POLITICAL COMMERCIAL ARCHIVE

A CATALOG AND GUIDE TO THE COLLECTION

Lynda Lee Kaid

Kathleen J. M. Haynes

Political Communication Center
University of Oklahoma
Norman

1991

Published by the Political Communication Center
610 Elm Avenue, Norman, Oklahoma 73019

Printed in the U.S.A.

The contents of this catalog were developed under a grant from the
U.S. Department of Education. However, those contents do not necessarily
represent the policy of the Department of Education, and you should not assume
endorsement by the Federal Government.

Cover designed by Roberta Wallace
Photographs produced by videoprinter directly from the archival materials

ACKNOWLEDGEMENTS

A project designed to bring bibliographic control to an archive of unique materials such as those contained in the Political Commercial Archive requires the talents and dedication of many people. First and foremost, the project owes a debt of gratitude to Louise Sutherland, Program Officer in the U. S. Department of Education's Strengthening Research Library Resources Program. Without her continuous encouragement and support, the entire project and this resulting catalog would not have been possible.

Dr. Robert Swisher, Director of the School of Library and Information Studies at the University of Oklahoma, was also an integral part of the project. The original head cataloger for the project, Charlene Rezabek, was instrumental in developing the cataloging guidelines and training catalogers for the local computer database.

The panel of expert consultants developed initial procedures and priorities for the project. These dedicated professionals, Dr. Jerry Saye, Wendy White-Hensen, and William Murphy, brought a wealth of experience and knowledge to this project. Jerry Saye is owed a special thanks for providing evaluation and suggestions for continued development at the conclusion of the project.

Expertise in the handling of the film, video, and audio aspects of the project was provided by Jane Gibbons Manier. Jane not only contributed superbly to the technological aspects of this project, but she served as an overall operations and facilities manager.

A number of graduate and undergraduate students also assisted with various phases of the project. Jane Garner and Rob Gobetz provided invaluable help with both cataloging and film and video operations. Other graduate students who worked in various phases of the operation included Jacques Taylor, Mike Chancellor, John Ballotti, Chris Leland, Dave Scott, Cindy Roper, and Dale Brashears. Several students assisted with the maintenance of the local computer database, including Belinda Stallings and Cynthia Owen. The project owes a special thanks to Pam McKeever who served as the organizational anchor of the project from beginning to end.

Finally, no one deserves more gratitude than Leroy Bridges, Chairman of the Advisory Board of the Political Communication Center at the University of Oklahoma. Leroy's initial support helped secure the funds to bring the Political Commercial Archive to the University of Oklahoma, and his continuing efforts to assist in the archive's projects cannot go unremarked.

i

TABLE OF CONTENTS

GUIDE TO THE COLLECTION

The Political Commercial Archive is the world's largest collection of political commercials and is nationally and internationally recognized as a major research resource. Many of the items in the collection are the only known, existing video or audio recordings of these particular political commercials. The archive currently contains over 40,000 individual radio and television commercials used in political campaigns from 1936 through the present time. The archive maintains an active acquisitions program, continuing to add current political spots in each election cycle.

At the time of the archive's location at the University of Oklahoma, the collection was completely without bibliographic control. This catalog is the result of the first phase of an effort to bring a systematic organization to the collection. The effort was funded by the **Strengthening Research Library Resources Program** of the **U. S. Department of Education.**

Importance of Political Advertising

During the past four decades, television's role in the political system has increased so dramatically that it is now the dominant form of communication in the political system. While news coverage and debates are undoubtedly important, it is electronic advertising which has become the most important aspect of this new communication between candidates and voters. Spending for television and radio time in the 1988 presidential campaign alone exceeded $80 million. Millions more are spent in races below the presidential level; as much as 50-75 percent of the campaign budgets for major statewide races is allocated to radio and television advertising.

A natural consequence of this growing importance of television advertising has been an increase in scholarly research. During the first sixteen years of television's use in politics (1952-1967), only seven studies of political television advertising were published in scholarly and professional journals. During the next fifteen years (1968-1982), there was an 800 percent increase in scholarly effort in the area; and in the succeeding years (1982-1990) the number of articles per year has tripled. These four decades have also seen a steady growth of books, convention papers, theses and dissertations devoted to the topic. Such increased interest emphasizes the need for increased access to original research materials.

Contents of the Archive

The Political Commercial Archive was founded by a private collector in 1959 and was purchased by the University of Oklahoma in 1985. When the archive was moved to the University of

2

Oklahoma, it became a part of the Political Communication Center in the Department of Communication. The Political Communication Center is an interdisciplinary unit which coordinates academic degree programs in political communication, facilitates research projects, sponsors conferences, oversees the Political Commercial Archive, and provides service to the academic and professional communities interested in political communication and political advertising.

At the time of the archive's purchase by the University of Oklahoma, the collection contained approximately 25,000 commercials in a variety of film, video, and audio formats. The collection has since grown to over 40,000 individual items.

The archive contains commercials from every election year from 1952 through 1990. All levels of races are included: presidential, U.S. Senatorial, U. S. Congressional, gubernatorial, state legislative, other statewide offices, state legislative, county and municipal, judicial, school board, etc. The archive has materials from all 50 states and some foreign countries. It also contains advertisements for and against ballot issues (or propositions) and an increasing number of advocacy commercials which deal with public and social policy questions.

Most of the commercials in the archive are in one of four media formats: 27 percent are on 16 mm film; 23 percent on 2 inch videotape; 34 percent on 3/4 inch videocassette, and 16 percent on audio tape. An increasing number of new acquisitions are on 1 inch videotape, as this has become the medium of choice in many production studios throughout the country. A small number of holdings are on 1/2" VHS cassettes, but these are not considered professional copies.

Bibliographic Control of the Collection

The establishment of bibliographic control for the Political Commercial Archive was the goal of the project which produced this catalog and guide. In order to be certain that proper procedures were followed in devising the cataloging system and preservation procedures for the project, a panel of experts was brought to the University of Oklahoma campus in November of 1988. The panel consisted of William Murphy (Chief of the Motion Picture, Sound, and Video Branch of the National Archives), Dr. Jerry Saye (Associate Professor in the School of Library Science, University of North Carolina), and Wendy White-Hensen (former senior cataloger for audio-visual materials at the Library of Congress). In conjunction with the Catalog Project Co-Directors, Dr. Lynda Lee Kaid and Dr. Kathleen J. M. Haynes, the expert panel set priorities and devised procedures for establishing bibliographic control of the archive.

As a result of the recommendations of the expert panel, the archive adopted a two-step bibliographic control system. First, a local computerized database was designed to provide detailed information on radio and television commercials on an item-by-item basis. Second, these individual records were then combined

into collection-level records, using the Archives and Manuscript
Control (AMC) format, and were added to the OCLC Union Catalog.
Thus, researchers can locate materials through OCLC and then
consult with Dr. Kaid to use the local computer database to
obtain additional information on each individual commercial item
held by the archive.

OCLC Access

The Political Commercial Archive is an independent member of
OCLC with the holdings code POI. The records added to OCLC
represent original cataloging using the AMC format. These
bibliographic records are based on the political career of an
individual. Thus, collections are organized according to the
names of candidates (with modifications made for certain other
types of materials). A given collection contains all of the
items produced for that individual for all political races at all
levels throughout his/her career which are owned by the archive.
This approach embraces the fundamental concept that archival
materials of all types must be understood in context.   The
physical description details the audio, video, and/or film
formats for each collection. A summary of the contents of the
collection, genre terms, and subject headings appropriate to
collection-level records are also provided.

In locating collections in OCLC, a researcher can best
proceed by searching the name of a candidate whose commercials
are sought. This can be done by constructing an author search, a
title search, or a combination author-title search using the
appropriate search statements. The author search statement is
based on the last name as the beginning element (**stev,adl,e** for a
record on Adlai E. Stevenson). The title search statement for
these records is based on the name in normal order (**adl,e,st.**)
The combination author/title search statement is based on the
candidate's last name and then the first name (**stev,adla.**)

The Political Commercial Archive is an additional access
point available through a corporate author search statement
(**=poli,com,a.**). In all these search statements, the qualifier
specifying the kind of material should be used to limit the
number of items retrieved. This qualifier is **/amc** for
manuscripts. Search statements may also be limited by
publication years in OCLC, but this approach is not appropriate
for the records of the Political Commercial Archive.

Descriptive cataloging, choice of access points, and name
heading elements conform to the standards set forth in <u>Archives,
Personal Papers, and Manuscripts</u>, 2nd edition, compiled by Steven
L. Hensen. <u>Archival Moving Image Materials: A Cataloging Manual</u>
by Wendy White-Hensen served as a source for cataloging decisions
and specifications. <u>Moving Image Materials: Genre Terms</u> compiled
by Martha M. Yee was the standard for genre terms chosen. Name
headings were verified in the Name Authority File of the Library
of Congress. Subject headings were chosen from the <u>Library of
Congress Subject Headings</u>.

Local Database

Information on individual commercials or sets of commercials can be obtained by using the local database compiled on each individual item in the archive. This database is maintained and continuously updated to include detailed information on each radio and television commercial. The database contains information on each commercial's audio or video format and physical condition. It also includes information on the candidate and the election in which the spot was used. For instance, the database indicates the political party of the candidate, the year of the election, the political office sought, the type of election (primary or general election), and numerous other descriptive fields which the computer software can utilize to retrieve commercials.

In the local database each commercial has been given a unique identification number. Working copies of many of the commercials have been compiled for use in performing the detailed cataloging necessary for the compilation of this database. These working copies make it possible to locate many items on 1/2 inch VHS videotapes, facilitating access to the collection's holdings by researchers. The availability of working copies of the materials is limited to items prioritized by the archive. These working copies are available only through coordination with Dr. Kaid.

Catalog Organization

The material contained in this catalog is basically a summary of data contained in the archive's collection-level records. Thus, the catalog entries are arranged alphabetically according to the candidate name.

Each entry consists of two parts (1) an entry line which includes the candidate's name, the physical description of the holdings, and, when available, the OCLC access number of the collection; and (2) a collection description which briefly indicates the extent of the archive's holdings as related to this particular candidate. In the latter description, information is included on the number of items held for each candidate, the years and elections for which items are available in the collection, and the political party of the candidate if known. Some of the information taken from the acquisition records of the original private collector could not be verified. The compilers welcome the reporting of any inaccuracies and inconsistencies so future editions of the catalog may be corrected.

For many items, a video representation is present, showing a still frame printed from one of the items in the collection. These video frames serve as examples of the visual content of the items.

It is important to note that this catalog is not a complete listing of the holdings of the Political Commercial Archive. In the bibliographic control project which produced this catalog, priority was given to the holdings contained on film and on 2 inch videotape. Audio recordings were processed only in order to produce collection-level records. Beyond the priority given to older holdings of the archive, the project also placed an emphasis on higher level elections. Thus, most of the holdings in this catalog relate to elections for President, U. S. Senate, U. S. Congress, and state governors.

Newer holdings, particularly those acquired after the current project's commencement in 1988, are not comprehensively included in this catalog. Commercials for lower level offices are also less heavily represented. These items will be included in OCLC as soon as feasible, and catalog updates will make these items accessible in the near future. Researchers who are seeking items from recent campaigns should attempt to access the items through OCLC or consult with local archive staff to determine the availability of these items. The archive maintains an active acquisitions program, and new items are acquired and processed in each election cycle.

Although the archive contains a substantial number of commercials for referenda, bond elections, propositions, and other special elections; these items are not included in this catalog because they were not given priority by the current bibliographic control project. Likewise, the catalog excludes advocacy and other specialized public affairs commercials. Users interested in these materials are encouraged to contact the archive for information about the holdings in this area.

Many of the items included in the catalog have not yet been entered into OCLC and thus do not contain OCLC numbers. Some entries in the catalog actually are more up-to-date than the OCLC entry as additions have been made for the purpose of compiling the catalog. These additions will be added to the relevant OCLC entry as soon as possible. Standard archival inventories, specialized guides, and other finding aids are planned for both the individual item records in the local database and the collection-level records.

Accessibility of the Archival Holdings

All items contained in the collection are available for use by researchers on-site. Advance consultation with the archive staff will facilitate the location of materials which a researcher wishes to view.

It is sometimes possible for a researcher to obtain a limited number of commercials from the archive for off-site usage in particular types of research projects. However, copyright restrictions limit such possibilities. In most cases, the Political Commercial Archive does not own the copyright to individual items. Archive staff can assist researchers in determining the educational and fair use tests to be applied in utilizing or copying various materials held by the archive.

The catalog project also maintains a videoprinter which can produce copies of individual frames from commercials. Researchers should consult with Dr. Kaid for information on access to this technology.

6

For further information about the archive or its holdings, interested users should contact:

Dr. Lynda Lee Kaid, Director
Catalog Project
Political Commercial Archive
Department of Communication
University of Oklahoma
Norman, OK 73019

(405) 325-3111

ABOUT THE AUTHORS

Lynda Lee Kaid is a Professor in the Department of Communication at the University of Oklahoma. She founded the Political Communication Center of which the Political Commercial Archive is a component. She is a former president of the Political Communication Division of the International Communication Association. She has authored several books and bibliographies on political communication and political advertising, including **New Perspectives on Political Advertising** and **Political Campaign Communication: A Bibliography and Guide to the Literature**. Her articles on political communication have appeared in numerous journals. A Fulbright Scholar, Kaid is currently working on several projects related to the impact of political television in Europe and recently co-edited **Mediated Politics in Two Cultures: Political Campaigning in the United States and France**.

Kathleen J. M. Haynes is an Assistant Professor in the School of Library and Information Studies at the University of Oklahoma. She teaches courses in descriptive and subject cataloging and other technical services areas. As a practitioner, she has experience in all types of libraries and has provided specialized information services on contract to government and industry. She has also planned, developed, and evaluated a wide range of technical and education programs. Her research areas include usability of online catalogs and issues in bibliographic control. An emerging research area is in the impact of telecommunications media upon learning outcomes and attitudes in distance education. She is a member of several professional associations. Committee assignments include the Education Committee for the Association for Library Collections and Technical Services, a division of the American Library Association.

ABBITT, Watt. 1 film reel (16 mm.). 24207556.

Collection contains 2 television commercials used during Abbitt's 1970 congressional campaign for District 4 of Virginia. (Democratic Party).

ABDNOR, James. 10 videocassettes (3/4 in. & 1/2 in.).

Collection contains 21 television commercials used during Abdnor's 1980 campaign for U.S. Senate in South Dakota and 11 television spots from his 1986 campaign for the same office. (Republican Party).

ABERCROMBIE, Neil. 2 videocassettes (3/4 in.).

Collection contains 1 television commercial used during Abercrombie's 1982 campaign for State Senate in Hawaii. Also includes 4 television spots from his 1986 campaign for U.S. Congress. (Democratic Party).

ABOUREZK, James. 2 film reels (16 mm.). 21368899.

Collection contains 18 television commercials used during Abourezk's campaign for the 1972 U.S. Senate in South Dakota. (Democratic Party).

ABRAMS, Robert. 1938 - . 2 videotapes (2 in.). 4 videocassettes (3/4 in.). 5 sound tape reels (7 1/2 ips.). 21352824.

Collection contains 20 radio commercials and 17 television commercials used during Abrams' 1974 campaign for Attorney General in New York. Also included are 4 television spots from his 1978, 7 television spots from his 1982, and 4 television spots from his 1986 Attorney General campaigns. (Democratic Party).

ABT, Clark. 4 videocassettes (3/4 in.).

Collection contains 8 television commercials used during Abt's 1986 campaign for U.S. Congress in Massachusetts. (Republican Party).

ABZUG, Bella. 2 videocassettes (3/4 in.).

Collection contains 6 television commercials from Abzug's 1976 campaign for U.S. Senate in New York and 3 television spots from her 1986 campaign for U.S. Congress in District 20 of New York. (Democratic Party).

ACKERMAN, Paul. 1 videocassette (3/4 in.).

Collection contains 1 television commercial used during Ackerman's 1982 campaign for county clerk in Tennessee.

ADAMS, Brock. 5 videocassettes (3/4 in.).

Collection contains 35 television commercials used during Brock's 1986 campaign for U.S. Senate in Washington. (Democratic Party).

ADAMS, J. Allen. 1932-. 1 film reel (16 mm.). 21726778.

Collection contains 1 television commercial available from the Adams' 1972 State Senate campaign in North Carolina, 14th District. (Democratic Party).

ADELMAN, Lynn S. 1939-. 2 videotapes (2 in.). 22186053.

Collection contains 2 television commercials from Adelman's 1974 congressional campaign in Wisconsin, 9th District. (Democratic Party).

ADINOLFI, Joseph. 1 film reel (16 mm). 24350632.

Collection contains 1 television commercial used during Adinolfi's 1969 campaign for Mayor in Connecticut. (Democratic Party).

AGNEW, Spiro. 1 film reel (16 mm). 1 videocassette (3/4 in.). 24350637.

Collection contains 1 television spot from Agnew's 1966 state campaign in Maryland and 5 television commercials used during his 1968 campaign as the vice-presidential candidate on the Nixon presidential ticket. (Republican Party).

AKAKA, Daniel K., 1924-. 1 videocassette (3/4 in.).

Collection contains 1 television commercial used during Akaka's 1986 campaign for U.S. Congress in District 2 of Hawaii. (Democratic Party).

ALBIN, Rick. 1 videocassette (3/4 in.).

Collection contains 1 television commercial used during Albin's 1986 campaign for U.S. Congress in District 1 of Arizona.

ALBOSTA, Don. 5 videocassettes (3/4 in.).

Collection contains 3 television spots from Albosta's 1984 campaign and 19 television commercials from his 1986 campaign for U.S. Congress in District 10 of Michigan. (Democratic Party).

ALEXANDER, Bill. 1 videocassette (3/4 in.).

Collection contains 2 television commercials from Alexander's 1974 congressional campaign in District 1 of Arkansas. (Democratic Party).

ALEXANDER, Lamar. 8 videocassettes (3/4 in.). 1 sound tape reel (7 1/2 ips.). 22137667.

Collection contains 17 television commercials and 2 radio commercials used during Alexander's 1978 campaign for Governor in Tennessee. Also includes 46 television commercials from his 1982 re-election campaign. (Republican Party).

ALIOTO, Joseph L. 1916 -. 25 videotapes (2 in.). 1 videocassette (3/4 in.). 1492295.

Collection contains 25 television commercials used during Alioto's 1971 campaign for Mayor in San Francisco and 7 television commercials used in his 1974 gubernatorial campaign in California. (Democratic Party).

ALLAIN, Bill. 1 videocassette (3/4 in.).

Collection contains 8 television commercials used during Allain's campaign for the 1983 gubernatorial election in Mississippi. (Democratic Party).

ALLEGRUCCI, Don. 1 videocassette (3/4 in.).

Collection contains 4 television commercials from Allegrucci's 1978 campaign for Congress in District 5 of Kansas. (Democratic Party).

ALLEN, Dick. 1 sound tape reel (7 1/2 ips.).

Collection contains 10 radio commercials used during Allen's campaign for the 1980 congressional election in District 10 in Michigan. (Republican Party).

ALLEN, Tom. 1 sound tape reel (7 1/2 ips.).

Collection contains 2 radio commercials used during Allen's 1972 campaign for a judgeship in Georgia. (Republican Party).

ALLISON, Ed. 1 film reel (16 mm.). 24350645.

Collection contains 4 television commercials used during Allison's 1968 campaign for State Land Commissioner in Arkansas.

ALLISON, Gary. 2 videocassettes (3/4 in.).

Collection contains 3 television commercials used during Allison's 1986 campaign for Congress in District 1 of Oklahoma. (Democratic Party).

ALLISON, Joan B. 1 videocassette (3/4 in.).

Collection contains 3 television spots from Allison's 1984 campaign for Superior Court Judge in Washington.

ALM, Dianne. 1 sound tape reel (7 1/2 ips).

Collection contains 1 radio commercial used during Alm's 1984 campaign for State Insurance Commissioner in North Dakota. (Republican Party).

ALTER, JoAnne. 1 videotape (2 in.). 24207562.

Collection contains 1 television commercial used during Alter's 1976 campaign for Lt. Governor in Illinois. (Democratic Party).

ALTMEYER, Jim. 1 videocassette (3/4 in.).

Collection contains 6 television commercials from Altmeyer's 1984 campaign for U.S. Congress in District 1 in West Virginia. (Republican Party).

AMESTOY, Jeff. 1 videocassette (3/4 in.).

Collection contains 3 television commercials from Amestoy's 1984 campaign for Attorney General in Vermont. (Republican Party).

ANAGOST, Katherine Cook. 1 sound tape reel (7 1/2 ips.).

Collection contains 1 radio commercial used during Anagost's 1980 campaign for State Supreme Court Justice in Illinois. (Republican Party).

ANANIA, Sam. 1 videotape (2 in.) 2420756.

Collection contains 1 television commercial used during Anania's campaign for a 1972 local election in Polk County, Iowa. (Democratic Party).

ANAYA, Toney. 1 videocassette (3/4 in.).

Collection contains 2 television spots from Anaya's 1982 campaign for Governor of New Mexico. (Democratic Party).

ANDERSON, Andy.   4 videocassettes (3/4 in.).

Collection contains 5 television commercials used during Anderson's 1982 campaign and 40 television commercials from his 1986 campaign for Governor of Hawaii. (Republican Party).

ANDERSON, Bob.   2 videocassettes (3/4 in.). 1 sound tape reel (7 1/2 ips.).

Collection contains 1 television and 3 radio commercial used during Anderson's 1982 campaign for Lt. Governor and 1 television spot from his 1986 campaign for Governor of Iowa. (Democratic Party).

ANDERSON, Bob.   1 videocassette (3/4 in.).

Collection contains 7 television commercials used during Anderson's 1986 campaign for U.S. Congress in District 11 of Michigan. (Democratic Party).

ANDERSON, John Bayard. 1922 -. 12 videotapes (16 mm.). 25 videocassettes (3/4 inch). 21133995.

Collection contains 53 television commercials used during Anderson's campaign for the 1972 gubernatorial election in Kansas. (Republican Party). Includes 27 commercials used in the 1980 presidential election. Collection also includes television debate from New Hampshire Democratic Primary, miscellaneous television news items related to Anderson's 1980 presidential candidacy, and several longer television programs/documentaries produced for his 1980 presidential campaign. (National Unity Party).

ANDERSON, Leroy. 1 sound tape reel (7 1/2 ips).

Collection contains 1 radio commercial used during Anderson's 1968 campaign for Governor of Montana. (Democratic Party).

ANDERSON, Richard. 2 videocassettes (3/4 in.).

Collection contains 3 television commercials used during Anderson's 1986 campaign for the U.S. Congress in District 9 of Michigan. (Democratic Party).

ANDERSON, Tom. 1 videotape (2 in.). 2 film reels (16 mm.). 24245059.

Collection contains 2 television commercials used during Anderson's 1970 campaign for Attorney General in Maryland. (Republican Party). Also contains 1 television commercial used during Anderson's 1976 presidential campaign. (Independent).

ANDERSON, Wendell Richard. 1933 -. 11 videotapes (2 in.). 2 film reels (16 mm.). 21180415.

Collection contains 27 television commercials used during Anderson's 1970 gubernatorial election and 6 television commercials used during his 1974 re-election campaign in Minnesota. (Democratic Party).

ANDERSON, William R. 1921 -. 1 videotape (2 in.). 1 sound tape reel (7 1/2 ips.). 21358319.

Collection contains 1 television commercial and 10 radio commercials used during Anderson's campaign for U.S. Congressional election in Tennessee, 6th District. (Democratic Party).

ANDREWS, Mark. 1926 -. 2 film reels (16 mm.). 3 video-cassettes (3/4 in. & 1/2 in.). 21416038.

Collection contains 19 television commercials used during Andrews' campaigns for the 1964 and 1972 U.S. Congressional elections in North Dakota. Also contains 56 television spots from his 1986 campaign for U.S. Senate. (Republican Party).

ANDREWS, Mike. 1 videocassette (3/4 in.).

Collection contains 1 television spot used during Andrews' 1980 campaign for U.S. Congress in District 2 of Texas. (Democratic Party).

ANDREWS, Taylor. 1 sound tape reel (7 1/2 ips). 22137723.

Collection contains 3 radio commercials used during Andrew's 1979 campaign for District Attorney in Cumberland County, Pennsylvania.

ANDRUS, Cecil. 1 film reel (16 mm.). 24207579.

Collection contains 15 television commercials used during Andrus' campaign for the 1972 gubernatorial election in Idaho. (Democratic Party).

ANGELO, Ernest. 1 videocassette (3/4 in.).

Collection contains 1 television commercial used during Angelo's 1982 campaign for State Senate in Texas in District 25. (Democratic Party).

ANGLY, Maurice. 1940 -. 1 videotape (2 in.). 21287324.

Collection contains 1 television commercial used during Angly's 1972 campaign for State Treasurer in Texas. (Republican Party).

ANNUNZIA, Frank. 1 sound tape reel (7 1/2 ips).

Collection contains 1 radio commercial used during Annunzia's 1984 campaign for Congress in District 11 of Illinois. (Democratic Party).

ANSPAUGH, Greg. 1 videocassette (3/4 in.).

Collection contains 4 television commercials used during Anspaugh's campaign for the State Representative in District 104 of Michigan.

ANTER, Richard. 3 videocassettes (3/4 in.). 24207587.

Collection contains 2 television commercials used during Anter's campaign for the 1982 congressional election in District 19 of Ohio. (Republican Party).

ANTHONY, Beryl. 3 videocassettes (3/4 in.).

Collection contains 12 television commercials from Anthony's 1978 campaign for Congress in District 4 of Arkansas. Also includes 1 television spot from her 1982 re-election campaign. (Democratic Party).

ANTONOVICH, Mike. 2 videocassettes (3/4 in.).

Collection contains 4 television commercials used during Antonovich's 1986 campaign for U.S. Senate in California. (Republican Party).

ARAGONA, Martin. 1 videotape (2 in.). 24350657.

Collection contains 1 television commercial used during Aragona's campaign for a 1978 local election in Maryland.

ARCHER, Dennis W.. 3 videocassettes (3/4 in.).

Collection contains 8 television commercials used during Archer's 1986 campaign for the State Supreme Court Judge in Michigan.

ARIEL, Douglas. 1950-. 1 videotape (2 in.). 21492308.

Collection contains 1 television commercial used during Ariel's 1972 campaign for State Representative in Massachusetts.

ARMSTRONG, Bea. 1 sound tape reel. (7 1/2 ips.).

Collection contains 2 radio commercials used during Armstrong's 1982 campaign for Governor of Illinois. (Libertarian Party).

ARMSTRONG, Bob. 1 film reel (16 mm.).

Collection contains 1 television commercial used during Armstrong's 1970 campaign for state commissioner in Texas. (Democratic Party).

ARMSTRONG, William.   1 videocassette (3/4 in.). 1 sound tape reel (7 1/2 ips).

Collection contains 5 television commercials from Armstrong's 1978 campaign for U.S. Senate in Colorado. Includes 1 radio commercial used during his 1972 campaign for Congress in District 5 of Colorado. (Republican Party).

ARNEBERGH, Roger. 1950-. 2 film reels (16 mm.). 21567391.

Collection contains 3 television commercials used during Arnebergh's 1973 campaign City Attorney in Los Angeles, California.   (Republican Party).

ARONSON, Marty. 1 videocassette (3/4 in.). 24207597.

Collection contains 2 television commercials used during Aronson's campaign for a 1982 election in Wisconsin.

ARRINGTON, Marvin.   1 videocassette (3/4 in.).

Collection contains 1 television commercial used during Arrington's 1980 campaign for Atlanta City Council President in Georgia.

ASHBROOK, John. 2 videotapes (2 in.). 1 videocassette (3/4 in.). 21244054.

Collection contains 4 television commercials used during Ashbrook's campaign for the 1972 presidential election. Includes 3 television commercials used during his campaign for the 1982 U.S. Senate election in Ohio. (Republican Party).

ASHCROFT, John. 1 videotape (2 in.). 2435066.

Collection contains 3 television commercials used during Ashcroft's 1974 campaign for State Auditor in Maryland. (Republican Party).

ASHE, Victor.   5 videocassettes (3/4 in.).

Collection contains 10 television spots from Ashe's 1984 campaign for U.S. Senate in Tennessee.   (Republican Party).

ASHWORTH, Don. 1 sound tape reel. (7 1/2 ips.).

Collection contains 1 radio commercial used during Ashworth's 1982 campaign for State Senate in Nevada.

ASHWORTH, L. Keith. 1 sound tape reel (7 1/2 ips.).

Collection contains 2 radio commercials used during Ashworth's campaign for the 1980 State Senate election in Nevada. (Democratic Party).

ASKEW, Reubin. 1928-. 2 videotapes (2 in.). 3 videocassettes (3/4 in.). 21243991.

Collection contains 10 television commercials used during Askew's campaign for the 1970 and 1974 gubernatorial elections in Florida. Also contains 12 television spots from Askew's 1984 primary campaigns for President. (Democratic Party).

This frame comes from a spot used in Askew's Florida gubernatorial campaign.

ASPIN, Les. 1 videotape (2 in.). 3 videocassettes (3/4 in.). 1 sound tape reel (7 1/2 ips.).

Collection contains 2 television spots from Aspin's campaign for the 1982 congressional election in District 1 of Wisconsin. Includes 4 television spots from his 1984 and 3 television spots from his 1986 re-election campaigns. Collection also contains 14 radio ads used from his 1972 campaign for the same office. (Democratic Party).

ATIYEH, Victor. 3 videocassettes (3/4 in.). 1 sound tape reel (7 1/2 ips.). 22044373.

Collection contains 23 television and 18 radio commercials from Atiyeh's 1978 campaign for Governor of Oregon and 6 television spots from his 1982 re-election campaign. (Republican Party).

ATKIN, Chet. 4 videocassettes (3/4 in.).

Collection contains 6 television spot from Atkin's 1984 primary campaign for U.S. Congress in District 5 of Massachusetts. (Democratic Party).

AUCOIN, Les. 10 videocassettes (3/4 in.). 24207607.

Collection contains 2 television commercials from AuCoin's 1974 campaign, 8 television commercials from his 1980 congressional race, 5 television commercials from his 1982 campaign, 7 television spots from his 1984 campaign, and 8 television spots from his 1986 campaign for U.S. Congress from District 1 in Oregon. (Democratic Party).

AURELIUS, William. 1 sound tape reel (7 1/2 ips.).

Collection contains 3 radio commercials used during Aurelius' campaign for the 1980 Judgeship of Common Pleas election in Cuyahoga County, Ohio.

AUSTER, Richard. 1 videocassette (3/4 in.).

Collection contains 1 television commercial used during Auster's 1982 campaign for U.S. Congress in District 5 of Arizona. (Libertarian Party).

AUSTIN, Richard. 1 videotape (2 in.). 21186283.

Collection contains four television commercials used during Austin's 1969 campaign for Mayor in Detroit, Michigan. (Democratic Party).

AYLWARD, James Patrick. 1920-. 1 videotape (2 in.). 21315031.

Collection contains 1 television commercial used during Aylward's 1972 campaign for Lt. Governor in Missouri. (Democratic Party).

BABBITT, Bruce. 4 videocassettes (3/4 in.). 21133966.

Collection contains 25 television commercials used during Babbitt's campaign for the 1982 gubernatorial election in Arizona, and Presidential election. (Democratic Party).

BABBITT, Wayne Hubert. 1928-. 1 videotape (2 in.). 22245539.

Collection contains 1 television commercial used during Babbitt's 1972 campaign for U.S. Senate in Arkansas. (Republican Party).

BABCOCK, Tim. 1919-. 1 sound tape reel (7 1/2 ips.). 21979461.

Collection contains 16 radio commercials used during Babcock's campaign for the 1966 U.S. Senate election in Montana. (Republican Party).

BABLITCH, Bill. 1 sound tape reel (7 1/2 ips.).

Collection contains 2 radio commercials used during Bablitch's campaign for a 1982 judgeship election in Wisconsin.

BACALL, Eva. 2 videocassettes (3/4 in.).

Collection contains 4 television commercials used during Bacall's 1986 campaign for Tuscon School Board in Arizona.

BACHMAN, George. 1 sound tape reel (7 1/2 ips.).

Collection contains 1 radio commercial used during Bachman's 1982 campaign for County Executive in Maryland.

BACHRACH, George. 7 videocassettes (3/4 in.).

Collection contains 11 television commercials used during Bachrach's 1986 campaign for U.S. Congress in District 8 of Massachusetts. (Democratic Party).

BADE, Jack. 1 videocassette (3/4 in.).

Collection contains 1 television commercial from Bade's 1980 primary campaign for U.S. Congress in District 7 of Georgia. (Democratic Party).

BADHAM, Bob. 3 videocassettes (3/4 in.).

Collection contains 2 television spots from Badham's 1984 campaign and 3 television spots from his 1986 campaign for U.S. Congress in District 40 of California. (Republican Party).

BADILLO, Herman. 1929-. 1 film reel (16 mm.). 1 videotape (2 in.). 2 videocassettes (3/4 in.). 21319703.

Collection contains 3 television commercials used in Badillo's 1973 campaign for Mayor in New York City and 5 television spots from his 1986 campaign for State Comptroller in New York. (Democratic Party).

BAGNEL, Anne Broyles. 1935-. 1 videocassette (3/4 in.). 22156008.

Collection contains 3 television commercials used in Bagnel's campaign for the 1982 U.S. congressional election in North Carolina, 5th District. (Democratic Party).

BAILEY, Don. 4 videotapes (2 in.). 24207614.

Collection contains 6 television commercials used during Bailey's campaign for Auditor General in Pennsylvania. (Democratic Party).

BAILEY, Robert L.. 1 videotape (2 in.). 24207625.

Collection contains 2 television commercials used during Bailey's campaign for an unknown 1986 Oklahoma election.

BAINUM, Stewart, Jr.. 1 videocassette (3/4 in.).

Collection contains 1 television commercial used during Bainum's 1986 campaign for Congress in District 8 of Oregon. (Democratic Party).

BAKALIS, Michael. 2 videotapes (2 in.). 24207636.

Collection contains 2 television commercials used during Bakalis' campaign for the 1978 gubernatorial election in Illinois. (Democratic Party).

BAKER, Cissy. 3 videocassettes (3/4 in.).

Collection contains 10 television commercials used during Baker's 1982 campaign for U.S. Congress in District 4 of Tennessee. (Republican Party).

BAKER, Edward H. 1 videocassette (3/4 in.).

Collection contains 1 television commercial used during Baker's campaign for the 1982 State House election in Tennessee. (Democratic Party).

BAKER, Howard. 11 videocassettes (3/4 in.).

Collection contains 34 television commercials used during Baker's 1980 campaign for President. Includes the New Hampshire Primary Debate and miscellaneous appearances during the primary campaign. (Republican Party).

BAKER, Russell "Tim." 3 videocassettes (3/4 in.).

Collection contains 10 television commercials used during Baker's 1986 campaign for Attorney General in Maryland. (Democratic Party).

BARANGER, Tom. 1 sound tape reel (7 1/2 ips.).

Collection contains 3 radio commercials used during Baranger's 1982 campaign for County Executive election in Maryland.

BARBEE, Allen Cromwell. 1910-. 2 videotapes (2 in.). 21319737.

Collection contains 2 television commercials used during Barbee's 1972 campaign for Lt. Governor in North Carolina. (Democratic Party).

BARBOR, Mike. 1 sound tape reel (7 1/2 ips.).

Collection contains 2 radio commercials used during Barbor's 1972 campaign for Public Service Commissioner in Georgia.

BARBOUR, Haley. 1 videocassette (3/4 in.). 24206399.

Collection contains 8 television commercials used during Barbour's campaign for the 1982 U.S. Senate election in Mississippi. (Republican Party).

BARCZAK, Gary. 1 videocassette (3/4 in.). 24207651.

Collection contains 1 television commercial used during Barczak's campaign for a 1982 Wisconsin election.

BARNES, Ben F. 1938-. 1 videotape (2 in.). 21319723.

Collection contains 1 television commercial used during Barnes' campaign for the 1973 gubernatorial election in Texas. (Democratic Party).

BARNES, Michael. 1 videocassette (3/4 in.). 1 sound tape reel (7 1/2 ips.).

Collection contains 1 radio commercial used during Barnes' campaign for the 1982 U.S. Congress election in District 8 in Maryland and 6 television commercials used during his 1986 campaign for U.S. Senate. (Democratic Party).

BARR, Burton. 3 videocassettes (3/4 in.).

Collection contains 7 television commercials used during Barr's 1986 campaign for Governor of Arizona. (Republican Party).

BARRARA, Roy. 1 videocassette (3/4 in.).

Collection contains 1 television commercial used during Barrara's 1986 campaign for Attorney General in Texas. (Republican Party).

BARRON, Dempsey. 1 videocassette (3/4 in.).

Collection contains 1 television commercial from Barron's 1980 campaign for State Senate in District 3 of Florida.

BARRY, Johnathon. 1 videocassette (3/4 in.).

Collection contains 2 television commercials used during Barry's 1986 campaign for U.S. senate in Wisconsin. (Republican Party).

BARRY, Marion. 1 sound tape reel (7 1/2 ips.).

Collection contains 8 radio commercials used during Barry's 1982 campaign for Mayor in Washington, D.C.

BARTLETT, Dewey F. 4 videotapes (2 in.). 21276392.

Collection contains 15 television commercials used during Bartlett's 1972 campaign for the U.S. Senate election in Oklahoma. (Republican Party).

BARTMAN, Tom. 1 sound tape reel (7 1/2 ips.).

Collection contains 1 radio commercial used during Bartman's 1979 campaign for a 1979 school election in California.

BARTON, Joe. 3 videocassettes (3/4 in.).

Collection contains 9 television spots form Barton's 1984 and 1986 campaigns for U.S. Congress in District 6 of Texas. (Republican Party).

BASHARA, George N. 1934-. 1 film reel (16 mm.). 22256840.

Collection contains 2 television commercials used during Bashara's campaign for a 1970 judgeship in Michigan.

BASKIN, Natalie. 1930-. 1 videotape (2 in.). 21352853.

Collection contains 1 television commercial used during Baskin's campaign for the 1974 judgeship election in Florida. (Democrat Party).

BASTION, David. 1 sound tape reel (7 1/2 ips.).

Collection contains 2 radio commercials used during Bastion's campaign for the 1982 State Senate election in District 15 in Maryland.

BATEMAN, Herbert. 7 videocassettes (3/4 in.). 1 sound tape reel (7 1/2 ips.).

Collection contains 12 radio commercials from Bateman's 1982 campaign, 11 television spots from his 1984 campaign, and 5 television spots from his 1986 campaign for U.S. Congress in District 1 of Virginia. (Republican Party).

BATES, James. 1 sound tape reel (7 1/2 ips.).

Collection contains 1 radio commercial used during Bates' campaign for the 1980 congressional election in District 41 in California. (Democratic Party).

BATES, Jim. 3 videotapes (2 in.). 24208251.

Collection contains 3 television commercials used during Bates' campaign for the 1986 Congress election in District 44 of California. (Democratic Party).

BAUCUS, Max. 3 videocassettes (3/4 in.).

Collection contains 11 television spots from Baucus' 1984 campaign for U.S. Senate in Montana. (Democratic Party).

BAUERNSCHMIDT, Charles. 1 sound tape reel (7 1/2 ips.).

Collection contains 1 radio commercial used during Bauernschmidt's 1982 campaign for a judgeship in Cleveland, Ohio.

BAXLEY, Bill. 12 videotapes (2 in.). 24208264.

Collection contains 19 television spots from Baxley's 1986 campaign for Governor in Alabama. (Democratic Party).

BAXTER, Wendy M.. 2 videocassettes (3/4 in.).

Collection contains 3 television commercials used during Baxter's 1986 campaign for a judgeship in Michigan.

BAYH, Birch. 1928-. 1 film reel (16 mm.). 2 videotapes (2 in.). 3 videocassettes (3/4 in.). 21352807.

Collection contains 3 television commercials used during Bayh's campaigns for the 1968 U.S. Senate election in Indiana and 1976 presidential election. Includes 63 commercials from Bayh's 1980 campaign for U.S. Senate in Indiana. (Democratic Party).

BEAL, Donald. 1 sound tape reel (7 1/2 ips.).

Collection contains 1 radio commercial used during Beal's 1972 campaign for Supervisor in Iowa. (Democratic Party).

BEALL, J. Glenn. 1927-. 5 film reels (16 mm.). 5 videotapes (2 in.). 21254603.

Collection contains 24 television commercials used during Beall's 1972 campaign for U.S. Senate in Maryland. (Republican Party).

BEAN, Jim. 3 videotapes (2 in.). 24208271.

Collection contains 3 television commercials used during Bean's campaign for an unknown 1986 Mississippi election.

24

This spot was used by Robin Beard to attack Sasser in a Senate campaign in Tennessee.

BEARD, Robin. 7 videocassettes (3/4 in.).

Collection contains 12 television commercials from Beard's 1982 campaign for the U.S. Senate in Tennessee. (Republican Party).

BEAUMONT, Bill. 1 sound tape reel (7 1/2 ips.).

Collection contains 1 radio commercial used during Beaumont's 1972 campaign for State Legislature in Arkansas.

BECK, Ray. 1 sound tape reel (7 1/2 ips.).

Collection contains 4 radio commercials used during Beck's campaign for the 1982 State Senate election in Maryland.

BECKER, Alan. 1 videocassette (3/4 in.).

Collection contains 4 television commercials used during Becker's 1982 campaign for U.S. Congress in Florida. (Democratic Party).

BEDELL, Berkley. 2 videocassettes (3/4 in.). 1 sound tape reel (7 1/2 ips.).

Collection contains 8 radio commercials used during Bedell's 1982 campaign and 25 television spots from his 1984 campaign for U.S. Congress in District 6 of Iowa. (Democratic Party).

BELAGA, Julie. 4 videocassettes (3/4 in.).

Collection contains 8 television commercials used during Belaga's 1986 campaign for Governor of Connecticut. (Republican Party).

BELL, Bob. 2 videocassettes (3/4 in.).

Collection contains 5 television commercials used during Bell's 1982 campaign for Governor of Georgia. (Republican Party).

BELL, Dale. 1 videocassette (3/4 in.).

Collection contains 14 television spots from Bell's 1984 campaign for Congressman At Large from South Dakota. (Republican Party).

BELL, Edward F. 1929-. 1 film reel (16 mm.). 1 videocassette (3/4 in.). 22198998.

Collection contains 1 television commercial used during Bell's 1970 campaign for a judgeship in Michigan.

BELL, Jeff. 8 videotapes (2 in.).

Collection contains 44 television commercials used during Bell's campaign for 1978 U.S. Senate in New Jersey. (Republican Party).

BELLMON, Henry. 3 videocassettes (3/4 in.). 1 film reel (16 mm.). 24357467.

Collection contains 35 television commercials used during Bellmon's 1974 campaign for the U.S. Senate election in Oklahoma. Also contains 6 television spots from Bellmon's 1986 campaign for Governor of Oklahoma. (Republican Party).

BELLOTTI, Francis X. 3 videotapes (2 in.). 21352834.

Collection contains 7 television commercials used during Bellotti's 1974 campaign for Attorney General in Massachusetts. (Democratic Party).

BELLUSO, Nick. 1 videocassette (3/4 in.). 1 videotape (2 in.).

Collection contains 1 television commercial for Belluso's 1978 campaign for Governor of Georgia. (Democratic Party).

BENEDICT, Al. 1 sound tape reel (7 1/2 ips.). 1 videocassette (3/4 in.).

Collection contains 2 radio commercials used during Benedict's campaign for the 1980 State Auditor General election in Pennsylvania. Includes 7 television spots from his 1984 campaign for State Treasurer. (Democratic Party).

BENET, Bill. 1 sound tape reel (7 1/2 ips.).

Collection contains 3 radio commercials used during Benet's campaign for the 1982 congressional election in District 30 of New York. (Democratic Party).

BENNETT, Gordon. 1 sound tape reel (7 1/2 ips).

Collection contains 3 radio commercials used during Bennett's campaign for a state office in Montana.

26

BENNETT, Robert F. 1927-. 3 videotapes (2 in.). 21352747.

Collection contains 12 television commercials used during Bennett's campaign for the 1974 gubernatorial election in Kansas. (Republican Party).

BENTLEY, Helen. 2 videotapes (2 in.). 8 videocassettes (3/4 in.). 24208281.

Collection contains 5 television commercials from 1984 and 4 television commercials from 1986 used in Bentley's campaigns for U.S. Congress in District 2 of Maryland. (Republican Party).

BENTLEY, Helen Delich. 1 sound tape reel (7 1/2 ips.).

Collection contains 5 radio commercials used during Bentley's campaign for the 1982 congressional election in District 2 in Maryland. (Republican Party).

BENTON, William. 1900-1973. 1 videocassette (2 in.). 22155972.

Collection contains 5 television commercials used during Benton's campaign for the 1950 U.S. Congress election in Iowa. (Democratic Party).

BENTSEN, Lloyd. 2 videotapes (2 in.). 3 videocassettes (3/4 in.). 21180440.

Collection contains 2 television commercials used during Bentsen's campaign for the 1970 U.S. Senate election in Texas. Also contains 32 television commercials from his 1982 re-election campaign. (Democratic Party).

Lloyd Bensten used this spot in his 1970 senatorial campaign in Texas.

BERG, Raymond K. 1 film reel (16 mm.). 24208290.

Collection contains 1 television commercial used during Berg's campaign for the 1972 State Attorney General election in Illinois. (Democratic Party).

BERGLAND, Bob. 1 film reel (16 mm.). 24208960.

Collection contains 3 television commercials used during Bergland's 1972 campaign for U.S. Congress for District 7 of Minnesota. (Democratic Party).

BERGLAND, David. 1 videocassette (3/4 in.). 21352792.

Collection contains 2 television commercials used during Bergland's campaign for the 1984 presidential election. (Libertarian Party).

BERKLEY, Dick L. 1 videotape (2 in.).

Collection contains 1 television commercial used during Berkley's 1978 campaign for Mayor in Kansas City.

BERMAN, Dan. 1 videocassette (3/4 in.).

Collection contains 2 television commercials from Berman's 1980 campaign for U.S. Senate in Utah. (Democratic Party).

BERNAL, Joe. 1927-. 1 videotape (2 in.). 21287296.

Collection contains 1 television commercial from Bernal's 1972 campaign for State Representative in Texas. (Democratic Party).

BERRYHILL, Clare. 1 videocassette (3/4 in.). 1 videotape (2 in.).

Collection contains 3 television commercials used during Berryhill's 1972 campaign for State Senate in District 3 of California. (Republican Party).

BERTINI, Catherine. 1 sound tape reel (7 1/2 ips.).

Collection contains 2 radio commercials used during Bertini's 1982 campaign for local office in Illinois. (Republican Party).

BETHAL, Paul D. 1 videotape (2 in.). 21426538.

Collection contains 3 television commercials used during Bethal's campaign for the 1972 U.S. Congress election in Florida, 13th District. (Republican Party).

BETHUNE, Ed. 1 videotape (2 in.). 1 videocassette (3/4 in.). 22441591.

Collection contains 1 television commercial used during Bethune's 1972 campaign for Attorney General in Arkansas. Also includes 12 television spots from Bethune's 1984 campaign for U.S. Senate from Arkansas. (Republican Party).

BETTS, Jim. 2 videocassettes (3/4 in.).

Collection contains 8 television commercials from Betts' 1980 campaign for U.S. Senate in Ohio. (Republican Party).

BEUTLER, Chris. 1 videocassette (3/4 in.).

Collection contains 6 television commercials used during Beutler's campaign for Governor of Nebraska. (Democratic Party).

BIBLE, Alan. 1909-. 1 film reel (16 mm.). 21416022.

Collection contains 41 television commercials used during Bible's 1968 campaign for U.S. Senate in Nevada. (Democratic Party).

BICKLE, Dwight. 1 sound tape reel (7 1/2 ips).

Collection contains 1 radio commercial used during Bickle's campaign in Idaho.

BICKNELL, Gene. 1 videocassette (3/4 in.).

Collection contains 1 television commercial used during Bicknell's 1986 campaign for Governor of Kansas.

BIDEN, Joseph. 2 videocassettes (3/4 in.).

Collection contains 3 television spots from Biden's 1984 campaign for U.S. Senate in Delaware. (Democratic Party).

**BILBRAY, James Hubert. 1 sound tape reel (7 1/2 ips.).
1 videocassette (3/4 in.).**

Collection contains 3 radio commercials used during Bilbray's campaign for the 1980 State Senate election in Nevada and 22 television commercials used during his 1986 campaign for Congressman-At-Large in Nevada. (Democratic Party).

BILIRAKIS, Mike. 3 videocassettes (3/4 in.).

Collection contains 8 television commercials used during Bilirakis' campaign for U.S. Congress in District 9 of Florida. (Republican Party).

BILLINGS, Leo. 1 videocassette (3/4 in.).

Collection contains 1 television commercial used during Billings' 1986 campaign for Congress in District 8 of Maryland.

BILLINGTON, Barry. 1 videocassette (3/4 in.).

Collection contains 1 television commercial from Billington's 1980 campaign for Congress in District 4 of Georgia.

BINGHAM, Clark. 1 sound tape reel. (7 1/2 ips.).

Collection contains 1 radio commercial used during Bingham's 1982 campaign for a local office in Nevada.

BIRCH, A.A. 1 videocassette (3/4 in.).

Collection contains 3 television commercials used during Birch's 1982 campaign for Criminal Court Judge in Tennessee.

BIRCH, Elizabeth. 1 sound tape reel (7 1/2 ips.).

Collection contains 1 radio commercial used during Birch's 1980 campaign for Supreme Court Justice in Michigan.

BIRD, Rose. 1 videocassette (3/4 in.).

Collection contains 2 television commercials used during Bird's 1986 campaign for Chief Justice in California.

BISHOP, C. Diane. 2 videocassettes (3/4 in.).

Collection contains 8 television commercials used during Bishop's 1986 campaign for State Superintendent of Schools in Arizona.

BIXLER, Jim. 1 sound tape reel (7 1/2 ips.).

Collection contains 1 radio commercial used during Bixler's 1980 campaign for Justice of the Peace in Nevada.

BLACK, Bill. 1 videocassette (3/4 in.).

Collection contains 1 television commercial used during Black's 1986 campaign for State Representative in Illinois.

BLACK, Bob. 1 videocassette (3/4 in.).

Collection contains 2 television commercials used in Black's 1980 campaign for Secretary of State. (Democratic Party).

BLACKBURN, Ben. 1 videocassette (3/4 in.).

Collection contains 3 television commercials used during Blackburn's 1982 campaign for Governor of Georgia. (Republican Party).

BLACKWELL, Earl R. 1923-. 1 videotape (2 in.). 1 sound tape reel (7 1/2 ips.). 21388344.

Collection contains 3 television commercials and 1 radio spot used during Blackwell's campaign for the 1972 gubernatorial election in Missouri. (Democratic Party).

BLAIR, G. Stanley. 1 film reel (16 mm.). 24208977.

Collection contains 5 television commercials used during Blair's 1970 campaign for Governor in Maryland. (Republican Party).

BLAIR, Paul. 1 videocassette (3/4 in.).

Collection contains 5 television spots used in Blair's 1975 campaign for Judge in Massachusetts.

BLANCHARD, Jim. 10 videocassettes (3/4 in.). 24209217.

Collection contains 21 television commercials used during Blanchard's 1982 campaign for Governor in Michigan. Also contains 25 television spots from his 1986 re-election campaign for the same office. (Democratic Party).

BLAND, Beth. 1 videocassette (3/4 in.).

Collection contains 1 television commercial used during Bland's campaign for the 1982 congressional election in District 8 of Washington. (Democratic Party).

BLAYLOCK, Len Everette. 1918-. 1 videotape (2 in.). 22199036.

Collection contains 1 television commercial from Blaylock's 1972 campaign for Governor in Arkansas. (Republican Party).

BLAZ, Ben. 5 videocassettes (3/4 in.).

Collection contains 12 television commercials used during Blaz's 1986 campaign for U.S. Congress from Guam. (Republican Party).

BLOBAUM, Roger. 1 sound tape reel (7 1/2 ips.). 22137675.

Contains television commercials used in Blobaum's campaign for the 1970 U.S. congressional election in Iowa. (Democratic Party).

BLOCH, Ed. 1 videocassette (3/4 in.).

Collection contains 1 television commercial used during Bloch's 1986 campaign for U.S. Congress in District 24 of New York. (Democratic Party).

BLOOM, Larry. 2 sound tape reels (7 1/2 ips).

Collection contains 2 radio commercial used during Bloom's 1984 campaign for State Attorney in Illinois. (Democratic Party).

BLOUIN, Michael T. 1945-. 1 videotape (2 in.). 22155957.

Collection contains 5 television commercials used during Blouin's 1974 campaign for U.S. Congress in Iowa. (Democratic Party).

BLOUNT, Winton M. 1921-. 8 videotapes (2 in.). 21248181.

Collection contains 17 television spots used during Blount's 1972 campaign for U.S. Senate in Alabama. (Republican Party).

BLUMENAUER, Earl. 1 videocassette (3/4 in.).

Collection contains 1 television commercial used during Bluemnauer's 1986 campaign for Portland City Council in Oregon.

BLUMENTHAL, Albert H. 1928-. 3 videotapes (2 in.). 21437420.

Collection contains 4 television spots from Blumenthal's 1973 campaign for Mayor of New York City. (Democratic Party).

BOE, Jason Douglas. 1929-. 2 videocassettes (3/4 in.). 22155993.

Collection contains 2 television spots from Boe's campaign for the 1974 U.S. Senate election in Oregon. (Democratic Party).

BOGGS, Lindy. 2 videocassettes (3/4 in.).

Collection contains 11 television commercials from Boggs' 1984 campaign for U.S. Congress in Louisiana. (Democratic Party).

BOGGS, Thomas Hale. 2 videotapes (2 in.). 21256309.

Collection contains 6 television commercials used during Boggs' 1970 campaign for U.S. Congress in Maryland. (Democratic Party).

BOHNER, Bill. 1 videocassette (3/4 in.). 24208989.

Collection contains 2 television commercials used during Bohner's 1982 campaign for Governor in New York. (Right to Life Party).

BOLLING, Richard. 1 film reel (16 mm.). 24209005.

Collection contains 1 television commercial used during Bolling's 1972 campaign for U.S. Congress in Maryland. (Democratic Party).

BOND, Christopher S. 1939-. 4 film reel (16 mm.). 18 videotapes (1 in.). 10 videocassettes (3/4 in. & 1/2 in.). 21368965.

This spot for Kit Bond's 1972 gubernatorial campaign in Missouri featured Bond's wife, Carolyn.

Collection contains 2 television spots from Bond's 1970 campaign for State Auditor, 32 television spots used in his 1972 campaign for Governor, 10 television spots from his 1976 re-election campaign, 40 television spots from his 1980 gubernatorial campaign, and 41 television spots used in Bond's campaign for the 1986 U.S. Senate. All elections in Missouri. (Republican Party).

BOND, Julian. 1 videocassette (3/4 in.).

Collection contains 3 television commercials used during Bond's 1986 campaign for U.S. Congress in District 5 of Georgia. (Democratic Party).

BONER, Bill. 3 videocassettes (3/4 in.).

Collection contains 10 television commercials used during Boner's 1986 campaign for U.S. Congress in District 5 of Tennessee. (Democratic Party).

BONETTI, Bob. 1 videotape (2 in.). 21887846.

Collection contains 1 television commercial used during Bonetti's 1974 campaign for Sheriff in California.

BONNER, Ray. 1 videocassette (3/4 in.).

Collection contains 1 television commercial from Bonner's 1980 campaign for Sheriff in Atlanta, Georgia.

BONORA, Matt. 1 sound tape reel (7 1/2 ips).

Collection contains 4 radio commercials used during Bonora's campaign for a local election in New York. (Democratic Party).

BOOSALIS, Helen. 5 videocassettes (3/4 in.).

Collection contains 51 television commercials used during Boosalis' 1986 campaign for Governor of Nebraska. (Democratic Party).

BOOZER, Vernon. 1 sound tape reel (7 1/2 ips.).

Collection contains 1 radio commercial used during Boozer's 1982 campaign for State Senate in District 9 of Maryland.

BOREN, David. 1941 -. 7 videotapes (2 in.). 3 videocassettes (3/4 in.). 24209015.

Collection contains 22 television commercials used during Boren's campaign for the 1974 gubernatorial election in Oklahoma, and 4 television spots from his 1984 U.S. Senate campaign in Oklahoma. (Democratic Party).

BOREN, Jim. 1 videocassette (3/4 in.).

Collection contains 1 television commercial used during Boren's 1986 campaign for Congress in Virginia. (Democratic Party).

This spot for David Boren's Senate campaign in Oklahoma displayed his symbolic "broom" used to sweep away the old guard politicians.

BORK, Robert. 1 sound tape reel (7 1/2 ips).

Collection contains 4 radio spots used against Bork during his 1987 Supreme Court nomination process.

BORMAN, Susan. 1 film reel (16 mm.). 24209024.

Collection contains 2 television commercials used during Borman's 1972 campaign for a judgeship in Michigan.

BORSKI, Bob. 6 videocassettes (3/4 in.).

Collection contains 6 television commercials used during Borski's 1982 campaign and 4 television spots from his 1986 campaign for U.S. Congress in District 3 of Pennsylvania. (Democratic Party).

34

BORYSZEWSKI, Ralph.   1 sound tape reel (7 1/2 ips.).

Collection contains 1 radio commercial used during Boryszewski's campaign for a 1980 election in New York.   (Libertarian Party).

BOSCH, Patricia. 1 film reel (16 mm.). 21631209.

Collection contains 1 television commercial from Bosch's 1974 campaign for Congress in Arizona. (Democratic Party).

BOSCHWITZ, Rudy.   7 videocassettes (3/4 in. & 1/2 in.).

Collection contains 1 television spot from Boschwitz's 1978 campaign and 60 television spots from his 1984 campaign for U.S. Senate in Minnesota.   (Republican Party).

BOTTONI, Jim.   1 sound tape reel (7 1/2 ips.).

Collection contains 1 radio commercial used during Bottoni's 1972 campaign for State Legislature in Wisconsin.   (Democratic Party).

BOUCHER, Rick.   1 videocassette (3/4 in.).

Collection contains 11 television spots from Boucher's 1984 campaign for Congress in Virginia.   (Democratic Party).

BOULTER, Beau. 3 videocassettes (3/4 in.).

Collection contains 10 television commercials from Boulter's 1986 campaign for U. S. Congress in Texas. (Republican Party).

BOURNE, Peter G., M.D. 1 videotape (2 in.). 24357493.

Collection contains 1 television commercial used during Bourne's 1980 response to accusations by the National Conservative Political Committee.

BOWEN, Otis R. 2 film reels (16 mm.). 4 videotapes (2 in.). 1 sound tape reel. 21369705.

Collection contains 16 television spot and 1 radio spot from Bowen's 1972 campaign for Governor in Indiana. (Republican Party).

This spot was used in Otis Bowen's 1972 campaign for governor of Indiana.

BOWES, William. 1 sound tape reel (7 1/2 ips).

Collection contains 1 radio commercial used during Bowes' 1968 campaign for City Commissioner in Portland, Oregon.

BOWLES, Hargrove Jr. 1919-. 1 film reel (16 mm.). 21892516.

Collection contains 13 television commercials used during Bowles' 1972 campaign for Governor in North Carolina. (Democratic Party).

BOYCE, Sam. 1 sound tape reel (7 1/2 ips).

Collection contains 1 radio commercial used during Boyce's 1968 campaign for Governor of Arizona.

BOYD, Paul. 1 sound tape reel (7 1/2 ips.). 1 videotape (2 in.). 21511186.

Collection contains 8 television and several radio commercials used during Boyd's 1972 campaign for State Senate in Idaho.

BRADEMAS, John. 4 videocassettes (3/4 in.).

Collection contains 3 television commercials used during Brademas' 1980 campaign for U.S. Congress in District 3 of Indiana. Also included are 5 television spots from an earlier congressional campaign. (Democratic Party).

BRADEN, Tom. 1 film reel (16 mm.). 24209031.

Collection contains 6 television commercials used during Braden's 1966 campaign for Lt. Governor in California. (Democratic Party).

BRADLEY, Bill. 2 videocassettes (3/4 in.).

Collection contains 5 television commercials from Bradley's 1978 campaign and 6 television spots from his 1984 campaign for U.S. Senate in New Jersey. (Democratic Party).

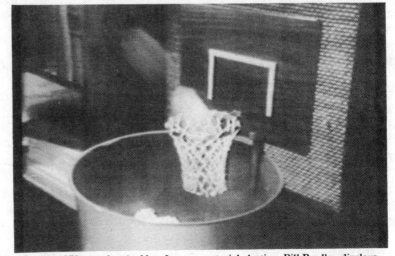

In this 1978 spot for the New Jersey senatorial election, Bill Bradley displays his famous basketball skills.

BRADLEY, Gerald.   2 videocassettes (3/4 in.).

Collection contains 9 television spots from Bradley's 1984 campaign for Congress in Illinois. (Democratic Party).

BRADLEY, Tom. 11 videotapes (1 in. & 2 in.). 24209036.

Collection contains 20 television commercials used during Bradley's campaign for the 1986 gubernatorial election in California. (Democratic Party).

BRADY, Larry.   1 videocassette (3/4 in.).

Collection contains 2 television spots from Brady's 1984 campaign for U.S. Congress in District 1 of New Hampshire. (Republican Party).

BRAMLETT, Leon. 1 videocassette (3/4 in.).

Collection contains 2 television commercials used during Bramlett's campaign for the 1983 gubernatorial election in Mississippi. (Republican Party).

BRANDENBURG, James Michael. 1942-. 1 sound tape reel (7 1/2 ips.). 21983865.

Collection contains 2 radio commercials used during Brandenburg's 1972 campaign for District attorney in New Mexico.

BRANDON, Doug. 1 videotape (2 in.). 21474894.

Collection contains 2 television commercials used during Brandon's campaign for Lt. Governor in Arkansas. (Democratic Party).

BRANDSTED, Terry.   1 sound tape reel (7 1/2 ips.).

Collection contains 11 radio commercials used during Brandsted's campaign for the 1982 gubernatorial election in Iowa. (Republican Party).

BRANSTAD, Terry.   4 videocassettes (3/4 in. & 1/2 in.).

Collection contains 2 television commercials used during Branstad's 1982 campaign and 8 television spots from his 1986 re-election campaign for Governor of Iowa. (Republican Party).

BRASHEAR, Kermit.   3 videocassettes (3/4 in. & 1.2 in.).

Collection contains 5 television commercials used during Brashear's 1986 primary campaign for Governor of Nebraska. (Republican Party).

BRAUN, Harry. 1 videocassette (3/4 in.).

Collection contains 2 television commercials used during Braun's 1986 campaign for U.S. Congress in District 1 of Arizona. (Democratic Party).

BRAUN, Warren. 1 videocassette (3/4 in.). 1 sound tape reel (7 1/2 ips.). 24209047.

Collection contains 2 television commercials and 4 radio commercials used during Braun's 1982 campaign for U.S. Congress in Wisconsin. (Democratic Party).

BRAY, Crandle. 2 videocassettes (3/4 in.).

Collection contains 24 television commercials used during Bray's 1986 campaign for U.S. Congress in District 6 of Georgia. (Democratic Party).

BREAUX, John. 6 videocassettes (3/4 in.).

Collection contains 75 television commercials used during Breaux's 1986 campaign for U.S. Senate in Louisiana. (Democratic Party).

BREECE, George. 2 videotapes (2 in.). 24209052.

Collection contains 8 television commercials used during Breece's 1976 campaign for Secretary of State in North Carolina. (Democratic Party).

BREITEL, Charles D. 6 videotapes (2 in.). 21315015.

Collection contains 6 television commercials used in Breitel's campaign for a 1973 judicial election in New York.

BREMER, Al. 1 sound tape reel (7 1/2 ips.).

Collection contains 2 radio commercials used during Bremer's campaign for the 1982 congressional election in District 6 in Iowa. (Republican Party).

BRENNAN, Jim. 4 videotapes (2 in.). 24209663.

Collection contains 4 television commercials used during Brennan's 1972 campaign for city attorney committee in Milwaukee, Wisconsin. (Democratic Party).

BRENNAN, Thomas. 1 videotape (2 in.). 24209677.

Collection contains 1 television commercial used during Brennan's 1976 campaign for U.S. Senate in Michigan. (Republican Party).

BREWER, Albert P. 1 film reel (16 mm.). 1 sound tape reel (3 3/4 ips.). 21416333.

Albert Brewer used this spot in his 1970 gubernatorial campaign in Alabama.

Collection contains 1 television commercial and 18 radio commercials used during Brewer's campaign for the 1970 gubernatorial election in Alabama. (Democratic Party).

BRICKLEY, Jim. 3 videocassettes (3/4 in.). 24209690.

Collection contains 11 television commercials used during Brickley's campaign for the 1982 gubernatorial election in Michigan. (Republican Party).

BRIGHTBILL, Chip. 1 videocassette (3/4 in.). 24209683.

Collection contains 1 television commercial used during Brightbill's 1982 campaign for State Senate in Pennsylvania. (Republican Party).

BRILL, Mike. 1 sound tape reel. (7 1/2 ips.).

Collection contains 1 radio commercial used during Brill's 1982 campaign for Mayor in Illinois. (Independent Party).

BRISCOE, Dolph. 1 videotape (2 in.). 21287258.

Collection contains 1 television commercial used in Briscoe's campaign for the 1972 gubernatorial election in Texas. (Democratic Party).

BRITT, Robin. 3 videocassettes (3/4 in.).

Collection contains 8 television commercials used during Britt's 1986 campaign for U.S. Congress in District 6 of North Carolina. (Democratic Party).

BROADBENT, Bob. 1 sound tape reel (7 1/2 ips.).

Collection contains 3 radio commercials used during Broadbent's campaign for the 1980 County Commissioner election in Nevada.

BROCK, Dave. 1 sound tape reel (7 1/2 ips).

Collection contains 1 radio commercial used during Brock's 1971 campaign for the U.S. Senate in New Hampshire. (Republican Party).

BROCK, William Emerson. 1930-. 1 film reel (16 mm.). 21358396.

Collection contains 27 television commercials used during Brock's 1970 campaign for U.S. Senate in Tennessee. (Republican Party).

BRODERICK, Ray. 1 film reel (16 mm.). 24357493.

Collection contains 16 television commercials used during Broderick's campaign for the 1970 gubernatorial election in Pennsylvania (Republican Party).

BROOKE, Edward. 2 videocassettes (3/4 in.).

Collection contains 8 television commercials from Brooke's 1978 campaign for U.S. Senate in Massachusetts. (Republican Party).

BROOKS, Jack. 1 videocassette (3/4 in.).

Collection contains 12 television commercials used during Brooks' 1982 campaign for U.S. Congress in Texas. (Democratic Party).

BROTZMAN, Don. 2 sound tape reels (7 1/2 ips.).

Collection contains 1 radio commercial used during Brotsman's 1970 campaign and 1 radio spot from his 1972 campaign for U.S. Congress in Colorado.

BROUJOS, John. 1 videotape (2 in.). 24209697.

Collection contains 3 television commercials used during Broujos' campaign for a 1984 election in Pennsylvania. (Democratic Party).

BROWN, Bill. 2 videocassette (3/4 in.). 24209703.

Collection contains 35 television commercials used during Brown's campaign for the 1982 gubernatorial election in Ohio. (Democratic Party).

BROWN, Clarence J. 3 videocassettes (3/4 in.). 24209708.

Collection contains 22 television commercials used during Brown's campaign for the 1982 gubernatorial election in Ohio. (Republican Party).

BROWN, Edmund G. "Pat." 2 videocassettes (3/4 in.). 1 film reel (16 mm.).

Collection contains several television spots from Brown's 1962 campaign and 19 television commercials from his 1966 campaign for Governor of California. (Democratic Party).

BROWN, Edmund G., Jr. "Jerry." 1938-. 1 videotape (2 in.). 7 videocassettes (3/4 in.). 21341107.

Collection contains 14 television commercials used during Brown's 1974 gubernatorial campaign and 4 television commercials used in his 1978 gubernatorial campaign; both in California. Includes 4 television commercials used during his 1976 campaign for President. Also included is a tape of the 1978 gubernatorial debate in California and a 30-minute television documentary used during his 1976 presidential primary in Wisconsin. (Democratic Party).

BROWN, Gary. 1 sound tape reel (7 1/2 ips).

Collection contains 1 radio commercial used during Brown's 1970 campaign for Congress in District 3 of Michigan. (Republican Party).

BROWN, George. 2 videocassettes (3/4 in.).

Collection contains 2 television spots from Brown's 1984 campaign for U.S. Congress in District 36 of California. (Democratic Party).

BROWN, John Y. 1 videocassette (3/4 in.).

Collection contains 13 television commercials from Brown's 1979 campaign for Governor of Kentucky. (Democratic Party).

BROWN, Millian. 1 sound tape reel. (7 1/2 ips.).

Collection contains 1 radio commercial used during Brown's 1982 campaign for Attorney General in Nevada. (Democratic Party).

BROWN, Sherrod. 3 videocassettes (3/4 in.). 24209714.

Collection contains 9 television commercials used during Brown's 1982 and 1986 campaigns for Secretary of State in Ohio. (Democratic Party).

BROWN, Sid. 1 videocassette (3/4 in.).

Collection contains 1 television commercial used during Brown's 1986 campaign for Associate District Judge in Oklahoma.

BROWN, Virgil E. 1 sound tape reel (7 1/2 ips.).

Collection contains 1 radio commercial used during Brown's 1980 campaign for Cuyahoga County Commissioner in Ohio.

BROYHILL, Jim. 10 videocassettes (3/4 in. & 1/2 in.).

Collection contains 18 television commercials used during Broyhill's 1986 campaign for U.S. Senate in North Carolina. (Republican Party).

BROYHILL, Joel T. 1919-. 2 videotapes (2 in.). 21254272.

Collection contains 2 television commercials used during Broyhill's 1970 campaign for U.S. Congress in Virginia. (Republican Party).

BRUCE, Terry. 2 videocassettes (3/4 in.).

Collection contains 5 television spots from Bruce's 1984 and 1986 campaigns for U.S. Congress in Illinois. (Democratic Party).

BRYAN, Richard. 1 sound tape reel. (7 1/2 ips.).

Collection contains 1 radio commercial used during Bryan's 1982 campaign for Attorney General in Nevada. (Democratic Party).

BUCHANAN, Mary Estill. 1 videocassette (3/4 in.).

Collection contains 2 television spots used during Buchanan's 1980 campaign for U.S. Senate in Colorado. (Republican Party).

BUCHANAN, Dennis. 1 videotape (3/4 in.). 24209720.

Collection contains 3 television commercials used during Buchanan's 1982 campaign for local office in Oregon.

BUCHMANN, George. 1 videotape (2 in.). 21631376.

Collection contains 1 commercial used during Buchmann's 1974 campaign for a judgeship in Florida. (Independent Party).

BUCKLEY, James Lane. 1923-. 1 sound tape reel (7 1/2 ips.). 3 film reels (16 mm.). 14 videotapes (2 in.). 1 videocassette (3/4 in.). 21191424.

Collection contains 24 television and 4 radio commercials used during Buckley's campaign for the 1970 U.S. senatorial election in New York. (Conservative Party). Includes 8 television commercials used during his re-election campaign for the 1976 U.S. senatorial election in New York and 18 commercials used in his 1980 re-election campaign for the same office. (Republican Party).

BUFORD. 1 videocassette (3/4 in.).

Collection contains 1 television commercial used during Buford's 1986 campaign for Associate District Judge in Oklahoma.

BUGLIOSI, Vincent. 2 videotapes (2 in.). 2 sound tape reels (7 1/2 ips.). 21341356.

Collection contains 10 radio commercials used during Bugliosi's 1972 and 1976 campaignss for Los Angeles District Attorney in California. Also includes 4 television commercials used during his 1974 campaign for Attorney General. (Democratic Party).

BUMPERS, Dale. 1 videotape (2 in.). 1 videocassette (3/4 in.). 21315045.

Collection contains 1 television commercial used during Bumpers' 1974 campaign for U.S. Senate in Arkansas. Also includes 12 television spots from his 1986 campaign for the same office. (Democratic Party).

BUNNING, Jim. 1931-. 6 videotapes (2 in.). 22245533.

Collection contains 7 television commercials used during Bunning's campaign for the 1983 gubernatorial election in Kentucky. (Republican Party).

BURCH, Francis Bill. 1 videocassette (3/4 in.).

Collection contains 6 television commercials from Burch's 1978 campaign for Governor of Maryland. (Democratic Party).

BURDEN, Carter. 3 videocassettes (3/4 in.).

Collection contains 21 television commercials from Burden's 1977 campaign for City Council in New York City and 2 television spots from his 1978 campaign for U.S. Congress in District 18 of New York. (Democratic Party).

BURDICK, Quentin N. 1908-. 3 film reels (16 mm.). 3 sound tape reels (7 1/2 ips.). 5 videotapes (2 in.). 21254589.

Collection contains 43 television commercials and 6 radio commercials used during Burdick's 1970 and 1976 campaigns for U.S. Senate in North Dakota. (Democratic Party).

BURGESS, John S. 1 sound tape reel (7 1/2 ips.).

Collection contains 3 radio commercials used during Burgess' 1972 campaign for Lt. Governor in Vermont.

BURKE, Edward. 1 sound tape reel (7 1/2 ips.).

Collection contains 4 radio commercials used during Burke's 1980 campaign for Attorney General in Illinois. (Democratic Party).

BURKE, Yvonne Brathwaite. 1932-. 1 videocassette (3/4 in.). 1 sound tape reel (7 1/2 ips.). 22044517.

Collection contains 6 television and 5 radio commercials used during Burke's 1978 campaign for Attorney General in California. (Democratic Party).

Yvonne Brathwaite Burke used this spot in her 1978 campaign for Attorney General in California.

BURNS, Edward P. 1 videotape (2 in.). 21511253.

Collection contains 1 television commercial used during Burns' 1972 campaign for Governor in North Dakota. (Democratic Party).

BURNS, John Carrol. 1 sound tape reel (7 1/2 ips.).

Collection contains 3 radio commercials used during Burns' 1982 campaign for Supreme Bench Judge in Baltimore, Maryland.

BURNS, Steve. 1 videocassette (3/4 in.).

Collection contains 3 television commercials used during Burns' 1986 campaign for Congress in District 1 of Nebraska. (Democratic Party).

BURRIS, John. 1 videocassette (3/4 in.).

Collection contains 4 television spots used in Burris' 1984 campaign for U.S. Senate in Delaware.

BURRIS, Roland. 1 videotape (1 in.). 1 sound tape reel (7 1/2 ips). 24209725.

Collection contains 2 television commercials used during Burris' campaign for a 1986 state office in Illinois and 2 radio commercials used during his 1982 campaign for State Comptroller in Illinois. (Democratic Party).

BURTON, John.   1 videocassette (3/4 in.).

Collection contains 3 television commercials used during Burton's 1980 campaign for U.S. Congress in District 5 of California. (Democratic Party).

BUSBEE, George. 1927-. 1 sound tape reel (7 1/2 ips.). 21887824.

Collection contains 2 radio commercials used during Busbee's campaign for the 1974 gubernatorial election in Georgia. (Democratic Party).

BUSCH, Joseph Peter. 1926-1975. 1 sound tape reel (7 1/2 ips.) 1 film reel (16 mm.). 21499042.

Collection contains 5 television commercials and 8 radio commercials used during Busch's 1973 campaign for District Attorney in California.

BUSCH, Pete.   2 videocassettes (3/4 in.).

Collection contains 6 television spots from Busch's 1984 campaign for U.S. Senate from Idaho.   (Democratic Party).

BUSH, George. 1924 -. 1 film reel (16 mm.). 35 videocassettes (3/4 in.). 8 videotapes (2 in.). 21254558.

George Bush lifts his granddaughter in this up-beat spot from his 1988 presidential campaign.

Collection contains 2 television commercials used in Bush's 1970 campaign for U.S. Senate Texas and 91 television commercials used during his 1980 presidential primary campaigns. Includes 1980 primary debates in New Hampshire, Illinois, and Texas and miscellaneous speeches and events (Republican National Convention speech). Also contains 61 television commercials used in his 1988 campaign for President and the 1988 presidential debates with Dukakis. (Republican Party).

In this 1988 presidential spot George Bush ridiculed Michael Dukakis's stand on defense.

BUSTAMONTE, Albert. 2 videocassettes (3/4 in.).

Collection contains 6 television spots from Bustamonte's 1984 campaign for U.S. Congress in District 23 of Texas. (Democratic Party).

BUTCHER, Jim. 1 videocassette (3/4 in.).

Collection contains 1 television commercial used during Butcher's 1986 campaign for Congress in District 5 of Indiana.

BUTLER, Carl. 1 film reel (16 mm.). 24209731.

Collection contains 3 television commercials from Butler's 1972 campaign for U.S. Congress in Mississippi. (Republican Party).

BUTTS, Nina. 1 videocassette (3/4 in.). 24357500.

Collection contains 2 television spots from Butts' 1986 campaign for U.S. Congress in District 10 of Texas. (Democratic Party).

BUXTON, Ron. 1 sound tape reel (7 1/2 ips.).

Collection contains 4 radio commercials from Buxton's 1980 campaign for State Senate in Pennsylvania. (Democratic Party).

BYCEL, Ben. 1 videocassette (3/4 in.).

Collection contains 1 television commercial used during Bycel's 1986 campaign for supervisor in Santa Barbara, California.

BYRD, Harold. 1 videocassette (3/4 in.).

Collection contains 3 television commercials used during Byrd's 1982 campaign for U.S. Congress in District 7 of Tennessee. (Democratic Party).

BYRD, Harry Flood, 1914 -. 2 film reels (16 mm.). 21416058.

Collection contains 11 television commercial used during Byrd's 1970 campaign for U.S. Senate in Virginia. (American Independent Party).

BYRD, Robert. 1 film reel (16 mm.). 24209977.

Collection contains 1 television commercial used during Byrd's 1970 campaign for U.S. Senate in West Virginia. (Democratic Party).

BYRNE, Garrett. 1 videotape (3/4 in.).

Collection contains 2 television commercials from Byrne's 1970 District attorney campaign in Suffolk County, Massachusetts.

BYRNE, Jane. 11 videocassettes (3/4 in.). 1 sound tape reel (7 1/2 ips.).

Collection contains 5 television commercials and 7 radio spots from 1979 and 23 television commercials from 1983, all used in Byrne campaigns for Mayor of Chicago, Illinois. Also includes 1983 televised mayoral debate with Harold Washington and Richard M. Daley. (Democratic Party).

BYRNES, John Carroll. 1 videotape (2 in.). 24209979.

Collection contains 2 television commercials used during Byrnes' campaign for the 1976 Congressional election in Maryland. (Democratic Party).

CAGLIARDI, Pat. 1 videocassette (3/4 in.).

Collection contains 2 television commercials used during Cagliardi's 1986 campaign for State Representative in Michigan.

CALABRESE, Anthony O. 1 sound tape reel (7 1/2 ips.).

Collection contains 3 radio commercials used during Calabrese's 1980 campaign for State Senate in Ohio. (Democratic Party).

CALDWELL, William W. 1925 -. 1 sound tape reel (7 1/2 ips.). 22137693.

Collection contains 5 radio commercials used during Caldwell's 1979 campaign for a judgeship in Dauphin County, Pennsylvania.

CALLAHAN, Sonny. 2 videocassettes (3/4 in.).

Collection contains 3 television spots from Callahan's 1984 campaign for U.S. Congress in District 1 of Alabama. (Republican Party).

CALLAN, Joseph. 1 videotape (2 in.). 24357514.

Collection contains 2 television commercials used during Callan's 1979 campaign for Circuit Court Judge of Branch 36 in Wisconsin.

CALTON, Stan. 1 sound tape reel (7 1/2 ips.).

Collection contains 2 radio commercials used during Calton's campaign for Governor of Nevada.

CAMPAIGNE, Tony. 1 sound tape reel (7 1/2 ips.).

Collection contains 12 radio commercials used during Campaigne's 1982 campaign for U.S. Congress in District 1 in New Hampshire. (Republican Party).

CAMPANELLA, Vince. 1 videocassette (3/4 in.). 24209985.

Collection contains 6 television commercials used during Campanella's campaign for the 1982 state election in Ohio. (Republican Party).

CAMPBELL, Ben Nighthorse. 1 videocassette (3/4 in.).

Collection contains 4 television commercials used during Campbell's 1986 campaign for Congress in District 3 of Colorado. (Democratic Party).

CAMPBELL, Bill. 2 videotapes (1 in.). 24209991.

Collection contains 4 television commercials used during Campbell's 1986 campaign for Controller Committee in California. (Republican Party).

CAMPBELL, Carroll. 1 videocassette (3/4 in.).

Collection contains 8 television spots from Campbell's 1984 campaign for U.S. Congress in North Carolina. (Republican Party).

CAMPBELL, Ed. 1 sound tape reel (7 1/2 ips.).

Collection contains 13 radio commercials used during Campbell's campaign for the 1982 gubernatorial election in Iowa. (Democratic Party).

CAMPBELL, Joe. 1 sound tape reel (7 1/2 ips).

Collection contains 1 radio commercial used during Campbell's 1970 campaign for the State Senate in New York. (Republican Party).

CANNON, Howard W. 1 videotape (2 in.). 1 videocassette (3/4 in.). 1 sound tape reel (7 1/2 ips.)   21358380.

Collection contains 33 television commercials used during Cannon's 1970 campaign, 29 television commercials used in his 1976 campaign, and 2 radio spots from his 1982 campaign for U.S. Senate; all in Nevada. (Democratic Party).

CANNON, Joe. 1 videotape (2 in.).

Collection contains 1 television commercial used during Cannon's campaign for a judgeship election in Oklahoma.

CANTOS, Earl. 3 videotapes (1 in.).   24209996.

Collection contains 3 television commercials used during Cantos' campaign for the 1986 State House election in California.

CANTRELL, Rose. 1 videocassette (3/4 in.).

Collection contains 2 television commercials used during Cantrell's campaign for the 1982 judgeship election in Tennessee. (Democratic Party).

CAPEHART, Homer Earl. 1897 - 1979. 1 film reel (16 mm.). 21382808.

Collection contains 1 television commercial used during Capehart's campaign for the 1962 U.S. senatorial election in Indiana. (Republican Party).

CAPONARA, Victor. 1 videocassette (3/4 in.).

Collection contains 1 television commercial used during Caponara's 1986 campaign for Albany City Judge in New York.

CARDIN, Ben. 1 videocassette (3/4 in.).

Collection contains 3 television commercials used during Cardin's 1986 campaign for Congress in District 3 of Maryland. (Democratic Party).

CAREY, Bernard. 1 sound tape reel (7 1/2 ips.).

Collection contains 4 radio commercials used during Carey's campaign for the 1980 State Attorney election in Illinois. (Republican Party).

CAREY, Eleanor. 3 videocassettes (3/4 in.).

Collection contains 10 television commercials used during Carey's 1986 campaign for Attorney General in Maryland. (Democratic Party).

CAREY, Hugh.   1 videocassette (3/4 in.).

Collection consists of 14 television commercials used in Carey's 1978 campaign for Governor of New York.   (Democratic Party).

CAREY, James.   1 videocassette (3/4 in.).

Collection contains 2 television spots from Carey's 1984 campaign for U.S. Congress in District 19 of California.   (Democratic Party).

CARLEY, David.   1 videocassette (3/4 in.). 2 videotapes (2 in.).

Collection contains 8 television commercials from Carley's 1978 campaign for Governor of Wisconsin.   (Democratic Party).

CARLIN, John.   1 videocassette (3/4 in.).

Collection contains 3 television commercials from Carlin's 1978 campaign for Governor of Kansas.   (Democratic Party).

CARMEN, Bill. 1 sound tape reel (7 1/2 ips).

Collection contains 1 radio commercial used during Carmen's 1971 campaign for Mayor in Massachusetts.

CARMICHAEL, Gilbert E. 11 videotapes (2 in.). 21631321.

Collection contains 12 television commercials used during Carmichael's campaign for the 1975 gubernatorial election in Mississippi. (Republican Party).

CARNEY, Jim, Jr. 1 videocassette (3/4 in.). 24210001.

Collection contains 6 television commercials used during Carney's campaign for the 1982 state office election in Ohio.

CARPENTER, John.   2 videocassettes (3/4 in.).

Collection contains 5 television spots from Carpenter's 1984 campaign for California State Assembly.

CARPER, J.E. 1 videotape (2 in.). 21887856.

Collection contains 2 television commercials used during Carper's 1974 campaign for Sheriff in California.

CARPER, Tom.   1 videocassette (3/4 in.).

Collection contains 2 television spots from Carper's 1984 campaign for Congressman At Large in Delaware. (Democratic Party).

CARR, Bob. 6 videocassettes (3/4 in.). 24210003.

Collection contains 9 television ads from Carr's 1976 campaign, 12 television commercials from his 1982 campaign, and 9 television commercials from his 1984 campaign; all for U.S. Congress in District 6 of Michigan. Includes 13 television commercials used during his 1986 campaign for Congress in District 6 of Michigan. (Democratic Party).

This spot was used in Larry Carr's 1970 gubernatorial campaign in Arkansas.

CARR, Larry. 1 film reel (16 mm.). 21887835.

Collection contains 1 television commercial used during Carr's campaign for the 1970 gubernatorial election in Arkansas. (Democratic Party).

CARRINGTON, John. 1 videocassette (3/4 in.).

Collection contains 6 television spots from Carrington's 1984 campaign for Lt. Governor of North Carolina.

CARROLL, James. 1 sound tape reel (7 1/2 ips.).

Collection contains 1 radio commercial used during Carroll's 1980 campaign for a judgeship in Cuyahoga County, Ohio.

CARROLL, Julian M. 1 videotape (2 in.). 1 videocassette (3/4 in.). 22155945.

Collection contains 11 television commercials used during Carroll's 1975 campaign for Governor in Kentucky. (Democratic Party).

CARTER, Doug. 7 videotapes (2 in.).

Collection contains 5 television commercials used during Carter's campaign for the 1974 state assemblyman election in District 7 of California. Includes 2 television commercials used during his campaign for the 1976 state assemblyman election in District 26 of California. (Republican Party).

CARTER, Jimmy. 5 film reels (16 mm.). 64 videocassettes (3/4 in.). 40 videotapes (2 in.).

Although it was not used as a campaign spot, this program produced for Jimmy Carter displayed an interesting use of claymation techniques.

Collection contains 171 television commercials used during Carter's campaign for the 1976 presidential election, 101 television spots from the 1980 presidential primaries, and 176 television commercials used during the 1980 re-election campaign. Collection also contains copies of televised debates in 1976 and 1980 and miscellaneous television news coverage, longer television documentaries, and speeches. (Democratic Party).

CARTEZ, Manny. 1 sound tape reel (7 1/2 ips.).

Collection contains 1 radio commercial used during Cartez's 1982 campaign for local office in Nevada.

CARVER, Richard. 1 sound tape reel (7 1/2 ips.).

Collection contains 2 radio commercials used during Carver's campaign for the 1980 U.S. Senate election in Illinois. (Republican Party).

CASE, Clifford P. 1904 - 1982. 1 videotape (2 in.). 21270318.

Collection contains 1 television commercial used during Case's 1972 campaign for U.S. Senate in New Jersey. (Republican Party).

CASEY, Dan. 1 videotape (2 in.). 24357524.

Collection contains 2 television commercials used during Casey's 1980 campaign for County Executive in Milwaukee, Wisconsin.

CASEY, Robert P. 1932 -. 1 film reel (16 mm.). 6 videocassettes (3/4 in.). 1 sound tape reel (7 1/2 ips.). 21923902.

Collection contains 70 television spots and several radio commercials from Casey's various statewide campaigns in Pennsylvania. (Democratic Party).

CASEY, Tom. 1 videocassette (3/4 in.).

Collection contains 5 television commercials used during Casey's 1986 campaign for a Jones County judgeship in Mississippi.

CASTLE, John. 4 videotapes (2 in.). 22256919.

Collection contains 6 television commercials used during the 1978 comptroller election in Illinois. (Republican Party).

CASTON, Bob. 1 sound tape reel (7 1/2 ips.).

Collection contains 2 radio commercials used during Caston's campaign for the 1976 Congressional election in Wisconsin.

CAVANAGH, Jerome P. 2 videotapes (2 in.). 21352729.

Collection contains 12 television commercials used during Cavanagh's campaign for the 1974 gubernatorial election in Michigan. (Democratic Party).

CAVANAUGH. 1 videocassette (3/4 in.). 24210006.

Collection contains 1 television commercial used during Cavanaugh's campaign for the 1982 judgeship election in Michigan.

CAYETANO. 2 videocassettes (3/4 in.).

Collection contains 12 television commercials used during Cayetano's 1986 campaign for Lt. Governor of Hawaii. (Democratic Party).

CECI, Louis J. 2 videotapes (2 in.). 24357535.

Collection contains 4 television commercials used during Ceci's 1980 campaign for State Supreme Court Judge in Wisconsin.

CELEBREZZE, Anthony J.. 2 videotapes (2 in.). 3 videocassettes (3/4 in.). 24210009.

Collection contains 5 television commercials used during Celebrezze's 1982 campaign for Attorney General and 4 television commercials used in his 1976 campaign for U.S. Congress in Ohio. Includes 8 television commercials used during his 1986 campaign for Attorney General. (Democratic Party).

CELEBREZZE, Frank D. 6 videotapes (1 in. & 2 in.). 24210012.

Collection contains 10 television commercials used during Celebrezze's 1986 campaign for a judgeship in Ohio. (Democratic Party).

CELEBREZZE, James P.   1 videocassette (3/4 in.).

Collection contains 2 television spots from Celebrezze's 1984 campaign for Supreme Court in Ohio. (Democratic Party).

CELESTE, Dick. 9 videocassettes (3/4 in.). 24210019.

Collection contains 30 television commercials used during Celeste's campaign for the 1982 gubernatorial election in Ohio. Includes 73 television commercials used during his 1986 re-election campaign. (Democratic Party).

CHAFEE, John H. 1922 -. 2 film reels (16 mm.). 3 videotapes (2 in.). 1 sound tape reel (7 1/2 ips.). 21276407.

Collection contains 12 television commercials and 1 radio commercial used during Chafee's 1968 campaign for Governor and his 1972 campaign for U.S. Senate in Rhode Island. (Republican Party).

CHAFFEE, Jim. 2 videotapes (2 in.). 21486400.

Collection contains 1 television commercial used during Chaffee's campaign for the 1972 sheriff election and 1 television commercial used in his campaign for the 1974 Sheriff election in Kansas. (Democratic Party).

CHANDLER, Debra. 1 videotape (2 in.). 24210835.

Collection contains 1 television commercial used during Chandler's 1986 campaign for U.S. Congress in District 7 of Alabama.

CHANDLER, Jack. 1 sound tape reel (7 1/2 ips.).

Collection contains 4 radio commercials used during Chandler's 1982 campaign for State Senate in District 7 in New Hampshire. (Republican Party).

CHANDLER, Rod. 2 videocassettes (3/4 in.).

Collection contains 2 television commercials used during Chandler's 1982 campaign and 2 television spots from his 1984 campaign for U.S. Congress in District 8 of Washington. (Republican Party).

CHAPMAN, Eugenia. 1 sound tape reel (7 1/2 ips.).

Collection contains 4 radio commercials used during Chapman's campaign for the 1982 Congressional election in District 10 of Illinois. (Democratic Party).

CHAPMAN, Sylvia. 1 sound tape reel (7 1/2 ips.).

Collection contains 7 radio commercials used during Chapman's campaign for the 1972 Congressional election in New Hampshire. (Democratic Party).

CHAPPIE, Eugene A. 1920-. 1 videotape (2 in.). 21341236.

Collection contains 1 television commercial used during Chappie's 1974 campaign for the State Representative in California.

CHAVEZ, Linda. 4 videocassettes (3/4 in.).

Collection contains 19 television spots from Chavez's 1986 campaign for the U.S. Senate in Maryland. (Libertarian Party).

CHEMA, Tom. 1 sound tape reel (7 1/2 ips.).

Collection contains 3 radio commercials used during Chema's campaign for the 1980 State Senate election in District 22 in Ohio. (Democratic Party).

CHENEY, Richard. 1 sound tape reel (7 1/2 ips).

Collection contains 1 radio commercial used during Cheney's 1984 campaign for U.S. Congress in Wyoming. (Republican Party).

CHERRY, Howard. 1 sound tape reel (7 1/2 ips).

Collection contains 1 radio commercial used during Cherry's 1970 campaign for the State House in Oregon. (Democratic Party).

CHILES, Lawton Mainor. 2 videotapes (2 in.). 24210838.

Collection contains 7 television commercials used during Chile's campaign for the 1976 U.S. Senate election in Florida. (Democratic Party).

CHOTKOWSKI, Dave. 1 videocassette (3/4 in.).

Collection contains 2 television spots from Chotkowski's 1984 campaign for State Representative in District 117 of Maine.

CHRISTENSEN, Vern. 1 sound tape reel. (7 1/2 ips.).

Collection contains 2 radio commercials used during Christensen's 1982 campaign for State Senate in District 5 in Nevada.

CHRISTENSEN, Walt. 1 film reel (16 mm.). 24210842.

Collection contains 1 television commercial used during Christensen's 1972 campaign for State Treasurer in North Dakota. (Democratic Party).

CHRISTIAN, Dave. 1 videocassette (3/4 in.).

Collection contains 3 television spots from Christian's 1984 campaign for U.S. Congress from Pennsylvania.

CHRISTOPHER, George. 1 film reel (16 mm.). 24210846.

Collection contains 2 television commercials used during Christopher's campaign for the 1966 gubernatorial election in California. (Republican Party).

CHRYSLER, Dick. 5 videocassettes (3/4 in.).

Collection contains 20 television spots used during Chrysler's 1986 campaign for Governor of Michigan. (Republican Party).

CHURCH, Frank. 3 film reels (16 mm.). 3 videotapes (2 in.). 2 videocassettes (3/4 in.). 21368917.

Collection contains 17 television commercials used during Church's campaign for the 1962 U.S. senatorial election in Idaho, 30 television commercials used in his 1968 re-election campaign. Includes 13 television commercials used in his 1976 campaign for president and 3 television spots from Church's 1980 campaign for U.S. Senate in Idaho. (Democratic Party).

CIANCI, Vincent A., Jr. "Buddy." 9 videotapes (2 in.). 1 videocassette (3/4 in.). 24357543.

Collection contains 27 television commercials used during Cianci's campaign for the 1980 gubernatorial campaign in Rhode Island. (Republican Party).

CICCO, John, Jr. 1 videocassette (1/2 in.).

Collection contains 2 television commercials used during Cicco's 1976 campaign for Congress in District 21 in Pennsylvania. (Democratic Party).

CLARK, Arthur. 1 videocassette (3/4 in.).

Collection contains 1 television spot from Clark's 1980 primary campaign for U.S. Congress in District 4 of Massachusetts. (Democratic Party).

CLARK, David. 1 sound tape reel (7 1/2 ips.).

Collection contains 2 radio commercials used during Clark's 1982 campaign for Washington, D.C. city council chairman. (Democratic Party).

CLARK, Dick. 1 videotape (2 in.). 1 videocassette (3/4 in.). 24210850.

This frame comes from a spot used in Dick Clark's 1978 senatorial campaign in Iowa.

Collection contains 1 television commercial used during Clark's 1972 campaign and 6 television commercials from his 1976 campaign for U.S. Senate in Iowa. (Democratic Party).

CLARK, Ed. 3 videotapes (2 in). 4 videocassettes (3/4 in.). 2 sound tape reels (7 1/2 ips.). 24357553.

Collection contains 5 television commercials and 10 radio spots used during Clark's 1980 campaign for Pres-ident. (Libertarian Party).

CLARK, Robert. 1 videocassette (3/4 in.). 24210853.

Collection contains 7 television commercials used during Clark's 1982 campaign for Congress in Mississippi. (Democratic Party).

CLARKE, James. 3 videocassettes (3/4 in.). 24210854.

Collection contains 14 television commercials used during Clarke's 1982 and 1984 campaigns for Congress in District 11 of North Carolina. (Democratic Party).

CLARKE, Mary Pat. 1 sound tape reel. (7 1/2 ips.).

Collection contains 4 radio commercials used during Clarke's 1982 campaign for local office in Maryland. (Democratic Party).

CLAY, Henry. 1 videocassette (3/4 in.). 24210857.

Collection contains 1 television commercial used during Clay's 1982 campaign for a judgeship in Michigan.

CLELAND, Max. 1942-. 1 film reel (16 mm.). 21631085.

Collection contains 2 television commercials from Cleland's 1974 campaign for Lt. Governor in Georgia. (Democratic Party).

CLEMENT, Annabelle O'Brien. 2 videocassettes (3/4 in.).

Collection contains 2 television commercials used during Clement's campaign for the 1982 gubernatorial election in Tennessee. (Democratic Party).

CLEMENT, Frank Goad. 1 film reel (16 mm.). 22164885.

Collection contains 1 television commercial used during Clement's 1962 campaign for Governor in Tennessee. (Democratic Party).

CLEMENTS, William. 6 videocassette (3/4 in.). 1 sound tape reel (7 1/2 ips).

Collection contains 2 television commercials from Clements' 1978 campaign for Governor and 2 television and 2 radio commercials from his 1982 campaign for Governor in Texas. Includes 71 television commercials used during his 1986 campaign for Congress in District 10 of Texas. (Republican Party).

CLEVELAND, Clyde. 1935-. 1 film reel (16 mm.). 21538637.

Collection contains 1 television commercial used during Cleveland's 1973 campaign for Common Council in Detroit, Michigan. (Democratic Party).

CLIMER, Kelly Bryant. 1 videotape (2 in.). 22245565.

Collection contains 1 television commercial used during Climer's 1972 campaign for Secretary of State in Arizona.

CLINGER, Bill. 7 videocassettes (3/4 in.).

Collection contains 16 television commercials used during Clinger's 1986 campaign for Congress in District 23 of Pennsylvania.
(Republican Party).

CLINTON, Bill. 3 videocassettes (3/4 in.).

Collection contains 6 television commercials used during Clinton's 1980 campaign for Governor of Arkansas. Also contains 21 television commercials from his 1984 re-election campaign. (Democratic Party).

CLOSE, Albert. 1 sound tape reel (7 1/2 ips).

Collection contains 1 radio commercial used during Close's 1984 campaign for Hartford County Judge in Maryland.

**CLOUD, Roger. 1 film reel (16 mm.). 2 videotapes (2 in.).
21191511.**

Collection contains 3 television commercials from Cloud's 1970
campaign for Governor in Ohio. (Republican Party).

COATS, Daniel. 3 videocassettes (3/4 in.).

Collection contains 13 television commercials used during Coats'
1986 campaign for Congress in Indiana. (Democratic Party).

COBB, Steve. 3 videocassettes (3/4 in.).

Collection contains 13 television commercials used during Cobb's
1986 campaign for U.S. Congress in Tennessee. (Republican Party).

COBEY, Bill. 5 videocassettes (3/4 in.).

Collection contains 11 television commercials used during Cobey's
1986 campaign for Congress in North Carolina. (Republican Party).

COCHRAN, THAD. 5 videocassettes (3/4 in.).

Collection contains 45 television spots form Cochran's 1984
campaign for U.S. Senate from Mississippi. (Republican Party).

COCKRILL, Sterling. 1 film reel (16 mm.). 24357287.

Collection contains 9 television commercials used during
Cockrill's 1968 campaign for Lt. Governor in Arkansas.
(Republican Party).

In this 1980 campaign for U.S. Senate in Wisconsin, Douglass Cofrin's
daughter appears beside a campaign poster.

**COFFEY, John. 1
videotape (2 in.).**

Collection contains 1
television commercial
from Coffey's 1978
campaign for Supreme
Court Judge in
Wisconsin.

**COFRIN, Douglass. 5
videotapes (2 in.).
24210861.**

Collection contains 12
television commercials
used during Cofrin's
1980 campaign for U.S.
Senate in Wisconsin.
(Republican Party).

COHEN, Allan S. 1 sound tape reel (7 1/2 ips.).

Collection contains 3 radio commercials used during Cohen's campaign for the 1982 County Council election in Maryland. (Democratic Party).

COHEN, Bill. 1 videotape (2 in.). 24210863.

Collection contains 1 television commercial used during Cohen's 1976 campaign for U.S. Congress in Massachusetts.

COHEN, Burt. 1 videocassette (3/4 in.).

Collection contains 5 television commercials used during Cohen's 1986 campaign for U.S. Congress in District 1 in New Hampshire. (Democratic Party).

COHEN, William. 2 film reels (16 mm.). 24210867.

Collection contains 5 television commercials used during Cohen's campaign for the 1972 congressional election in District 2 of Minnesota. (Republican Party).

COHEN, William, S. 1940 -. 3 videocassettes (3/4 in.).

Collection contains 16 television spots from Cohen's 1986 campaign for U.S. Senate in Maine. (Republican Party).

COLEMAN, Marshall. 1 sound tape reel (7 1/2 ips.).

Collection contains 23 radio commercials used during Coleman's campaign for the 1981 gubernatorial election in Virginia. (Republican Party).

COLEMAN, Mary Stallings. 1 videotape (2 in.). 1 sound tape reel (7 1/2 ips.). 21348089.

Collection contains 1 television commercial used during Coleman's campaign for the 1972 state supreme court judge election and 1 radio commercial from her 1980 campaign for the same office.

COLEMAN, Ronald. 1 sound tape reel (7 1/2 ips.).

Collection contains 1 radio commercial used during Coleman's 1982 congressional campaign in District 16 of Texas. (Democratic Party).

COLLINS, Candiss. 1 sound tape reel (7 1/2 ips).

Collection contains 1 radio commercial used during Collins' 1984 campaign for Congress in District 7 of Illinois. (Democratic Party).

COLLINS, Johnny. 1 sound tape reel (7 1/2 ips.).

Collection contains 1 radio commercial used during Collins' 1982 campaign for State House in District 48 of California. (Democratic Party).

COLLINS, LeRoy. 1 film reel (16 mm.). 24357294.

Collection contains 1 television commercial used during Collins' campaign for the 1968 U.S. Senate election in Florida. (Democratic Party).

COLLINS, Martha Layne. 1 videocassette (3/4 in.).

Collection contains 12 television spots from Collins' 1983 campaign for Governor of Kentucky. (Democratic Party).

COLLINS, Tom. 1 sound tape reel (7 1/2 ips.).

Collection contains 3 radio commercials used during Collins' campaign for the 1980 County Attorney election in Maricopa County in Arizona. (Republican Party).

COLLIS, Conway H. 1 videotape (1 in.). 24213144.

Collection contains 1 television commercial used during Collis' campaign for a 1986 election in California.

COLON, Rafael. Hernandes. 8 videocassettes (3/4 in.).

Collection contains 12 television commercials for Colon's 1976 campaign for Governor in Puerto Rico and 2 television spots from his 1980 campaign for Governor. (Popular Democratic Party).

COLUMBO, Robert J., Jr. 1 sound tape reel. (7 1/2 ips.).

Collection contains 1 radio commercial used during Columbo's 1982 campaign for a judgeship in Michigan.

COLVIN, Milton. 1 film reel (16 mm.). 24210948.

Collection contains 3 television commercials used during Colvin's campaign for the 1970 U.S. Senate election in Virginia. (Democratic Party).

COMBS, Bert. 2 film reels (16 mm.). 24210950.

Collection contains 20 television commercials used during Combs' campaign for the 1971 gubernatorial election in Kentucky. (Democratic Party).

CONLIN, Roxanne.   1 sound tape reel (7 1/2 ips.).

Collection contains 8 radio commercials used during Conlin's 1982 campaign for Governor in Iowa.   (Democratic Party).

CONLIN, Michael. 1 videotape (2 in.). 24357303.

Collection contains 2 television commercials used during Conlin's 1978 campaign for U.S. Congress in Michigan.   (Republican Party).

CONMY, Patrick A.   1 sound tape reel (7 1/2 ips.).

Collection contains 1 radio commercial used during Conmy's re-election campaign for the 1980 State Legislature election in District 47 in North Dakota.   (Republican Party).

CONNALLY, John.   7 videotapes (2 in.). 7 videocassettes (3/4 in.). 24357314.

Collection contains 34 television commercials used during Connally's primary campaigns for the 1980 presidential election. Also includes the New Hampshire primary debate and miscellaneous other speeches and debates. (Republican Party).

CONNALLY, Wayne. 1 film reel (16 mm.). 1 videotape (2 in.). 21511287.

Collection contains 5 television commercials from Connally's 1972 campaign for Lt. Governor in Texas. (Democratic Party).

CONNELL, Des.   1 sound tape reel (7 1/2 ips.).

Collection contains 8 radio commercials used during Connell's campaign for the 1972 District Attorney election in Oregon.

CONNOLLY, Mike. 2 videocassettes (3/4 in.).

Collection contains 2 television commercials used during Connolly's 1986 campaign for Secretary of State in Massachusetts. (Democratic Party).

CONNORS, Arlene. 3 videotapes (2 in.). 24357325.

Collection contains 3 television commercials used during Connors' campaign for the 1980 Circuit Court Judge of Branch 36 in Wisconsin.

CONRAD, Ken. 2 videocassettes (3/4 in.).

Collection contains 23 television commercials used during Conrad's 1986 campaign for U.S. Senate in North Dakota. (Democratic Party).

62

CONRAD, Larry A. 1 videotape (2 in.). 21191469.

Collection contains 2 television commercials used during Conrad's campaign for the 1970 Secretary of State in Indiana. (Democratic Party).

COOK, Rodney. 1 sound tape reel (7 1/2 ips.).

Collection contains 3 radio commercials used during Cook's campaign for the 1972 Congressional election in District 5 in Georgia. (Republican Party).

COON, Ken. 1 film reel (16 mm.). 21630881.

Collection contains 4 television commercials used during Coon's campaign for the 1974 gubernatorial election in Arizona. (Republican Party).

COOPER, Jessica. 3 videocassettes (3/4 in.).

Collection contains 3 television commercials used during Cooper's 1986 campaign for a judgeship in Michigan.

COOPER, Jim. 3 videocassettes (3/4 in.).

Collection contains 8 television commercials used during Cooper's 1982 campaign for U.S. Congress in Tennessee. (Democratic Party).

COPE, Mike. 1 videocassette (3/4 in.).

Collection contains 1 television commercial used during Cope's 1986 campaign in Ohio.

CORAM, Dick. 1 sound tape reel (7 1/2 ips.).

Collection contains 5 radio commercials used during Coram's campaign for the 1972 State Senate election in Oregon.

CORCORAN, Tom. 1 videotape (2 in.). 24210952.

Collection contains 3 television commercials from Corcoran's campaign for U.S. Senate in Illinois. (Republican Party).

CORMAN, Doyle. 1 videocassette (3/4 in.).

Collection contains 4 television commercials for Corman's 1978 campaign for State Senate.

CORWIN, Darlene. 3 videocassettes (3/4 in.).

Collection contains 1 television commercial used during Corwin's 1986 campaign for Rock Island County Clerk in Illinois.

CORY, Ken.   3 videocassettes (3/4 in.).

Collection contains 6 television commercials from Cory's 1974 campaign for State Controller in California and 1 television commercial from his 1980 campaign for the same office. (Democratic Party).

COSENTINO, Jerry. 2 videotapes (2 in.).   1 sound tape reel (7 1/2 ips.).   24211067.

Collection contains 5 radio spots from Cosentino's 1982 campaign for Secretary of State and 2 television commercials used during his 1986 campaign for State Treasurer in Illinois. (Democratic Party).

COSTA, Jim.   1 videocassette (3/4 in.).

Collection contains 1 television commercial from Costa's 1980 campaign for California State Assembly.

COSTELLO, John W.. 1 sound tape reel (71/2 ips).

Collection contains 6 radio commercials used during Costello's campaign for Lt. Governor in Massachusetts. (Democratic Party).

COTTER, William Ross. 1926-1981. 1 videotape (2 in.). 21256360.

Collection contains 1 television commercial used during Cotter's 1972 campaign for U.S. Congress in Connecticut. (Democratic Party).

COUGHLIN, Larry. 3 videocassettes (3/4 in.).

Collection contains 6 television commercials used during Coughlin's 1986 campaign for Congress in District 13 of Pennsylvania.

COURTWRIGHT, Morris. 2 videotapes (2 in.). 24211187.

Collection contains 2 television commercials used during Courtwright's campaign for the 1986 State House election in Arizona.

COWPER, Steve.   7 videocassettes (3/4 in.).

Collection contains 14 television spots from Cowper's 1984 campaign for Governor of Alaska. (Democratic Party).

COX, Bill. 1 videocassette (3/4 in.).

Collection contains 1 television commercial used during Cox's 1986 campaign for the State House in District 34 of Maryland.

64

COYNE, Jim. 2 videocassettes (3/4 in.). 1 sound tape reel (7 1/2 ips.).

Collection contains 7 television spots and 1 radio spots from Coyne's 1980 campaign and 5 television spots and 7 radio spots from his 1982 campaign for U.S. Congress in District 8 of Pennsylvania. (Republican Party).

COYNE, Ray. 1 sound tape reel (7 1/2 ips).

Collection contains 1 radio commercial used during Coyne's 1984 campaign for a state office in Illinois. (Democratic Party).

CRAIG, Ed. 1 sound tape reel (7 1/2 ips.).

Collection contains 1 radio commercial used during Craig's campaign for the 1982 Register of Probate election in New Hampshire.

CRAIG, Larry. 2 videocassettes (3/4 in.).

Collection contains 6 television spots from Craig's 1984 campaign for U.S. Congress from District 1 in Idaho. (Republican Party).

CRANE, Daniel B. 1936-. 1 sound tape reel (7 1/2 ips.). 1 videocassette (3/4 in.). 21930049.

Collection contains 6 radio commercials used during Crane's 1978 campaign for U.S. Congress in Illinois. Also contains 2 television commercials from his 1984 campaign for U.S. Congress. (Republican party).

CRANE, Phil. 2 videocassettes (3/4 in.).

Collection contains Crane's participation in the 1980 Republican New Hampshire primary presidential debate and in the Republican Unity Dinner in 1980. (Republican Party).

CRANE, Robert. 8 videocassettes (3/4 in.).

Collection contains 22 television commercials used during Crane's 1986 campaign for State Treasurer in Massachusetts. (Democratic Party).

CRANSTON, Alan MacGregor. 2 film reels (16 mm.). 16 videotapes (2 in.). 11 videocassettes (3/4 in.). 21341174.

Collection contains 5 television commercials used during Cranston's campaign for the 1968 U.S. Senate in California, 3 television commercials used in his 1974 re-election campaign, and 62 television commercials used in his 1986 re-election campaign. Also contains 19 television spots used during his 1984 primary campaigns for President. (Democratic Party).

CRAPSEY, Jean. 1 film reel (16 mm.). 24357330.

Collection contains 1 television commercial used during Crapsey's campaign for a 1970 school affiliated election in New York. (Republican Party).

CRAVIN, John. 1 sound tape reel (7 1/2 ips).

Collection contains 1 radio commercial used during Cravin's 1971 campaign for city council.

CREEL, William. 1 videotape (2 in.). 21479167.

Collection contains 2 television commercials used during Creel's campaign for the 1972 labor commissioner election in North Carolina. (Democratic Party).

CREEN, John. 1 sound tape reel. (7 1/2 ips.).

Collection contains 1 radio commercials used during Creen's 1982 campaign for Congress in District 43 of California. (Republican Party).

CRESTO, Dominic. 1 sound tape reel (7 1/2 ips.).

Collection contains 5 radio commercials used during Cresto's campaign for the 1972 Attorney General election in Rhode Island. (Democratic Party).

CROSS, Richard. 1 videocassette (3/4 in.).

Collection contains 1 television commercial used during Cross' 1982 campaign for State Senate in Texas. (Republican Party).

CROWLEY, Roger. 2 sound tape reels (7 1/2 ips.).

Collection contains 8 radio commercials used during Crowley's campaign for the 1972 gubernatorial election in New Hampshire. (Democratic Party).

CRYTS, Wayne. 1 videocassette (3/4 in.).

Collection contains 7 television commercials used during Cryts' campaign for Congress in District 8 of Missouri.

CULVER, John C. 1932-. 6 videotapes (2 in.). 2 videocassettes (3/4 in.). 22226326.

Collection Contains 11 television commercials used during Culver's campaign for the 1974 U.S. Senate and 25 television spots from his 1980 re-election campaign for U.S. Senate; both in Iowa. (Democratic Party).

CUNNINGHAM, George. 2 videocassettes (3/4 in.).

Collection contains 9 television spots from Cunningham's 1984 campaign for U. S .Senate in South Dakota. (Democratic Party).

**CUOMO, Mario Matthew.
2 videotapes (2 in.).
9 videocassettes (3/4
in.). 1 sound tape
reel (7 1/2 ips).
21348168.**

Collection contains 2 television commercials used during Cuomo's campaign for the 1974 gubernatorial election in New York. Includes 17 television and 9 radio commercials used in his campaign for the 1982 gubernatorial election also in New York. Includes 11 television commercials used during his 1986 campaign for Governor of New York. (Democratic Party).

This frame comes from a 1982 Mario Cuomo gubernatorial campaign in New York.

**CURB, Mike. 8 videotapes (1 in.). 1 videocassette (3/4 in.).
24211310.**

Collection contains 8 television commercials used during Curb's 1980 campaign for Lt. Governor in California. Includes 1 television commercial used during his 1986 campaign for the same office. (Republican Party).

**CURRAN, J. Joseph. 1 videotape (2 in.). 1 videocassette
(3/4 in.). 24213268.**

Collection contains 1 television commercial used during Curran's campaign for the 1976 congressional election in Maryland. Includes 2 television commercials used during his 1986 campaign for Attorney General in Maryland. (Democratic Party).

**CURRY, Bill. 3 sound tape reels (7 1/2 ips.). 1 videocassette
(3/4 in.).**

Collection contains 9 radio commercials and 2 television commer-cials used during Curry's 1982 congressional campaign in District 6 in Connecticut. (Democratic Party).

CURTIS, Carl T. 1905-. 2 film reels (16 mm.). 1 sound tape reel (7 1/2 ips.). 21358360.

Collection contains 8 television commercials and 7 radio spots used during Curtis' 1972 campaign for U.S. Senate in Nebraska. (Republican Party).

CURTIS, Kenneth M. 1931-. 1 sound tape reel (7 1/2 ips.). 21892571.

Collection contains 6 radio commercials used during Curtis' campaign for the 1970 gubernatorial election in Maine. (Democratic Party).

CUSACK, Bill. 1 videocassette (3/4 in.).

Collection contains 1 television commercial used during Cusack's 1986 campaign for Scott County Treasurer in Iowa.

CUSMA, Rene. 1 videocassette (3/4 in.).

Collection contains 3 television commercials used during Cusma's 1986 campaign for Portland Metro Committee.

CUTLER, Lynn. 2 videocassettes (3/4 in.). 2 sound tape reels (7 1/2 ips.).

Collection contains 6 television commercials and 6 radio spots from Cutler's campaigns for U.S. Congress in District 3 of Iowa. (Democratic Party).

D'AMATO, Al. 11 videotapes (2 in.). 4 videocassettes (3/4 in.). 24357337.

Collection contains 35 television commercials used during D'Amato's campaign for the 1980 U.S. Senate in New York. Includes 31 television commercials used during his 1986 re-election campaign. (Republican Party).

This spot was used in Al D'Amato's 1980 campaign for the U.S. Senate in New York.

D'AMICO, Gerry. 5 videocassettes (3/4 in.).

Collection contains 13 television commercials used during D'Amico's 1986 campaign for Lt. Governor of Maine. (Democratic Party).

D'AMOURS, Norman. 1 sound tape reel (7 1/2 ips.). 1 sound tape reel. (15 ips.). 1 videocassette (3/4 in.).

Collection contains 15 radio commercials used during D'Amours' 1982 congressional campaign in District 1 of New Hampshire and 8 television spots from his 1984 campaign for U.S. Senate in New Hampshire. (Democratic Party).

DAILEY, John P. 1 sound tape reel (7 1/2 ips.).

Collection contains 9 radio commercials used during Dailey's 1982 campaign for State Treasurer in Illinois. (Republican Party).

DALEY, Richard M. 4 videocassettes (3/4 in.). 1 sound tape reel (7 1/2 ips.).

Collection contains 2 radio and 38 television commercials used during Daley's 1983 primary campaign for Mayor of Chicago. Includes 1 television spot from Daley's 1980 campaign for Chicago State's Attorney. Also includes 1983 mayoral debate with Jane Byrne and Harold Washington. (Democratic Party).

DALLESANDRO, Lou. 1 sound tape reel (7 1/2 ips.).

Collection contains 6 radio commercials used during Dallesandro's campaign for the 1982 gubernatorial election in New Hampshire. (Republican Party).

DALTON, Dan. 1 sound tape reel (7 1/2 ips.).

Collection contains 1 radio commercial used during Dalton's campaign for the 1981 State Senate election in New Jersey. (Democratic Party).

DALTON, John. 1 film reel (16 mm.). 21499026.

Collection contains 1 television commercial used during Dalton's 1973 campaign for Lt. Governor in Virginia. (Republican Party).

DALY, Gene B.. 1 sound tape reel (7 1/2 ips).

Collection contains 1 radio commercial used during Daly's 1968 campaign for Attorney General in Montana. (Democratic Party).

**DANFORTH, John C. 4 film reel (16 mm.). 2 videotapes (2 in.).
1 videocassette (3/4 in.). 21388370.**

Collection contains 2 television commercials used during
Danforth's campaign for the 1970 U.S. Senate, 7 television
commercials used during his 1972 Attorney General campaign, and
12 television commercials used in his 1976 U.S. Senate campaign,
and 4 television spots form his 1982 re-election campaign in
Missouri. (Republican Party).

DANIEL, Bob. 1 videotape (2 in.). 24212062.

Collection contains 2 television commercials used during Daniel's
campaign for the 1976 congressional election in Virginia.

DANIEL, Mike. 2 videocassettes (3/4 in.).

Collection contains 2 television commercials used during Daniel's
1986 campaign for Governor of South Carolina. (Democratic Party).

DANIELS, Jack. 2 film reels (16 mm.). 21726233.

Collection contains 20 television commercials used during
Daniels' 1972 campaign U.S. Senate in New Mexico. (Democratic
Party).

DANINNY, Rudy. 1 sound tape reel (7 1/2 ips.).

Collection contains 1 radio commercial used during Daninny's
campaign for the 1972 State House election in Pennsylvania.
(Republican Party).

DARDEN, Buddy. 3 videocassette (3/4 in.).

Collection contains 1 television commercial used during Darden's
campaign for the 1983 congressional election in Georgia. Includes
8 television commercials used during his 1986 campaign for U.S.
Congress in District 7 of Georgia. (Democratic Party).

DARROW, Clarence. 1 videocassette (3/4 in.).

Collection contains 1 television commercial used during Darrow's
1986 campaign for Judicial Circuit Judge in District 14 of
Illinois.

DASCHLE, Tom. 22 videocassettes (3/4 in.).

Collection contains 13 television commercials from Daschle's 1978
congressional campaign in District 1 in South Dakota and 7
television spots for his 1980, 10 spots from his 1982 campaign,
and 9 television spots from his 1984 re-election campaigns for
the same office. Includes 62 television commercials used during
his 1986 campaign for U.S. Senate. (Democratic Party).

DAUB, Tom. 9 videocassettes (3/4 in.).

Collection contains 62 television commercials used during Daub's 1986 campaign for U.S. Senate in South Dakota. (Democratic Party).

DAVIS, Bob. 3 videocassette (3/4 in.).

Collection contains 4 television commercials used during Davis' 1986 campaign for Congress in District 11 in Michigan. (Republican Party).

DAVIS, Deane C. 1900-. 1 videotape (2 in.). 1 videocassette (3/4 in.). 21180430.

Collection contains 5 television commercials used during Davis' campaign for the 1970 gubernatorial election in Vermont. (Republican Party).

DAVIS, Dock. 1 videocassette (3/4 in.).

Collection contains 1 television commercial for Davis' 1980 campaign for U.S. Congress in Georgia. (Democratic Party).

DAVIS, Drew. 1 videocassette (3/4 in.).

Collection contains 1 television commercial from Davis' 1980 campaign for State Representative.

DAVIS, Gray. 2 videotapes (1 in.). 2 videocassettes (3/4 in.). 24212161.

Collection contains 10 television commercials used during Davis' 1986 campaign for State Controller in California. (Democratic Party).

DAVIS, Jimmie. 1902-. 1 videotape (2 in.). 21248193.

Collection contains 1 television commercial used during Davis' campaign for the 1973 gubernatorial election in Louisiana. (Democratic Party).

DAVIS, J.M. "Mac". 1 sound tape reel (7 1/2 ips.).

Collection contains 1 radio commercial used during Davis' campaign for the 1982 State Senate election in Wisconsin.

DAVIS, Leon. 1 sound tape reel (7 1/2 ips.).

Collection contains 1 radio commercial used during Davis' campaign for the 1980 Congressional election in District 2 in Illinois. (Democratic Party).

DAVIS, Lynn. 2 film reels (16 mm.). 24357347.

Collection contains 5 television commercials used during Davis' 1968 campaign for Secretary of State in Arkansas.

DAVIS, Miles.   1 sound tape reel (7 1/2 ips.).

Collection contains 2 radio commercials used during Davis' 1980 campaign for State Legislature in Harrisburg, Pennsylvania.

DAVIS, Myrtle.   1 videocassette (3/4 in.).

Collection contains 2 television spots from Davis' 1981 campaign for City Council in Atlanta, Georgia.

DAVIS, Peter. 1 videotape (2 in.).

Collection contains 1 television commercial used during Davis' campaign for a congressional election during the 1970's.

DAVIS, Phil. 2 videocassettes (3/4 in.).

Collection contains 5 television commercials used during Davis' 1986 campaign for Congress in District 4 of Arizona. (Democratic Party).

DAVIS, Richard.   1 sound tape reel (7 1/2 ips.).

Collection contains 5 radio commercials used during Davis' 1982 campaign for U.S. Senate in Virginia.   (Democratic Party).

DAVIS, William E. 1 sound tape reel (7 1/2 ips.). 1 film reel (16 mm.). 22156018.

Collection contains 12 radio and 9 television commercials used during Davis' 1972 campaign for U.S. Senate in Idaho. (Democratic Party).

DAY, Kathleen. 1 sound tape reel (7 1/2 ips).

Collection contains 4 radio commercials used during Day's campaign for a state office in Idaho. (Democratic Party).

DAY, Lon. 1 videocassette (3/4 in.).

Collection contains 1 television commercial used during Day's Congressional campaign in Georgia.

DAYTON, Mark.   1 sound tape reel (7 1/2 ips.).

Collection contains 13 radio commercials used during Dayton's campaign for the 1982 Senate election in Minnesota.   (Democratic Party).

72

DE FAZIO, Peter. 1 videocassette (3/4 in.).

Collection contains 12 television commercials used during De Fazio's 1986 campaign for Congress in District 4 of Connecticut. (Democratic Party).

DE GRANDIS.   1 sound tape reel (7 1/2 ips.).

Collection contains 1 radio commercial used during De Grandis' campaign for the 1980 Judgeship of Common Pleas election in Cuyahoga County, Ohio.

DE JAEGHER, Bob. 1 videocassette (3/4 in.).

Collection contains 1 television commercial used during De Jaegher's 1986 campaign for state Congress in District 72 of Illinois.

DE NUCCI, Joe. 4 videocassettes (3/4 in.).

Collection contains 4 television commercials used during De Nucci's 1986 campaign for State Auditor. (Democratic Party).

DE SIMONE, Herbert.   1 sound tape reel (7 1/2 ips.).

Collection contains 16 radio commercials used during De Simone's campaign for the 1972 Supervisor election in Rhode Island. (Republican Party).

DE WEESE, Bill.   1 sound tape reel (7 1/2 ips.).

Collection contains 6 radio commercials used during De Weese's campaign for the 1972 mayoral election in Portland, Oregon.

DEARMOND, Sue. 1 videocassette (3/4 in.).

Collection contains 1 television commercial used during DeArmond's 1986 campaign for Tuscon School Board in Arizona.

DEATHRIDGE, Cleta. 2 videotapes (1 in.). 1 videocassette (1/2 in.).   24260720.

Collection contains 6 television commercials used during Deathridge's primary campaign for the 1986 Lt. Governor's election in Oklahoma. (Democratic Party).

DECKARD, Joel.   1 videocassette (3/4 in.).

Collection contains 5 television commercials used during Deckard's 1982 campaign for U.S. Congress in District 8 of Indiana.   (Republican Party).

DECONCINI, Dennis. 3 videocassettes (3/4 in.).

Collection contains 22 television commercials used during DeConcini's 1982 campaign for U.S. Senate in Arizona. (Democratic Party).

DEELY, Bill. 2 videotapes (2 in.). 21983915.

Collection contains 2 television commercials used during Deely's campaign for the 1973 local election in Nassau County, New York. (Democratic Party).

DEGNAN, John. 8 videotapes (2 in). 1 videocassette (3/4 in.). 24357356.

Collection contains 8 television commercials used during Degnan's campaign for the 1981 gubernatorial election in New Jersey. (Democratic Party).

DEJONG, Fred. 1 sound tape reel (7 1/2 ips.).

Collection contains 1 radio commercial used during Dejong's 1982 campaign for County Executive in District 4 of Baltimore County in Maryland. (Democratic Party).

DEMUZIO, Vince. 1 videotape (2 in.). 24219935.

Collection contains 1 television commercial used during Demuzio's 1976 campaign for State of Secretary in Illinois. (Democratic Party).

DENARDIS, Larry. 2 videocassettes (3/4 in.).

Collection contains 13 television commercials from DeNardis' 1982 and 1984 campaign for U.S. Congress in District 3 of Connecticut. (Republican Party).

DENTON, Jeremiah A. 2 videotapes (2 in.). 11 videocassettes (3/4 in.). 24219938.

Collection contains 21 television commercials used during Denton's campaign for the 1986 U.S. Senate election in Alabama. (Republican Party).

DERMER, Jay. 1 film reel (16 mm.). 24211930.

Collection contains 5 television commercials used during Dermer's campaign for the 1972 congressional election in District 14 of Florida. (Democratic Party).

DERRICK, Butler. 1 film reel (16 mm.). 1 videocassette (3/4 in.). 21431655.

Collection contains 7 television commercials used during Derrick's 1974 campaign for U.S. Congress in South Carolina in District 3, and 4 television spots from his 1980 re-election campaign for the same office. (Democratic Party).

DERRYBERRY, Larry Dale. 1939-. 2 videotapes (2 in.). 1 videocassette (3/4 in.). 21191461.

Collection contains 9 television commercials used during Derryberry's campaigns for Attorney General, and 27 television commercials used during his 1978 gubernatorial primary campaign in Oklahoma. (Democratic Party).

DESIMONE, Herbert. 3 film reels (16 mm.). 24219965.

Collection contains 2 television commercials used during DeSimone's campaign for the 1970 gubernatorial election and 11 television commercials used during his 1972 gubernatorial election in Alabama. (Republican Party).

DEUKMEJIAN, George. 15 videotapes (1 in. & 2 in.). 4 videocassettes (3/4 in.). 24219941.

Collection contains 44 television commercials used during Deukmejian's campaign for the 1986 gubernatorial election in California. (Republican Party).

DI FAZIO, Lucien. 1 sound tape reel (7 1/2 ips.).

Collection contains 2 radio commercials used during Di Fazio's 1982 campaign for U.S. Senate of Connecticut. (Democratic Party).

DI PRETE, Ed. 1 videocassette (3/4 in.).

Collection contains 3 television commercials used during Di Prete's 1986 campaign for Governor of Rhode Island.

DIAMOND, G. William. 2 videocassettes (3/4 in.).

Collection contains 14 television commercials used during Diamond's 1986 campaign for Governor of Maine. (Democratic Party).

DICHEK, Leonard. 1 sound tape reel (7 1/2 ips.).

Collection contains 12 radio commercials used during Dichek's campaign for the 1972 Board of Education election in Los Angeles, California.

DICK, Nancy. 2 videocassettes (3/4 in.).

Collection contains 11 television spots from Dick's 1984 campaign for U.S. Senate in Colorado. (Democratic Party).

DICKINSON, Fred O. 1 film reel (16 mm.). 2 videotapes (2 in.). 21340674.

Collection contains 10 television commercials used during Dickinson's 1974 campaign for State Comptroller in Florida. (Democratic Party).

DICKENSON, William L. 1925 -. 3 videocassettes (3/4 in.).

Collection contains 8 television commercials from Dickenson's 1984 campaign and 1 television spot from his 1986 campaign for U.S. Congress in District 2 of Alabama. (Republican Party).

DIDIER, George. 1 videotape (2 in.). 24357369.

Collection contains 2 television commercials used during Didier's 1980 campaign for State Legislature in District 34 in Illinois.

DIFALCO, Anthony. 1938-. 1 film reel (16 mm.). 21511245.

Collection contains 6 commercials used during DiFalco's 1973 campaign for City Council President in New York. (Democratic Party).

DIGGS, Anna. 1 film reel (16 mm.). 24219943.

Collection contains 2 television commercials used during Diggs' 1970 campaign for a judgeship in Michigan.

DILLARD, Ben. 1 sound tape reel (7 1/2 ips.).

Collection contains 5 radio commercials used during Dillard's 1972 campaign for Chairman of Commissioners in Georgia. (Republican Party).

DILLEY, Robert D. 1926-. 1 sound tape reel (7 1/2 ips.). 2 videotapes (2 in.). 21930074.

Collection contains 1 radio and 2 television commercials used during Dilley's campaign for the 1972 gubernatorial election in Iowa. (American Independent Party).

DIMINI, Rudy. 1 sound tape reel (7 1/2 ips.).

Collection contains 1 radio commercial used during Dimini's 1980 campaign for State House in District 106 in Pennsylvania. (Republican Party).

DINENNA, Eric. 1 videocassette (3/4 in.).

Collection contains 2 television commercials used during DiNenna's 1978 campaign for Baltimore County Executive in Maryland. (Democratic Party).

DIRKSEN, Everett McKinley. 1 film reel (16 mm.). 1 videotape (2 in.). 21180462.

Collection contains 25 television commercials used during Dirksen's campaign for the 1968 U.S. senatorial election in Illinois. (Republican Party).

DIXON, Alan John. 1927-. 1 film reel (16 mm.). 4 videocassettes (3/4 in.). 1 sound tape reel (7 1/2 ips.). 21476112.

Collection contains 2 television commercials used during Dixon's 1976 campaign for Secretary of State in Illinois, and 10 television spots and 15 radio spots from his 1980 campaign for U.S. Senate in Illinois. Includes 2 television commercials used during his 1986 campaign for U.S. Senate. (Democratic Party).

DIXON, Arrington. 1 sound tape reel (7 1/2 ips.).

Collection contains 3 radio commercials used during Dixon's 1982 campaign for City Council in the District of Columbia.

DIXON, Isaiah (Ike). 1 sound tape reel. (7 1/2 ips.).

Collection contains 4 radio commercials used during Dixon's 1982 campaign for State House in Maryland.

DIXON, Katie. 1 videocassette (3/4 in.). 24357054.

Collection contains 1 television commercial used during Dixon's campaign for a 1982 city office in Vermont.

DOAK, John. 2 videocassettes (3/4 in.).

Collection contains 4 television commercials used during Doak's 1982 campaign for a judgeship in Tennessee.

DOCKING, Robert. 1 videotape (2 in.). 24219945.

Collection contains 1 television commercial used during Docking's 1972 campaign for Governor in Kansas. (Democratic Party).

DOCKING, Tom. 3 videocassettes (3/4 in.).

Collection contains 26 television commercials used during Docking's 1986 campaign for Governor of Kansas. (Democratic Party).

DODD, Chris. 3 videocassettes (3/4 in.).

Collection contains 11 television commercials used during Dodd's 1986 campaign for U.S. Senate in Connecticut. (Democratic Party).

DODD, Pat. 1 videocassette (3/4 in.).

Collection contains 2 television spots from Dodd's 1981 primary campaign for Governor of New Jersey. (Democratic Party).

DODD, Thomas J. 1907-1971. 1 sound tape reel (7 1/2 ips.). 21979481.

Collection contains 6 radio commercials used during Dodd's 1970 campaign for 1970 U.S. Senate in Connecticut. (Independent).

DODERER, Minnette. 1923-. 1 sound tape reel (7 1/2 ips.). 1 film reel (16 mm.). 21979506.

Collection contains 1 radio and 2 television spots from Doderer's 1970 campaign for Lt. Governor in Iowa. (Democratic Party).

DODSON, Henry. 1 videocassette (3/4 in.).

Collection contains 1 television spot used during Dodson's 1986 campaign for County Commissioner in Georgia. (Democratic Party).

DOGGETT, Lloyd. 6 videotapes (1 in. & 2 in.). 8 videocassettes (3/4 in.). 24219947.

Collection contains 34 television spots used during Doggett's 1984 campaign for U.S. Senate in Texas. (Democratic Party).

DOHERTY, Ed. 1 sound tape reel (7 1/2 ips).

Collection contains 1 radio commercial used during Doherty's 1968 campaign for Governor. (Republican Party).

DOHERTY, Tom. 1 film reel (16 mm.). 21920839.

Collection contains 1 television commercial used during Doherty's campaign for the 1973 District attorney election in Wisconsin.

DOLE, Robert. 1923-. 14 videocassettes (3/4 in.). 18 videotapes (2 in.). 5 videocassettes (3/4 in.). 21348156.

Collection contains 29 television items (including debates) from Dole's 1974 campaign for U.S. Senate in Kansas and 15 television spots used during his re-election campaign in 1980. Includes 7 television spots from his 1980 campaign for President and 23 television spots used in his 1988 presidential campaign. Collection also includes appearance by Dole in the 1980 New Hampshire presidential primary debate. (Republican Party).

DOMENICI, Peter. 1 videocassette (3/4 in.). 1 sound tape reel (7 1/2 ips.).

Collection contains 2 radio commercials used during Domenici's 1972 campaign for U.S. Senate in New Mexico and 1 television spot from his 1984 campaign for the same office. (Republican Party).

DOMINA, David. 1 videocassette (3/4 in.).

Collection contains 3 television commercials used during Domina's 1986 campaign for Governor of Nebraska. (Democratic Party).

DOMINICK, Peter H. 1915-. 1 film reel (16 mm.). 21421474.

Collection contains 1 television commercial used during Dominick's campaign for the 1974 U.S. senatorial election in Colorado. (Republican Party).

DONNELLY, Brian. 1 sound tape reel (7 1/2 ips.).

Collection contains 1 radio commercial used during Donnelly's campaign for the 1980 Corporation Commissioner election in Arizona.

DONNELLY, John. 1 sound tape reel (7 1/2 ips.).

Collection contains 6 radio commercials used during Donnelly's 1980 campaign for a judgeship in Cuyahoga County, Ohio. (Democratic Party).

DONNEWALD, Jim. 1 sound tape reel. (7 1/2 ips.).

Collection contains 4 radio commercials used during Donnewald's 1982 campaign for State Treasurer in Illinois. (Democratic Party).

DOOLITTLE, John. 5 videocassettes (3/4 in.).

Collection contains 9 television commercials used in Doolittle's 1984 campaign for State Senate in California. (Republican Party).

DORGAN, Byron L. 2 videotapes (2 in.). 5 videocassette (3/4 in.). 1 sound tape reel (7 1/2 ips.). 24357063.

Collection contains 23 television commercials and 9 radio spots used during Dorgan's 1980 campaign for the U.S. Congress and 3 commercials used in his 1982 congressional campaign; both campaigns for Congressman At Large in North Dakota. Includes 7 television commercials used during his 1986 campaign for the same office. (Democratic Party).

**DORN, William Jennings Bryan. 1916-. 1 film reel (16 mm.).
21437408.**

Collection contains 15 television commercials used during Dorn's
campaign for the 1974 gubernatorial election in South Carolina.
(Democratic Party).

DORNAN, Robert. 1 sound tape reel (7 1/2 ips.).

Collection contains 3 radio commercials used during Dornan's
campaign for the 1980 Congressional election in District 27 in
California. (Republican Party).

DOUGHERTY, Charles. 1 sound tape reel (7 1/2 ips.).

Collection contains 2 radio commercials used during Dougherty's
campaign for the 1980 Congressional election in District 4 in
Pennsylvania. (Republican Party).

DOUGLAS, Paul Howard. 1892-. 2 film reels (16 mm.). 21381861.

Collection contains 33 television commercials used during
Douglas' campaign for the 1966 U.S. senatorial campaign in
Illinois. (Democratic Party).

DOUGLASS, John. 1 sound tape reel. (7 1/2 ips.).

Collection contains 2 radio commercials used during Douglas' 1983
campaign for local offices in Maryland. (Democratic Party).

DOWD. 1 sound tape reel (7 1/2 ips.).

Collection contains 4 radio commercials used during Dowd's 1980
campaign for a judgeship in Ohio. (Republican Party).

DOWD, Edward L. 1 videotape (2 in.). 21276421.

Collection contains 1 television commercial used during Dowd's
campaign for the 1972 gubernatorial election in Missouri. (Democratic Party).

DOWDY, W. 4 videocassette (3/4 in.). 24219949.

Collection contains 12 television commercials used during Dowdy's
1982, 1984 and 1986 campaigns for U.S. Congress in District 4 of
Mississippi. (Democratic Party).

**DOWNING, Bill. 1 videocassette (3/4 in.). 1 sound tape reel.
24219950.**

Collection contains 1 television commercial and 1 radio spot used
during Downing's campaign for Lake County commissioner in Ohio.

80

DRESCHER, John P. 1 sound tape reel (7 1/2 ips.).

Collection contains 1 radio commercial used during Drescher's campaign for the 1982 State Assembly Committee election in Wisconsin. (Democratic Party).

DRINAN, Robert F. 1 videotape (2 in.). 21248173.

Collection contains 1 television commercial used during Drinan's 1970 campaign for U.S. Congress in Massachusetts, 4th District. (Democratic Party).

DRONEY, John J. 6 videotapes (2 in.). 21270293.

Collection contains 6 television commercials used during Droney's 1972 campaign for U.S. Senate in Massachusetts. (Democratic Party).

DU PONT, Elise R. W. 1 videocassette (3/4 in.).

Collection contains 3 television spots for du Pont's 1984 campaign for Congresswoman At Large from Delaware. (Republican Party).

DU PONT, Pierre S., IV. 1935 -. 4 videocassettes (3/4 in.). 21368948.

Collection contains 18 television commercials used during DuPont's campaigns for the 1980 gubernatorial election in Delaware and the 1988 presidential election. (Republican Party).

DUDLEY, Dudley. 3 videocassettes (3/4 in.).

Collection contains 5 television commercials for Dudley's 1984 campaign for U.S. Congress in District 1 in New Hampshire.

DUFF, Brian. 1 videotape (2 in).

Collection contains 1 television commercial used during Duff's campaign for an appellate court judicial election in Illinois. (Republican Party).

DUFFEY, Joseph D. 10 videotapes (2 in.). 21255440.

Collection contains 21 television commercials used during Duffey's campaign for the 1970 U.S. senatorial election in Connecticut. (Democratic Party).

DUFFY, Patrick J. 1 sound tape reel (7 1/2 ips.).

Collection contains 1 radio commercial used during Duffy's campaign for the 1982 election in Baltimore, Maryland.

DUKAKIS, Michael. 19 videocassettes (3/4 in.). 1 film reel (16 mm.). 12 videotapes (2 in.). 21180478.

Collection contains 1 television commercial used during Dukakis' campaign for the 1974 gubernatorial election, 16 television commercials used in his 1982 gubernatorial campaign, and 6 television commercials used in his 1986 gubernatorial campaign, all in Massachusetts. Includes 121 television commercials used in his campaign for the 1988 presidential election. (Democratic Party).

This spot was used by Michael Dukakis in his 1986 gubernatorial campaign in Massachusetts.

DUNCAN, Bob. 2 videocassettes (3/4 in.). 1 sound tape reel (7 1/2 ips).

Contains 2 television commercials used during Duncan's 1974 campaign for Congress in District 3 of Oregon and 4 television spots from his 1980 campaign for the same office. Includes 1 radio commercial used during Duncan's 1968 campaign for U.S. Senate. (Democratic Party).

DUNN, James. 3 videocassettes (3/4 in.). 1 sound tape reel (7 1/2 ips). 24219956.

Collection contains 12 television commercials used during Dunn's campaign for the 1982 and 1986 congressional elections in District 6 of Michigan. Also includes 1 television spot from his 1984 campaign for U.S. Senate. Includes 1 radio commercial used during his 1966 campaign for U.S. Senate. (Republican Party).

DUNN, Peter. 2 videocassettes (3/4 in.).

Collection contains 14 television commercials used during Dunn's 1982 campaign for U.S. Senate in Arizona. (Republican Party).

DUNN, Richard D. 1 film reel (16 mm.). 21492257.

Collection contains 1 television commercial used during Dunn's 1976 campaign for a judgeship in Wayne County, Michigan. (Democratic Party).

DUNN, Winfield. 6 videocassettes (3/4 in.).

Collection contains 49 television commercials used during Dunn's 1986 campaign for Governor of Tennessee. (Republican Party).

DUNNE, George. 1 sound tape reel (7 1/2 ips.).

Collection contains 9 radio commercials used during Dunne's 1982 campaign for a local office in Illinois. (Democratic Party).

DUPAY, Bob. 1 sound tape reel (7 1/2 ips.).

Collection contains 1 radio commercial used during Dupay's campaign for the 1982 Congressional election in District 2 in New Hampshire. (Democratic Party).

DUPONT, Dick. 1 sound tape reel (7 1/2 ips.).

Collection contains 1 radio commercial used during Dupont's campaign for the 1982 County Sheriff election in Hillsboro County in New Hampshire. (Democratic Party).

DURBIN, Richard. 4 videocassettes (3/4 in.).

Collection contains 7 television spots from Durbin's 1984 campaign and 6 television spots from his 1986 campaign for U.S. Congress in Illinois. (Democratic Party).

DURENBERGER, David. 2 videocassettes (3/4 in.).

Collection consists of 11 television commercials from Durenberger's campaigns for U.S. Senate in Minnesota. (Republican Party).

DURHAM, Kathy. 1 sound tape reel (7 1/2 ips.).

Collection contains 1 radio commercial used during Durham's campaign for the 1980 State Representative election in District 160 in Pennsylvania. (Republican Party).

DURYEA, Perry. 2 videocassettes (3/4 in.).

Collection contains 20 television commercials used in Duryea's 1978 campaign for Governor of New York. (Republican Party).

DUVALL, Clive. 1 film reel (16 mm.). 4 videocassettes (3/4 in.). 24219953.

Collection contains 8 television commercials used during Duvall's 1970 campaign and 6 television commercials used during his 1978 campaign for U.S. Senate in Virginia. (Democratic Party).

DWORAK, Leo J. 1 videotape (2 in.). 21511264.

Collection contains 1 television commercial used during Dworak's 1969 campaign for Mayor in Nebraska.

DWYER, R. Budd. 2 videotapes (2 in.). 1 videocassette (3/4 in.). 24221631.

Collection contains 5 television commercials used during Dwyer's campaign for the 1984 State Treasurer election in Pennsylvania.

DYAS, Hess. 1 videotape (2 in.). 21352766.

Collection contains 6 television commercials used during Dyas' campaign for the 1974 U.S. congressional election in Nebraska. (Democratic Party).

DYKE, William D. 1930 -. 1 videotape (2 in.). 22186025.

Collection contains 1 television commercial used during Dyke's campaign for the 1974 gubernatorial election in Wisconsin. (Republican Party).

DYKE, Ann. 1 sound tape reel (7 1/2 ips.).

Collection contains 3 radio commercials used during Dyke's 1980 campaign for Judgeship of Common Pleas in Cuyahoga County, Ohio. (Democratic Party).

DYNALLY, Mervyn. 1 sound tape reel (7 1/2 ips.).

Collection contains 3 radio commercials used during Dynally's campaign for the 1980 Congressional election in District 31 in California. (Democratic Party).

DYSON, Roy. 1 videocassette (3/4 in.).

Collection contains 3 television commercials from Dyson's 1986 campaign for Congress in District 1 of Maryland. (Democratic Party).

EADS, Lee. 1 videotape (2 in.). 21498993.

Collection contains 1 television commercial used during Eads' 1970 campaign for Sheriff in Indianapolis, Indiana. (Republican Party).

EAGLETON, Norma. 1 videocassette (3/4 in.).

Collection contains 5 television ads from Eagleton's 1980 campaign for Corporation Commission in Oklahoma.

**EAGLETON, Thomas F. 1929 -. 1 film reel (16 mm.).
5 videocassettes (3/4 in.). 21431682.**

Collection contains 10 television commercials used during
Eagleton's 1974 campaign for U.S. Senate in Missouri and 11
television spots from his 1980 campaign for the same office.
(Democratic Party).

**EARL, Anthony S. "Tony." 1 videocassette (3/4 in.). 2 sound tape
reels (7 1/2 ips.). 22164847.**

Collection contains 3 radio commercials used during Earl's 1974
campaign for Attorney General and 10 television spots and 6 radio
spots from his 1982 campaign for Governor in Wisconsin .
(Democratic Party).

EAST, John P. 1 videotape (2 in.). 24357076.

Collection contains 1 television commercial used during East's
1980 campaign for U.S. Senate in North Carolina. (Republican
Party).

EASTON, John. 2 videocassettes (3/4 in.).

Collection contains 16 television commercials from Easton's 1984
campaign for Governor of Vermont. (Republican Party).

**ECKART, Dennis E. 1950 -. 2 videocassettes (3/4 in.). 1 sound
tape reel (7 1/2 ips.).**

Collection contains 2 television commercials used during Eckart's
1982 campaign for U.S. Congress and 2 radio commercials from his
1980 race for the same office in Ohio. (Democratic Party).

ECKERD, Jack. 3 videotapes (2 in.). 21388409.

Collection contains 4 television commercials used during Eckerd's
1974 campaign for U.S. Senate in Florida. (Republican Party).

ECKERT, Fred. 3 videocassettes (3/4 in.).

Collection contains 4 television commercials used during Eckert's
1986 campaign for U.S. Senate in Connecticut. (Republican Party).

EDDY, Roger. 1 videocassette (3/4 in.).

Collection contains 3 television commercials used during Eddy's
1986 campaign for U.S. Senate in Connecticut. (Republican Party).

EDGAR, James. 1 videotape (2 in.). 1 videocassette (3/4 in.). 1 sound tape reel (7 1/3 ips.). 24221498.

Collection contains 6 television and 7 radio commercials used during Edgar's 1986 campaign for Secretary of State in Illinois. (Republican Party).

EDGAR, Robert W. 1943 -. 1 sound tape reel (7 1/2 ips.). 8 videocassettes (3/4 in.).

Collection contains 8 television spots from Edgar's 1984 campaign for U.S. Congress and 37 television commercials used during Edgar's 1986 campaign for U.S. Senate in Pennsylvania. Also contains 2 radio commercials from his 1980 campaign for U.S. Congress. (Democratic Party).

EDMISTEN, Rufus. 2 videocassettes (3/4 in.).

Collection contains 45 television commercials from Edmisten's 1984 campaign for Governor of North Carolina. (Democratic Party).

EDMONDSON, Ed. 1919 -. 8 videotape (2 in.). 1 film reel (16 mm.). 21287228.

Collection contains 19 television commercials used during Edmondson's 1972 campaign for the U.S. Senate, and 6 television commercials used in his 1974 campaign for the U.S. Senate in Oklahoma. (Democratic Party).

EDMONDSON, J. Howard. 2 videocassettes (3/4 in.).

Collection contains a video excerpt from an address made by Edmondson to a joint legislative session in Oklahoma in 1959 while he was Governor and 6 television spots from his 1964 primary campaign for the U.S. Senate in Oklahoma. (Democratic Party).

EDWARDS, Edwin. 3 videocassettes (3/4 in.).

Collection contains 49 television commercials used during Edwards' campaign for the 1983 gubernatorial election in Louisiana. (Democratic Party).

EDWARDS, Ellis. 2 videocassettes (3/4 in.).

Collection contains 5 television commercials used during Edwards' 1986 campaign for State Treasurer in Oklahoma. (Democratic Party).

EDWARDS, James B. 1927 -. 1 videotape (2 in.). 21421443.

Collection contains 4 television commercials used during Edwards' 1974 campaign for Governor in South Carolina. (Republican Party).

EGAN, John. 1 videocassette (3/4 in.).

Collection contains 3 television commercials from Egan's 1983 campaign for Mayor of Philadelphia, Pennsylvania.

EGGERS, Paul. 2 film reel (16 mm.).

Collection contains 12 television commercials used during Eggers' 1970 campaign for Governor in Texas. (Republican Party).

EIKENBERRY, Ken. 1 videocassette (3/4 in.).

Collection contains 2 television spots from Eikenberry's 1984 campaign for Attorney General in Washington. (Republican Party).

EISENHOWER, Dwight D. 1 videocassette (3/4 in.). 3 film reels (16 mm.). 21128363.

This famous animated figure appeared in an Eisenhower 1952 campaign commercial created by Walt Disney Studios.

Collection contains 27 television commercials from Eisenhower's 1952 and 1956 presidential elections. (Republican Party).

ELKIN, Richard A. 4 videotapes (2 in.). 24221504.

Collection contains 5 television commercials used during Elkin's campaign for the 1976 gubernatorial election in North Dakota. (Republican Party).

ELROD, Richard Jay. 1934 -. 1 videotape (2 in.). 21268962.

Collection contains 1 television commercial used during Elrod's 1970 campaign for Sheriffin Illinois. (Democratic Party).

EMBERTON, Tom. 9 videotapes (2 in.). 2 film reels (16 mm.). 21270284.

Collection contains 19 television commercials used during Emberton's campaign for the 1971 gubernatorial election in Kentucky. (Republican Party).

EMERSON, Bill. 3 videocassettes (3/4 in.).

Collection contains 9 television commercials from Emerson's 1986 campaign for Congress of Missouri. (Republican Party).

EMERY, David. 1 videotape (2 in.). 24221509.

Collection contains 1 television commercial used during Emery's 1982 campaign for U.S. Senate in Maine. (Republican Party).

ENFREKIN, Sarah. 2 videotapes (2 in.). 24221516.

Collection contains 2 television commercials used during Enfrekin's campaign in a 1986 Mississippi election.

ENGDAHL, Lynn. 1 videocassette (3/4 in.).

Collection contains 1 television commercial from Engdahl's 1980 campaign for U.S. Congress in Oregon. (Republican Party).

ENGLER, Coleen. 3 videocassettes (3/4 in.).

Collection contains 4 television commercials used during Engler's 1986 campaign for Governor of Michigan. (Republican Party).

ENGLISH, Glenn. 1 videocassette (3/4 in.). 24357082.

Collection contains 3 television commercials used during English's campaign for the 1978 congressional election in Oklahoma. (Democratic Party).

EPPERSON, Stu. 2 videocassettes (3/4 in.).

Collection contains 3 television commercials used during Epperson's 1986 campaign for Congress in District 5 of North Carolina. (Republican Party).

EPTON, Bernard. 2 videocassettes (3/4 in.).

Collection contains 11 television commercials used during Epton's 1983 campaign for Mayor in Chicago, Illinois. (Republican Party).

ERBAR, Tom. 1 videocassette (3/4 in.).

Collection contains 5 television spots from Erbar's 1980 campaign for State Senate in District 22 of Oklahoma. (Democratic Party).

ERDREICH, Ben. 3 videocassettes (3/4 in.).

Collection contains 2 television commercials used in Erdreich's 1984 campaign for U.S. Congress in District 6 of Alabama. Includes 5 television commercials used during his 1986 re-election campaign. (Democratic Party).

ERICKSON, John. 1 film reel (16 mm.). 24221526.

Collection contains 15 television commercials used during Erickson's campaign for the 1970 U.S. Senate election in Wisconsin. (Republican Party).

ERTEL, Alan. 5 videotapes (2 in.). 1 videocassette (3/4 in.). 24221641.

Collection contains 5 television commercials used during Ertel's 1984 campaign for Attorney General in Pennsylvania. Also includes 2 television spots from his 1982 Governor's campaign. (Democratic Party).

ESCH, Marvin Leonel. 2 videotapes (2 in.). 24221647.

Collection contains 6 television commercials used during Esch's 1976 campaign for U.S. Senate in Michigan. (Republican Party).

ESKIND, Jane Greenebaum. 1933 -. 1 film reel (16 mm.). 3 videocassettes (3/4 in.). 21421280.

Collection contains 4 television commercials used during Eskind's 1976 campaign for U.S. Senate in Tennessee. Includes 32 television commercials used during her 1986 campaign for Governor of Tennessee. (Democratic Party).

ESPY, Mike. 1 videocassette (3/4 in.).

Collection contains 11 television commercials used during Espy's 1986 campaign for Congress in District 2 of Mississippi. (Democratic Party).

EU, March Fong. 1 videotape (2 in.). 1 sound tape reel (7 1/2 ips.). 21340775.

Collection contains 1 television commercial used during the 1974 Secretary of State election in California and 1 radio spot used in the 1982 campaign for the same office. (Democratic Party).

EVANS, Brock. 1 videocassette (3/4 in.).

Collection contains 4 television commercials from Evans' 1984 campaign for U.S. Congress in District 1 of Washington. (Democratic Party).

EVANS, Cooper. 1 videocassette (3/4 in.). 1 sound tape reel (7 1/2 in.).

Collection contains 1 television spot from Evans' 1980 campaign for U.S. Congress in District 3 of Iowa and 9 radio spots from his 1982 campaign for the same office. (Republican Party).

EVANS, Dan. 1 film reel (16 mm.). 24357089.

Collection contains 10 television commercials used during Evans'
1968 campaign for Governor in Washington. (Republican Party).

EVANS, Jimmy. 6 videotapes (2 in.). 24221651.

Collection contains 6 television commercials used during Evans'
campaign for a 1986 Alabama election.

**EVANS, Lane. 3 videotapes (2 in.). 6 videocassettes (3/4 in.).
24221963.**

Collection contains 9 television commercials used during Evans'
1982 and 1984 campaigns for U.S. Congress in District 17 for
Illinois. Includes 7 television commercials used during his 1986
campaign for Congress in District 17. (Democratic Party).

EVANS, Tom. 3 videocassettes (3/4 in.).

Collection contains 5 television commercials from Evans' 1980
campaign for Congressman At Large in Delaware and 5 television
spots from his 1982 re-election campaign. (Republican Party).

EVERETT, Jim. 1 videocassette (3/4 in.).

Collection contains 1 television commercial used during Everett's
campaign for the 1982 probate judge election in Tennessee.

EYNON, Jim. 1 videocassette (3/4 in.).

Collection contains 1 television commercial used during Eynon's
1986 campaign for Congress in District 10 of Indiana. (Republican
Party).

FADELEY. 1 sound tape reel (7 1/2 ips.).

Collection contains 3 radio commercials used during Fadeley's
campaign for the 1972 Congressional election in Oregon.

FADEM, Joyce. 1 sound tape reel (7 1/2 ips.).

Collection contains 6 radio commercials used during Fadem's
campaign for the 1972 Junior College Trustee election in California.

FAHNER, Ty. 1 sound tape reel (7 1/2 ips.).

Collection contains 5 radio commercials used during Fahner's
campaign for the 1982 Attorney General election in Illinois.
(Republican Party).

FAIR, Robert J. 1 videotape (2 in.). 24221663.

Collection contains 2 television commercials used during Fair's campaign for the 1976 gubernatorial election in Indiana. (Democratic Party).

FARELL, Mary. 1 sound tape reel (7 1/2 ips.).

Collection contains 1 radio commercial used during Farell's campaign for the 1980 State Senate election in Pennsylvania.

FARENTHOLD, Frances T. 3 videotapes (2 in.). 1 sound tape reel (7 1/2 ips.). 21421457.

Collection contains 4 television and 5 radio commercials used during Farenthold's 1972 campaign for Governor of Texas. (Democratic Party).

FARLEY, Frances. 2 videocassettes (3/4 in.).

Collection contains 13 television commercials used during Farley's 1982 and 1984 campaigns U.S. Congress District 2 of Utah. (Democratic Party).

FARMER, William. 1 videocassette (3/4 in.).

Collection contains 2 television commercials used during the 1982 judgeship election in Tennessee.

FARR, William S. 1935 -. 1 film reel (16 mm.). 22226289.

Collection contains 4 television commercials used during Farr's campaign for the 1970 Attorney General election in Michigan. (Republican Party).

FARRIS, Milton. 1 videocassette (3/4 in.).

Collection contains 3 television commercials used during Farris' 1986 campaign for Fulton County Commissioner in Georgia.

FASCELL, Dante. 1 videotape (2 in.). 2 videocassettes (3/4 in.). 1 sound tape reel (7 1/2 ips.). 24222341.

Collection contains television and 1 radio commercials used during Fascell's 1978, 1982 and 1984 campaigns for Congress in Florida. (Democratic Party).

FASRI, Frank. 1 videocassette (3/4 in.).

Collection contains 5 television commercials used during Fasri's 1982 campaign for Governor of Hawaii. (Republican Party).

FAUBUS, Orval Eugene. 1910 -. 1 videotape (2 in.). 21315055.

Collection contains 1 television commercial used during Faubus' 1974 campaign for Governor in Arkansas. (Democratic Party).

FAULISO, Joe. 1 sound tape reel (7 1/2 ips.).

Collection contains 3 radio commercials used during Fauliso's 1982 campaign for Lt. Governor of Connecticut. (Democratic Party).

FAZIO, Vic. 1 videocassette (3/4 in.).

Collection contains 1 television spot from Fazio's 1980 campaign for Congress in District 4 of California. (Democratic Party).

FEDER, John. 1 sound tape reel (7 1/2 ips.).

Collection contains 3 radio commercials used during Feder's campaign for the 1982 judgeship election in Maryland.

FEIGHAN, Ed. 7 videocassettes (3/4 in.).

Collection contains 7 television spots used during Feighan's 1982 campaign and 8 television spots from his 1984 campaign for U.S. Congress in District 19 of Ohio. Includes 22 television spots from his 1986 campaign for Congress. (Democratic Party).

FEINSTEIN, Dianne. 1 film reel (16 mm.). 1 videotape (2 in.). 21248206.

Collection contains 19 television commercials used during Feinstein's 1971 mayoral campaign in San Francisco, California. (Independent Party).

FELLMAN, Dick. 1 videocassette (3/4 in.).

Collection contains 5 television commercials used during Fellman's 1982 campaign for U.S. Congress in District 2 in Nebraska. (Democratic Party).

FENTON, Ray. 2 videotapes (2 in.). 24222347.

Collection contains 2 television commercials used during Fenton's campaign for the 1970 local election in Polk County, Iowa. (Democratic Party).

FENWICK, Millicent. 7 videocassettes (3/4 in.). 1 sound tape reel (7 1/2 ips.).

Collection contains 21 television commercials and 34 radio spots used during Fenwick's 1982 primary campaign for U.S. Senate in New Jersey. (Republican Party).

FERENCY, Zoltan. 1 videocassette (3/4 in.). 24222353.

Collection contains 6 television commercials used during Ferency's campaign for the 1982 gubernatorial election in Michigan. (Democratic Party).

FERGUSON, Glenn. 1 videocassette (3/4 in.).

Collection contains 1 television commercial used during Ferguson's campaign for a 1982 local election in Tennessee.

FERGUSON, Tom. 1 videocassette (3/4 in.). 24222366.

Collection contains 2 television commercials used during Ferguson's campaign for the 1982 state auditor election in Ohio. (Democratic Party).

FERRARO, Geraldine. 4 videocassettes (3/4 in.). 21368955.

Collection contains 2 television commercials used during Ferraro's campaign as the vice-presidential candidate on the Mondale presidential ticket in the 1984 presidential election. Also includes her acceptance speech at the Democratic National Convention. Other commercials used in the Mondale-Ferraro campaign are included in the Mondale Collection. (Democratic Party).

FERRE, Maurice. 1 videotape (2 in.). 21268947.

Collection contains 2 television commercials used during Ferre's campaign for the 1970 mayoral election in Florida. (Democratic Party).

FESS, Bill. 1 videocassette (3/4 in.).

Collection contains 3 television commercials used during Fess' 1982 campaign for U.S. Senate in Ohio. (Republican Party).

FIEDLER, Bobbi. 1 sound tape reel (3 3/4 ips.). 1 sound tape reel (7 1/2 in.). 22044352.

Collection contains 2 radio commercials used during Fiedler's 1977 campaign for school board in Los Angeles, California. Also includes 4 radio commercials used during Fiedler's campaign for the 1980 Congressional election in District 21 in California. (Republican Party).

FIELDS, Jack. 1 videocassette (3/4 in.).

Collection contains 4 television commercials from Fields' 1984 campaign for U S Congress in District 8 of Texas. (Republican Party).

FIGEL. 1 videocassette (3/4 in.).

Collection contains 1 television commercial used during Figel's 1986 campaign for Sheriff in Fort Wayne, Indiana.

FINCH, Cliff. 1 videocassette (3/4 in.).

Collection contains 1 television spot from Finch's 1980 primary campaign for President. (Democratic Party).

FINCH, Sharon Tevis. 1 film reel (16 mm.). 24222375.

Collection contains 1 television commercial used during Finch's 1972 campaign for a judgeship in Michigan.

FINCH, Walter G. 1 videotape (2 in.). 21191412.

Collection contains 1 television commercial used during Finch's campaign for the 1970 U.S. senatorial election in Maryland. (Republican Party).

FINCHER, Dan. 1 videocassette (3/4 in.).

Collection contains 1 television commercial used during Fincher's campaign in the 1983 special election for Congress in Georgia.

FINDLEY, Paul. 3 videotapes (2 in). 1 videocassette (3/4 in.). 24357096.

Collection contains 11 television commercials used during Findley's 1980 campaign and 1 commercial from his 1982 campaign for U.S. Congress in District 10 of illinois. (Republican Party).

FINE, Ralph Adam. 2 videotapes (2 in.). 24357105.

Collection contains 5 television commercials used during Fine's campaign for the 1979 judicial election in Wisconsin.

FINK, Adrian. 1 film reel (16 mm.). 24357118.

Collection contains 2 television commercials used during Fink's campaign for the 1970 congressional election in Ohio. (Republican Party).

FINKBEINER, Carty. 1 videotape (2 in.). 24222385.

Collection contains 1 television commercial used during Finkbeiner's campaign for the 1976 Congressional election in Ohio. (Republican Party).

FINLEY, Morgan. 2 sound tape reels (7 1/2 ips.).

Collection contains 3 radio commercials from Finley's 1980 campaign for Clerk of the Circuit Court and 10 radio commercials used during his 1982 campaign for the same office in Illinois.

FINLEY, Morris. 1 videocassette (3/4 in.).

Collection contains 1 television commercial used during Finley's 1986 campaign for Atlanta City Council in Georgia.

FINNEGAN, Dave. 1 videocassette (3/4 in.).

Collection contains 11 television commercials used during Finnegan's campaign for the 1983 mayoral election in Boston, Massachusetts.

FINNEY, Jervis Spencer. 1931 -. 1 film reel (16 mm.). 21498901.

Collection contains 5 television commercials used during Finney's 1974 campaign for a county office in Maryland. (Republican Party).

FINNEY, Joan. 1 videocassette (3/4 in.).

Collection contains 1 television commercial used during Finney's 1986 campaign for State Treasurer in Kansas. (Democratic Party).

FINNIGAN, Dan. 1 sound tape reel (7 1/2 ips.).

Collection contains 1 radio commercial used during Finnigan's campaign for the 1980 State Senate election in District 39 in California. (Democratic Party).

FIRESTONE, George. 1 videotape (2 in.). 1 videocassette (3/4 in.). 24222394.

Collection contains 1 television commercial used during Firestone's 1978 campaign for State Senate in Florida. Also contains 1 television spot from his 1982 re-election campaign for Secretary of State in Florida. (Democratic Party).

FISCHER, Dick. 4 videocassettes (3/4 in.).

Collection contains 10 television spots used during Fischer's 1978 campaign for Mayor of Anchorage, Alaska.

FISHER, Joe. 2 videocassettes (3/4 in.).

Collection contains 5 television spots from Fisher's 1980 campaign for U.S. Congress in District 10 of Virginia. (Democratic Party).

FISHER, Lee. 1 videocassette (3/4 in.).

Collection contains 6 television commercial used during Fisher's 1982 campaign for State Senate in Ohio. (Democratic Party).

FISHER, Leslie R. 1 videocassette (3/4 in.).

Collection contains 4 television commercials used during Fisher's 1970 campaign for State Superintendent of Public Instruction in Oklahoma.

FITHIAN, Floyd. 1 videocassette (3/4 in.).

Collection contains 2 television commercials used during Fithian's 1982 campaign for U.S. Senate in Indiana. (Democratic Party).

FITZGERALD, Jerry. 4 videocassettes (3/4 in.).

Collection contains 6 television spots from Fitzgerald's 1978 campaign for Governor, 6 television commercials from his 1982 campaign for Governor, and 8 television commercials from his 1984 campaign for U.S. Congress in District 5; all in Iowa. (Democratic Party).

FITZGERALD, William. 1 videocassette (3/4 in.). 24222401.

Collection contains 6 television commercials used during Fitzgerald's campaign for the 1982 gubernatorial election in Michigan. (Democratic Party).

FITZPATRICK, Bob. 1 videocassette (3/4 in.). 24222408.

Collection contains 1 television commercial used during Fitzpatrick's campaign for the 1982 state election in Michigan. (Democratic Party).

FITZPATRICK, David. 1 videotape. (2 in.). 24357125.

Collection contains 1 television commercial used during Fitzpatrick's 1980 campaign in Ohio.

FITZPATRICK, Richard. 1 videocassette (3/4 in.).

Collection contains 3 television commercials used during Fitzpatrick's 1986 campaign for State Senator in Michigan. (Democratic Party).

FLAHERTY, Pete. 1 videocassette (3/4 in.).

Collection contains 12 television commercials from Flaherty's 1978 campaign for Governor of Pennsylvania. (Democratic Party).

FLORIO, James.   3 videocassettes (3/4 in.).   1 sound tape reel (7 1/2 ips.).

Collection contains 25 television spots and 8 radio commercials used in Florio's 1981 campaign for Governor of New Jersey and 6 television spots used in his campaign for U.S. Congress in 1984. (Democratic Party).

FLOURNOY, Houston I. 3 videotapes (2 in.). 21341297.

Collection contains 3 television commercials contained in Flournoy's campaign for the 1974 gubernatorial election in California. (Republican Party).

FLYNN, Jim. 1 videocassette (3/4 in.). 24222413.

Collection contains 1 television commercial used during Flynn's 1982 campaign for Lt. Governor in Wisconsin. (Democratic Party).

FLYNN, Matt. 2 videocassettes (3/4 in.).

Collection contains 6 television commercials used during Flynn's 1986 campaign for U.S. Senate in Wisconsin. (Democratic Party).

FLYNN, Ray. 1 videocassette (3/4 in.).

Collection contains 5 television commercials used during Flynn's campaign for the 1983 mayoral election in Boston, Massachusetts.

FLYNT, John J. 1 film reel (16 mm.). 21426555.

Collection contains 1 television commercial used during Flynt's campaign for the 1976 U.S. congressional election in Georgia. (Democratic Party).

FOGLIETTA, Tom.   2 videocassettes (3/4 in.).

Collection contains 1 television spot from Foglietta's 1984 campaign for U.S. Congress in District 1 of Pennsylvania. Includes 1 television commercial used during his 1986 campaign for Congress in District 1. (Democratic Party).

FOLKES, John. 2 videocassettes (3/4 in.).

Collection contains 3 television commercials used during Folkes' campaign for Superintendent of Public Instruction in Oklahoma.

FOLSOM, Jim. 7 videotapes (2 in.). 1 videocassette (3/4 in.). 24222422.

Collection contains 12 television commercials used during Folsom's 1986 campaign for Lt. Governor in Alabama. (Democratic Party).

FONTANA, Raymond Joseph. 1923 -. 1 videotape (2 in.). 21256315.

Collection contains 3 television commercials used during Fontana's 1972 campaign for Register of Probate in Massachusetts. (Republican Party).

FORD, Bud. 1 videocassette (3/4 in.).

Collection contains 1 television commercial used during Ford's 1986 campaign for State Senate in Illinois.

FORD, Gerald R. 1913 -. 4 videocassettes (3/4 in.). 78 videotapes (2 in.). 21140194.

Collection contains 169 television commercials used during Ford's campaign for the 1976 presidential election. (Republican Party).

FORD, Geraldine Bledsoe. 1 videocassette (3/4 in.). 24222630.

Collection contains 1 television commercial used during Ford's 1982 campaign for a judgeship in Michigan.

FORD, Wendell H. 1924 - . 7 videotapes (2 in.). 1 film reel (16 mm.). 2 videocassettes (3/4 in.). 21254281.

Collection contains 18 television commercials used during Ford's 1972 campaign for Governor Kentucky and 7 television spots from his 1980 campaign for Senate. Includes 7 television spots from during his 1986 campaign for U.S. Senate. (Democratic Party).

FORE, Rick. 1 sound tape reel. (7 1/2 ips.).

Collection contains 1 radio commercial used during Fore's 1982 campaign for U.S. Senate in Nevada. (Republican Party).

FOREORSTER, Tom. 1 sound tape reel (7 1/2 ips.).

Collection contains 15 radio commercials used during Foreorster's campaign for the 1972 County Commissioner election in Pennsylvania.

FOSTER, Smith. 1 film reel (16 mm.). 21474881.

Collection contains 2 television commercials used during Foster's 1978 campaign for U.S. Congress in Georgia. (Democratic Party).

FOWLER, Wyche, Jr. 1940 -. 6 videocassettes (3/4 in). 1 sound tape reel (7 1/2 ips.).

Collection contains 4 radio commercials used during Fowler's campaign for the 1972 Congressional election in Georgia, and 65 television commercials used during his 1986 campaign for U.S. Senate in Georgia. (Democratic Party).

FRAAS, Lee. 1 sound tape reel (7 1/2 ips).

Collection contains 1 radio commercial used during Fraas' 1966 campaign for judge in North Dakota.

FRANK, Barney. 3 videocassettes (3/4 in.). 24222632.

Collection contains 2 television commercials used during Frank's 1980 campaign and 2 television commercials from his 1982 campaign for U.S. Congress in District 4 of Massachusetts. (Democratic Party).

FRANKEL, Dave. 1 sound tape reel (7 1/2 ips.).

Collection contains 3 radio commercials used during Frankel's campaign for the 1980 State Senate election in Pennsylvania. (Democratic Party).

FRANKLIN, Webb. 7 videocassettes (3/4 in.). 24222640.

Collection contains 8 television commercials used during Franklin's 1982 and 1984 campaigns for U.S. Congress in District 2 of Mississippi. Includes 12 television commercials used during his 1986 re-election campaign. (Republican Party).

FRANZENBURG, Paul. 1916-. 1 film reel (16 mm.). 21426481.

Collection contains 17 television commercials used during Franzenburg's campaign for the 1968 gubernatorial election in Iowa. (Democratic Party).

FREEDMAN, Deborah. 1 sound tape reel (7 1/2 ips.).

Collection contains 4 radio commercials used during Freedman's campaign for the 1982 Congressional election in District 3 in Maryland. (Democratic Party).

FREEMAN, Debra. 1 sound tape reel. (7 1/2 ips.).

Collection contains 3 radio commercials used during Freeman's 1983 campaign for local offices in Maryland. (Democratic Party).

FREEMAN, Orville L. 1 film reel (16 mm.). 21382832.

Collection contains 7 television commercials used during Freeman's campaign for the 1960 gubernatorial campaign in Minnesota. (Democratic Party).

FREEMAN, Woody. 2 videocassettes (3/4 in.).

Collection contains 8 television spots from Freeman's 1984 campaign for Governor of Arkansas. (Republican Party).

FRENZAL, Bill. 1 sound tape reel (3 3/4 ips.). 21892598.

Collection contains 8 radio commercials used during Frenzal's campaign for the 1972 U.S. Congressional election in Minnesota. (Republican Party).

FRENZI, Joe. 1 sound tape reel (7 1/2 ips.).

Collection contains 2 radio commercials used during Frenzi's 1982 campaign for a judgeship in Wisconsin.

FREY, Lou. 2 videocassettes (3/4 in.).

Collection contains 4 television commercials used during Frey's 1986 campaign for Governor of Florida. (Republican Party).

FRISBIE, Ray. 1 film reel (16 mm.). 24222645.

Collection contains 6 television commercials used during Frisbie's campaign for the 1972 gubernatorial election in Kansas. (Republican Party).

FROMAN, Gordon J. 1 sound tape reel (7 1/2 ips.).

Collection contains 1 radio commercial used during Froman's campaign for the 1980 County Commissioner election in District 12 in Kent County, Michigan. (Democratic Party).

FROMM, John. 1 sound tape reel (7 1/2 ips.).

Collection contains 3 radio commercials used during Fromm's campaign for the 1980 County Board of Supervisors election in Cerro Gordo County, Iowa.

FROST, Marianna. 1 videocassette (3/4 in.).

Collection contains 3 television commercials used during Frost's campaign for the 1982 congressional election in District 4 of Tennessee. (Republican Party).

FULBRIGHT, J. William. 1905-. 1 film reel (16 mm.). 7 videotapes (2 in.). 21186324.

Collection contains 22 television commercials used during Fulbright's campaign for the 1968 and 1974 U.S. senatorial elections in Arkansas. (Democratic Party).

FULTON, Richard. 3 videocassettes (3/4 in.).

Collection contains 34 television commercials used during Fulton's campaign for Mayor of Nashville, Tennessee. (Democratic Party).

FULTON, Robert D. 1929-. 1 sound tape reel (7 1/2 ips.). 1 videotape (2 in.). 22164857.

Collection contains 5 radio and 1 television spot used during Fulton's 1970 campaign for Governor in Iowa. (Democratic Party).

GABLE, Robert Elledy. 1934-. 3 videotapes (2 in.). 1 film reel (16 mm.). 21727428.

Collection contains 10 television commercials used during Gable's 1972 campaign for U.S. Senate, 7 television spots used during his 1974 gubernatorial election in Kentucky. (Republican Party).

GAGNON, Paul. 1 sound tape reel (7 1/2 ips.).

Collection contains 1 radio commercial used during Gagnon's 1982 campaign for local office in Hillsboro County. (Democratic Party).

GALBREATH, Charles. 1 videocassette (3/4 in.).

Collection contains 6 television commercials used during Galbreath's 1982 campaign for Public Defender in Tennessee.

GALIFIANAKIS, Nick. 1928-. 3 videotapes (2 in.). 21270265.

Collection contains 12 television spots from Galifianakis' 1972 campaign for U.S. Senate in North Carolina. (Democratic party).

GALLAGHER, Tom. 2 videocassettes (3/4 in.).

Collection contains 36 television commercials used during Gallagher's 1986 campaign for Governor of Florida. (Republican Party).

GALLEGOS, Eugene. 1 sound tape reel (7 1/2 ips.).

Collection contains 11 radio commercials used during Gallegos' campaign for the 1972 Congressional election in District 1 in New Mexico. (Democratic Party).

GALLEN, Hugh. 1 sound tape reel (7 1/2 ips.).

Collection contains 9 radio commercials used during Gallen's 1982 campaign for Governor of New Hampshire. (Democratic Party).

GAMBRELL, David Henry. 1929-. 1 film reel (16 mm.). 21538699.

Collection contains 5 television commercials used during Gambrell's campaign for the 1974 gubernatorial election in Georgia. (Democratic Party).

GANDER, Joan. 1 videotape (2 in.). 21727047.

Collection contains 1 television commercial used during Gander's campaign for the 1975 school board election in Milwaukee, Wisconsin.

GANDY, Evelyn. 1 videocassette (3/4 in.).

Collection contains 15 television commercials from Gandy's 1983 primary campaign for Governor of Mississippi. (Democratic Party).

GANN, Paul. 2 videotapes (2 in.). 1 videocassette (3/4 in.). 24357135.

Collection contains 8 television commercials used during Gann's campaign for the 1980 U.S. Senate election in California. (Republican Party).

GANNON, William. 1 sound tape reel (7 1/2 ips.). 22256908.

Collection contains 7 radio commercials used during Gannon's campaign for the 1974 gubernatorial election in Iowa. (Democratic Party).

GARAMENDI, John. 1 videotape (2 in.). 3 videocassettes (3/4 in.). 21319774.

Collection contains 1 television commercial used during Garamendi's 1974 campaign State Representative in California. Also includes 9 television commercials used during his 1986 campaign for statewide office. (Democratic Party).

GARCIA, George. 1 videocassette (3/4 in.).

Collection contains 1 television spot from Garcia's 1980 campaign for California State Assembly.

GARDNER, Booth. 1 videocassette (3/4 in.).

Collection contains 24 television spots used during Gardner's 1984 campaign for Governor of Washington. (Democratic Party).

GARDNER, Jim. 1933-. 2 film reels (16 mm.). 4 videotapes (2 in.). 21276381.

Collection contains 17 television commercials used during Gardner's 1972 campaign for Governor in North Carolina. (Republican Party).

GARDNER, Samuel C. 1 film reel (16 mm.). 24222656.

Collection contains 2 television commercials used during Gardner's 1972 campaign for a judgeship in Michigan.

GARLAND, Ray L. 1934-. 1 videotape (2 in.). 21186233.

Collection contains 3 television commercials used during Garland's 1970 campaign for U.S. Senate in Virginia. (Republican Party).

GARMAN, Rita B.. 1 videocassettes (3/4 in.).

Collection contains 1 television commercial used during Garman's 1986 campaign for a judgeship in Illinois. (Republican Party).

GARN, Jake. 2 videocassettes (3/4 in.).

Collection contains 11 television commercials used during Garn's 1986 campaign for U.S. Senate in Utah. (Republican Party).

GARRAHY, J. Joseph. 6 videocassettes (3/4 in.). 2 sound tape reels (7 1/2 ips.). 21892590.

Collection contains 6 radio commercials used during Garrahy's 1968 campaign for Lt. Governor, 1 television commercial from his 1976, 5 television commercials from his 1978, 18 television commercials and 16 radio spots from his 1980, and 12 television spots from his 1982 gubernatorial campaigns in Rhode Island. (Democratic Party).

GARRETT, Bill. 1 videocassette (3/4 in.).

Collection contains 2 television commercials used during Garrett's 1982 campaign for Metropolitan Trustee of Nashville, Tennessee.

GARRETT, James P. 1 videotape (2 in.). 21315023.

Collection contains 2 television commercials used during Garrett's 1966 campaign for Attorney General in Oklahoma. (Democratic Party).

GARVEY, Ed. 8 videocassettes (3/4 in.).

Collection contains 36 television commercials used during Garn's 1986 campaign for U.S. Senator in Wisconsin. (Democratic Party).

GARY, Raymond. 1 videocassette (3/4 in.).

Collection consists of 2 television commercials used during Gary's 1954 campaign for Governor of Oklahoma. (Democratic Party).

GEARY, Tom. 1 videotape (2 in.). 21741476.

Collection contains 1 television spot from Geary's 1972 campaign for State Representative in North Carolina. (Republican Party).

**GEJDENSON, Samuel. 3 sound tape reels (7 1/2 ips.).
5 videocassettes (3/4 in.).**

Collection contains 9 radio commercials and 7 television commercials used during Gejdenson's 1982 congressional campaign in District 2 of Connecticut. Includes 16 television commercials used during his 1986 campaign for for the same office. (Democratic Party).

GEKAS, George W. 1 videocassette (3/4 in.). 24222744.

Collection contains 4 television commercials used during Gekas' campaign for the 1982 congressional election in District 17 of Pennsylvania. (Republican Party).

GELFAND, Eugene. 1 sound tape reel (7 1/2 ips.).

Collection contains 1 radio commercial used during Gelfand's 1979 campaign for a Superior Court Judgeship in Pennsylvania. (Democratic Party).

GEORGE, Gary. 2 videocassettes (3/4 in.).

Collection contains 11 television commercials used during George's 1986 campaign for U.S. Senate in Wisconsin. (Democratic Party).

GEORGOPOLUS, Lovis. 1 sound tape reel (7 1/2 ips.).

Collection contains 4 radio commercials used during Georgopolus' campaign for the 1982 Executive Council election in New Hampshire. (Republican Party).

GEPHARDT, Richard A. 1941-. 7 videocassettes (3/4 in.). 21426520.

Collection contains 24 television commercials used during Gephardt's campaign for the 1988 presidential election. (Democratic Party).

GIBBONS, Mark. 1 videocassette (3/4 in.).

Collection contains 1 television commercial used during Gibbons' 1986 campaign for Lt. Governor in Florida. (Democratic Party).

GIBSON, Kenneth. 1 videocassette (3/4 in.). 1 sound tape reel (7 1/2 ips.).

Collection contains 3 television commercials and 1 radio spot from Gibson's 1981 campaign in New Jersey. (Democratic Party).

GILBERT, Alice. 1932-. 1 film reel (16 mm.). 21421308.

Collection contains 1 television commercial used during Gilbert's 1976 campaign for a judgeship in Oakland County, Michigan.

GILLIGAN, John J. 3 film reels (16 mm.). 1 videocassette (3/4 in.). 21437427.

Collection contains 10 television spots from Gilligan's 1974 campaign for Governor in Ohio. (Democratic Party).

GILLMOR, Paul. 1 videocassette (3/4 in.). 1 videotape (2 in.). 24222664.

Collection contains 8 television commercials used during Gillmor's 1986 campaign for Governor of Ohio. (Republican Party).

GILMORE, Jim. 1 sound tape reel (7 1/2 ips.).

Collection contains 1 radio commercial used during Gilmore's campaign for the 1980 Congressional election in Michigan.

GINGRICH, Newt. 3 videocassettes (3/4 in.).

Collection contains 1 television spot from Gingrich's 1980 congressional campaign in Georgia and 4 television spots from his 1982 re-election campaign. Includes 2 television commercials used during his 1986 campaign for Congress in District 6. (Republican Party).

GINN, Bo. 2 videocassettes (3/4 in.).

Collection contains 13 television commercials used during Ginn's 1982 campaign for Governor of Georgia. (Democratic Party).

GISCARD D'ESTAING, Valerie. 3 videotapes (3/4 in.).

Collection contains the 1981 television debate between Giscard D'Estaing and François Mitterrand during the election for President of France.

GISSENDANNER, Shirley M. 1 sound tape reel. (7 1/2 ips.).

Collection contains 1 radio commercial used during Gissendanner's 1982 campaign for U. S. Congress in District 44 of California. (Republican Party).

GIVOT, Steve. 1 sound tape reel (7 1/2 ips).

Collection contains 1 radio commercial used during Givot's 1984 campaign for the U.S. Senate in Illinois. (Libertarian Party).

GLANCEY, Joseph R. 1 sound tape reel (7 1/2 ips.).
1 videocassette (3/4 in.). 21984417.

Collection contains 3 radio and 2 television commercials used
during Glancey's 1979 campaign for a judgeship in Pennsylvania.

GLEASON, Jim. 1 film reel (16 mm.). 24222675.

Collection contains 3 television commercials used during
Gleason's campaign for County Executive in Maryland.

GLENN, John. 1921-. 6 videotapes (1 in. & 2 in.). 9
videocassettes (3/4 in.). 21180451.

This John Glenn campaign spot capitalized on his fame as a former astronaut.

Collection contains 2
television commercials
used during Glenn's
1970 campaign, 11
television commercials
used in his 1974
campaign, 7 television
spots from the 1980
campaign, and 10
television commercials
used in his 1986
campaign; all for U.S.
Senate in Ohio. Also
includes 80
commercials used by
Glenn in 1984 primary
campaign for
President.
(Democratic Party).

GLICKMAN, Dan. 2 videocassettes (3/4 in.).

Collection contains 8 television commercials used during
Glickman's 1986 campaign for Congress in District 4 of Kansas.
(Democratic Party).

GODOY, Robert. 1 videotape (2 in.). 24222683.

Collection contains 1 television commercial used during Godoy's
campaign for the 1978 state representative election in District
117 of Florida.

GODWIN, Mills E. 1914-. 2 film reels (16 mm.). 1 videotape
(2 in.). 21319685.

Collection contains 9 television commercials used during Godwin's
campaign for the 1973 gubernatorial election in Virginia.
(Republican Party).

GOJACK, Mary.   1 videocassette (3/4 in.).

Collection consists of 6 television spots from Gojack's 1980 campaign for U.S. Senate in Nevada.   (Democratic Party).

GOLA, Tom.   1 sound tape reel.   (7 1/2 ips.).

Collection contains 5 radio commercials used during Gola's 1983 campaign for Mayor in Pennsylvania. (Republican Party).

GOLDBERG, Joyce. 1 videotape (2 in.). 2 film reels (16 mm.).

Collection contains 3 television commercials used during Goldberg's 1972 campaign for Metro Commissioner, and 1 television commercial used during his campaign for the 1974 State House, both in Florida. (Democratic Party).

GOLDBERG, Arthur. 1 film reel (16 mm.). 24357214.

Collection contains 14 television commercials used during Goldberg's 1970 campaign for Governor in New York.   (Democratic Party).

GOLDMARK, John. 1 film reel (16 mm.). 22137713.

Collection contains 1 television item used after Goldmark's defeat in the 1962 state senatorial election in Washington. (Democratic Party).

GOLDSCHMIDT, Neil E. 1940-. 1 film reel (16 mm.). 2 sound tape reels (7 1/2 ips.). 1 videocassette (3/4 in.). 21567335.

Collection contains 11 television commercials and 10 radio commercial used during Goldschmidt's campaign for the 1972 Mayoral election in Portland, Oregon. Includes 36 television commercials used during his 1986 campaign for Governor. (Democratic Party).

GOLDSMITH, Steve. 1 videotape (2 in.). 24356606.

Collection contains 2 television commercials used during Goldsmith's 1982 campaign for Prosecutor in Indiana.   (Republican Party).

GOLDSTEIN, Louis. 1 film reel (16 mm.). 1 sound tape reel (7 1/2 in.).   24222690.

Collection contains 1 television commercial used during Goldstein's 1970 campaign for state office in Maryland. Also contains 3 radio commercials used during his 1982 campaign for State Comptroller in Maryland.   (Democratic Party).

GOLDWATER, Barry M.
1909-. 9 film reels
(16 mm.)., 8 sound
tape reels (3 3/4
ips.). 2 videocas-
settes (3/4 in.).
21145121.

Barry Goldwater's 1964 presidential campaign spots usually featured this famous Goldwater slogan.

Collection contains 51
items on television,
1 television commer-
cial, and 15 items on
radio, used during
Goldwater's campaign
for the 1964 presi-
dential election. Also
includes 24 television
spots from Goldwater's
1980 campaign for U.S.
Senate in Arizona.
(Republican Party).

GOODE, Wilson. 2 videocassettes (3/4 in.). 1 sound tape reel
(7 1/2 ips.).

Collection contains 6 radio commercials and 38 television commercials used during Goode's 1983 campaign for Mayor in
Philadelphia, Pennsylvania. (Democratic Party).

GOODELL, Charles E. 1926 -1987. 3 videotapes (2 in.). 21243984.

Collection contains 3 television commercials used during
Goodell's campaign for the 1970 U.S. senatorial election in New
York. (Republican Party).

GOODLING, William F. 1 sound tape reel (7 1/2 ips.).

Collection contains 2 radio commercials used during Goodling's
campaign for the 1980 congressional election in District 19 in
Pennsylvania. (Republican Party).

GOODMAN, William. 1 sound tape reel (7 1/2 ips.).

Collection contains 1 radio commercial used during Goodman's
campaign for the 1982 County Council election in Baltimore County
in Maryland. (Democratic Party).

GORDON, Bart. 3 videocassettes (3/4 in.).

Collection contains 4 television commercials used during Gordon's
1986 campaign for Congress in District 6 of Tennessee.
(Democratic Party).

GORDON, Milton G. 1 videotape (2 in.). 1 sound tape reel (7 1/2 ips.). 21191500.

Collection contains 1 television commercial and 1 radio commercial used during Gordon's 1970 campaign for State Treasurer in California. (Democratic Party).

GORE, Albert. 1948 -. 12 videocassettes (3/4 in.). 2 film reels (16 mm.). 21511298.

Collection contains 12 television commercials used during Gore's 1970 campaign for U.S. Senate, 4 television commercials used in his 1984 campaign for U.S. Senate, and 1 television commercial used during his 1986 campaign for U.S. Senate; all in Tennessee. Includes 43 television commercials used during his 1988 campaign for President. (Democratic Party).

GORTON, Slade. 1 videotape (2 in.). 15 videocassettes (3/4 in.).

Collection contains 32 television commercial used during Gorton's campaign for the 1980 U.S. Senate election in Washington. Also includes a 30-minute call-in television program from the same election. Includes 51 television commercials used during his 1986 campaign for U.S. Senate. (Republican Party).

GOSLEE, Georgia. 1 sound tape reel. (7 1/2 ips.).

Collection contains 2 radio commercials used during Goslee's 1982 campaign for a judgeship in Maryland.

GOYKE, Gary. 1 videotape (2 in.). 24356616.

Collection contains 4 television commercials used during Goyke's 1980 campaign for Congress in Wisconsin. (Democratic Party).

GRADDICK, Charles. 15 videotapes (2 in.). 24224422.

Collection contains 20 television spots from Graddick's 1986 campaign for Governor in Alabama. (Democratic Party).

GRADISON, Willis D. 1928 -. 1 videotape (2 in.). 21421452.

Collection contains 1 television commercial used during Gradison's campaign for the 1974 U.S. congressional election in Ohio, District 1. (Republican Party).

GRADY, John. 3 videotapes (2 in.). 21741111.

Collection contains 1 television commercial used during Grady's campaign for the 1974 U.S. senatorial election in Florida. (Independent Party). Includes 4 television commercials used during his campaign for the 1976 U.S. Senate election in Florida. (Republican Party).

GRAHAM, Robert. 2 videotapes (2 in.). 4 videocassettes (3/4 in.). 24224424.

Collection contains 13 television commercials used during Graham's campaign for the 1978 gubernatorial election in Florida. Includes 12 television commercials used during his 1986 campaign for U.S. Senate. (Democratic Party).

GRAMM, Phil. 12 videocassettes (3/4 in.). 21368940.

Collection contains 35 television commercials used during Gramm's campaign for the 1984 U.S. senatorial election in Texas. (Republican Party).

GRANT, Bill. 1 videocassette (3/4 in.).

Collection contains 4 television commercials used during Grant's 1986 campaign for Congress in District 2 of Florida.

GRANT, Jerome David. 1 videotape (2 in.). 24224427.

Collection contains 1 television commercial used during Grant's 1972 campaign for a judgeship in Wisconsin.

GRASSLEY, Charles "Chuck". 5 videocassettes (3/4 in.). 1 sound tape reel (7 1/2 ips.).

Collection contains 17 television commercials and 10 radio spots used in Grassley's 1980 campaign for U.S. Senate in Iowa. Includes 1 television commercial used during his 1986 re-election campaign. (Republican Party).

GRASSO, Ella. 1 videotape (2 in.). 2 videocassettes (3/4 in.). 21276352.

Collection contains 2 television spots from Grasso's 1972 congressional campaign in District 6, 4 television spots from her 1974 gubernatorial campaign, and 5 television spots from her 1978 gubernatorial campaign; all in Connecticut. (Democratic Party).

GRATIAS, Art. 1 sound tape reel (7 1/2 ips.).

Collection contains 3 radio commercials used during Gratias' campaign for the 1982 State Senate election in Iowa.

GRAVEL, Mike. 1930 -. 1 film reel (16 mm.). 1 videocassette (3/4 in.). 21369667.

Collection contains 1 television item used during Gravel's campaign for the 1968 U.S. Senate and 1 television documentary used in his 1974 campaign for U.S. Senate in Alaska. (Democratic Party).

GRAVES, Bill. 2 videocassettes (3/4 in.).

Collection contains 1 television commercial used during Graves' 1986 campaign for Secretary of State in Kansas. (Republican Party).

GRAY, Bill. 1 sound tape reel (7 1/2 ips.).

Collection contains 1 radio commercial used during Gray's campaign for the 1980 State Representative election in District 103 in Pennsylvania. (Republican Party).

GRAY, David. 1 videocassette (3/4 in.).

Collection contains 1 television commercials used during Gray's 1982 campaign for a judgeship in Tennessee.

GRAY, KARL. 1 videotape (2 in.). 24356624.

Collection contains 1 television commercial used during Gray's campaign for the 1978 judicial election in Oklahoma.

GRAY, Ken. 2 videocassettes (3/4 in.).

Collection contains 6 television commercials used during Gray's 1986 campaign for Congress in District 22 of Illinois. (Republican Party).

GRAY, Sid. 1 videotape (2 in.). 24356634.

Collection contains 2 television commercials used during Gray's 1981 campaign for a judgeship in Branch 21 in Wisconsin.

GRAY, Sterling. 1 videocassette (3/4 in.).

Collection contains 1 television commercial used during Gray's 1982 campaign for a judgeship in Tennessee.

GREEN, Bruce. 1 sound tape reel (7 1/2 ips.).

Collection contains 3 radio commercials used during Green's campaign for the 1980 U.S. Senate election in Illinois. (Libertarian Party).

GREEN, Mark. 2 videocassettes (3/4 in.).

Collection contains 3 television commercials used during Green's 1986 campaign for U.S. Senate in New York. (Democratic Party).

GREEN, William. 5 videotapes (2 in.). 2 videocassettes (3/4 in.). 24224432.

Collection contains 12 television commercials used during Green's 1976 campaign for the U.S. Senate in Pennsylvania and 11 television commercials from his 1979 campaign for Mayor of Philadelphia. (Democratic Party).

GREENHALGH, William W. 1 videotape (2 in.). 21486426.

Collection contains 5 television commercials used during Green-halgh's 1970 campaign for County Executive in Maryland. (Democratic Party).

GREENWOOD, Gordon Hicks. 1909 -. 1 videotape (2 in.). 21479151.

Collection contains 2 television commercials used during Greenwood's campaign for the 1972 state representative election in North Carolina. (Democratic Party).

GREGG, Judd. 1 sound tape reel (7 1/2 ips.).

Collection contains 5 radio commercials used during Gregg's 1982 congressional campaign in District 2 in New Hampshire. (Republican Party).

GRIBBS, Katherine. 1 film reel (16 mm.). 21630787.

Collection contains 4 television commercials used during Gribbs' campaign for the 1973 City Council election in Detroit, Michigan. (Democratic Party).

GRIFFIN, Brian. 2 videocassettes (3/4 in.).

Collection contains 10 television commercials used during Griffin's 1986 campaign for Attorney General in Oklahoma. (Republican Party).

GRIFFIN, Robert P. 1923 -. 2 film reels (16 mm.). 6 videotapes (2 in.). 1 videocassette (3/4 in.). 21287305.

Collection contains 2 television commercials used during Griffin's campaign for the 1966 U.S. senatorial election, 4 television commercials used during his 1972 re-election campaign, and 5 television commercials used during his 1978 re-election campaign in Michigan. Includes 2 television commercials used during his 1986 campaign for Supreme Court Judge. (Republican Party).

GRIFFITH, James B. 1 sound tape reel (7 1/2 ips.). 22198966.

Collection contains 4 radio commercials used during Griffith's 1974 campaign for State Auditor in Wyoming. (Republican Party).

GRIMES, Gerald. 1 videocassette (3/4 in.).

Collection contains 2 television commercials used during Grimes' 1986 campaign for Insurance Commissioner in Oklahoma.

GRODIN, Joe. 1 videotape (2 in.). 24224435.

Collection contains 3 television commercials used during Grodin's 1986 campaign for a judgeship in California.

GROENER, Ralph.   1 videocassette (3/4 in.).

Collection contains 1 television spot from Groener's 1980 campaign for Clackamas County Commissioner.   (Democratic Party).

GROTBERG, John. 1 sound tape reel (7 1/2 ips).

Collection contains 1 radio commercial used during Grotberg's 1984 campaign for Congress in Illinois. (Republican Party).

GROVER, Bert. 1 videotape (2 in.). 24356647.

Collection contains 1 television commercial used during Grover's campaign for the 1981 school election in Wisconsin.

GROVER, Henry. 6 videotapes (2 in.). 21741145.

Collection contains 24 television commercials used during Grover's campaign for the 1972 gubernatorial election in Texas. (Republican Party).

GROWE, Joan.   5 videocassettes (3/4 in.).

Collection contains 16 television spots from Growe's 1984 campaign for U.S. Senate in Minnesota.   (Democratic Party).

GRUBER, Don. 1 videotape (2 in.). 24224439.

Collection contains 1 television commercial used during Gruber's campaign for the 1978 State Senate election in Florida. (Republican Party).

GRUENING, Clark.   1 videocassette (3/4 in.).

Collection contains 18 spots from Gruening's 1980 campaign for U.S. Senate in Alaska.   (Democratic Party).

GRYFING, A. 1 videotape (2 in.). 24224445.

Collection contains 1 television commercial used during Gryfing's campaign in a 1986 Mississippi election.

GUARINO, Joe. 1 sound tape reel (7 1/2 ips).

Collection contains 2 radio commercials used during Guarino's 1986 campaign for Congress in New York. (Republican Party).

GUDE, Gilbert. 1 sound tape reel (7 1/2 ips.).

Collection contains 6 radio commercials used during Gude's campaign for the 1972 congressional election. (Republican Party).

GUENTHER, Herbert V. 2 videotapes (2 in.). 24224447.

Collection contains 2 television commercials used during Guenther's campaign for a 1986 Arizona election.

GUEST, James. 2 videocassettes (3/4 in.).

Collection contains 10 television commercials used during Guest's campaign for the 1982 U.S. senatorial election in Vermont. (Democratic Party).

GUGLIELMO, Tony. 1 videocassette (3/4 in.). 1 sound tape reel (7 1/2 ips.).

Collection contains 1 radio commercial and 6 television commercials used during Guglielmo's 1982 congressional campaign in District 2 in Connecticut. (Republican Party).

GUIN, Jim. 1 videotape (2 in.). 24224450.

Collection contains 1 television commercial used during Guin's campaign for a 1986 Alabama election.

GUNDERSON, Al. 1 sound tape reel. (7 1/2 ips.).

Collection contains 1 radio commercial used during Gunderson's 1982 campaign for a judgeship in Nevada.

GUNTER, William D. "Bill." 1934 -. 3 videotapes (2 in.). 5 videocassettes (3/4 in.). 21511175.

Collection contains 7 television commercials used during Gunter's 1974 campaign and 16 television commercials from his 1980 campaign, both for the U.S. Senate in Florida. Also includes 9 television spots from his 1986 campaign for Insurance Commissioner. (Democratic Party).

GURNEY, Edward J. 1914 -. 1 film reel (16 mm.). 21416242.

Collection contains 18 television commercials used during Gurney's campaign for the 1968 U.S. senatorial election in Florida. (Republican Party).

GUSTAFSON, Rick. 1 videocassettes (3/4 in.).

Collection contains 3 television spots used during Gustafson's 1986 campaign for Metro Executive in Portland, Oregon.

GUY, William L. 1919 -. 2 film reels (16 mm.). 21431893.

Collection contains 12 television spots used during Guy's 1974 campaign for U.S. Senate in North Dakota. (Democratic Party).

GUZZI, Paul. 2 videotapes (2 in.). 21741074.

Collection contains 2 television commercials used during Guzzi's campaign for the 1974 Secretary of State election in Massachusetts. (Democratic Party).

GWIN, Jim. 1 videocassette (3/4 in.).

Collection contains 6 television commercials used during Gwin's 1986 campaign for State Senator in Ohio. (Democratic Party).

HAABSTAD, Bud. 1 sound tape reel (7 1/2 ips.).

Collection contains 2 radio commercials used during Haabstad's campaign for the 1980 U.S. Senate election in Pennsylvania. (Republican Party).

HAAS, Virginia. 1 videotape (2 in.). 22198974.

Collection contains 1 television commercial used during Haas' 1972 campaign County Clerk in Wisconsin.

HAAVEN, Jon O. 1 film reel (16 mm.). 3 videotapes (2 in.). 1 sound tape reel (7 1/2 ips.). 21276435.

Collection contains 36 television commercials and 28 radio spots used during Haaven's campaign for the 1972 U.S. congressional election in Minnesota. (Republican Party).

HACKETT, Luther Frederick. 1933 -. 4 videotapes (2 in.). 21416210.

Collection contains 4 television commercials used during Hackett's campaign for the 1972 gubernatorial election in Vermont. (Republican Party).

HADIN, Charles H. 1 film reel (16 mm.). 21538687.

Collection contains 1 television commercial used during Hadin's campaign for the 1972 Secretary of State election in West Virginia. (Republican Party).

HAGAN, Anthony. 1 videocassette (3/4 in.).

Collection contains 2 television commercials used during Hagan's campaign for a 1982 judgeship election in Tennessee.

HAGAN, Tim. 2 videocassette (3/4 in.).

Collection contains 2 television commercials used during Hagan's campaign for a 1982 county commissioner election in Ohio. (Democratic Party).

HAGEN, Paul. 1 film reels (16 mm.). 24356653.

Collection contains 2 television commercials used during Hagen's campaign for the 1970 state commissioner's election in South Dakota. (Democratic Party).

HALE, Elaine. 1 videotape (1 in.). 24224452.

Collection contains 1 television commercial used during Hale's 1986 campaign for Mayor in California.

HALL, David. 2 videocassettes (3/4 in.).

Collection consists of 1 television commercial used during Hall's 1970 campaign for Governor of Oklahoma. Also included is a 1971 television news documentary on Hall's first 100 days as Governor of Oklahoma. (Democratic Party).

HALL, Gus. 3 videotapes (2 in.). 1 sound tape reel (3 3/4 ips.). 21270257.

Collection contains 3 television commercials and 1 radio commercial used during Hall's campaign for the 1972 presidential election. Includes 1 radio commercial used during his 1984 campaign for President. (Communist Party).

HALL, Robert. 1 sound tape reel (7 1/2 ips.).

Collection contains 2 radio commercials used during Hall's campaign for the 1980 Metropolitan Sanitary District Commissioner election in Illinois. (Republican Party).

HALLETT, Carol. 4 videotapes (2 in.). 4 videocassettes (3/4 in.). 24356661.

Collection contains 7 television commercials used during Hallett's campaign for the 1982 Lt. Governor's election in California. Includes 2 television commercials used during his 1986 campaign for Lt. Governor. (Republican Party).

HALLOWAY, Harry. 2 videotapes (2 in.). 24356667.

Collection contains 2 television commercials used during Halloway's 1972 and 1980 campaigns for Circuit Court Judge in Wisconsin.

HALLOWAY. 1 videotape (2 in.). 24224483.

Collection contains 1 television commercial used during Halloway's campaign for a 1972 judgeship election.

HALMRAST, Gerald. 1 videotape (2 in.). 24227114.

Collection contains 1 television commercial used during Halmrast's campaign for a 1976 local election in North Dakota.

HAMILTON, Lee. 2 film reels (16 mm.). 21421503.

Collection contains 2 television commercials used during Hamilton's campaign for the 1966 U.S. congressional election in Indiana. (Democratic Party).

HAMILTON, Milton. 1 videocassette (3/4 in.).

Collection contains 3 television commercials used during Hamilton's campaign for a 1982 state election in Tennessee.

HAMMOND, George Donald. 1906 -. 3 videotapes (2 in.). 1 film reel (16 mm.). 21256329.

Collection contains 4 television commercials used during Hammond's 1972 campaign for State Senate in Massachusetts. (Republican Party).

HAMMOND, Jay. 2 videocassettes (3/4 in.).

Collection consists of 4 television commercials from Hammond's 1978 campaign for Governor of Alaska. (Republican Party).

HAMMOND, John. 1 sound tape reel (7 1/2 ips.).

Collection contains 2 radio commercials used during Hammond's campaign for the 1982 County Executive election in Maryland.

HAMPERS, Joyce. 9 videocassettes (3/4 in.).

Collection contains 32 television commercials used during Hampers' 1986 campaign for State Treasurer in Massachusetts. (Republican Party).

HANAWAY, Dan. 1 videocassette (3/4 in.).

Collection contains 2 television commercials used during Hanaway's 1986 campaign for Attorney General in Wisconsin. (Republican Party).

HANCE, Kent. 1 videocassette (3/4 in.).

Collection contains 2 television commercials used during Hance's 1986 campaign for Governor of Texas. (Republican Party).

HAND, Lloyd. 1 film reel (16 mm.). 24227129.

Collection contains 5 television commercials used during Hand's 1966 campaign for Lt. Governor in California. (Democratic Party).

HANEY, Ann. 1 videocassette (3/4 in.).

Collection contains 13 television commercials used during Haney's 1986 campaign for Congress in District 2 of Wisconsin. (Republican Party).

HANLON, Neil. 1 sound tape reel (7 1/2 ips.).

Collection contains 6 radio commercials used during Hanlon's 1982 congressional campaign in District 5 of Connecticut. (Republican Party).

HANNEMAN, Carl. 1 videotape (2 in.). 24356672.

Collection contains 1 television commercial used during Hanneman's campaign for the 1980 sheriff's election in Milwaukee, Wisconsin.

HANNEMANN, Mufi. 2 videocassettes (3/4 in.).

Collection contains 15 television commercials used during Hannemann's 1986 campaign for Congress in District 1 of Hawaii. (Democratic Party).

HANSEN, Bill. 1 sound tape reel (7 1/2 ips.).

Collection contains 1 radio commercial used during Hansen's campaign for the 1980 congressional election in District 3 in Iowa. (Republican Party).

HANSEN, Clifford P., 1912 -. 3 film reels (16 mm.). 21369681.

Collection contains 16 television commercials used during Hansen's 1966 and 1972 campaigns for U.S. Senate in Wyoming. (Republican Party).

HANSEN, George.   1930 -.   2 videocassettes (3/4 in.). 1 film reel (16 mm.).

Collection contains 4 television commercials used during Hansen's 1968 campaign U.S. Senate and 4 television spots from his 1984 campaign for U.S. Congress in District 2 of Idaho.   (Republican Party).

HANSEN, George.   1 sound tape reel (7 1/2 ips.). 24356682.

Collection contains 5 radio commercials used during Hansen's campaign for the 1972 U.S. Senate election in Iowa.   (Republican Party).

HANSEN, James. 3 videocassette (3/4 in.).

Collection contains 4 television commercials used during Hansen's campaign for the 1982 congressional election in District 1 of Utah. Includes 6 television commercials used during his 1986 campaign for Congress in District 1. (Republican Party).

HANSEN, Jay. 1 videocassette (3/4 in.).

Collection contains 1 television commercial used during Hansen's 1986 campaign for Judicial Court Judge in Illinois. (Republican Party).

HANSEN, Orval. 1 sound tape reel (7 1/2 ips.). 22199007.

Collection contains 5 radio commercials used during Hansen's campaign for the 1972 U.S. senatorial election in Idaho. (Republican Party).

HANSEN, Phillip. 12 videotapes (2 in.). 1 sound tape reel (3 3/4 ips.). 21631400.

Collection contains 12 television commercials and 9 radio commercials used during Hansen's campaign for the 1972 U.S. senatorial election in Minnesota. (Republican Party).

HANSON, Bob.   1 videocassette (3/4 in.).

Collection contains 3 television commercials from Hanson's 1980 campaign for State Treasurer in North Dakota.

HARBOR, William H. 1920 -. 3 sound tape reels (7 1/2 ips.). 22164835.

Collection contains 3 radio commercials used during Harbor's 1972 campaign for Lt. Governor in Iowa. (Republican Party).

HARE, F. 2 videotapes (2 in.). 24227138.

Collection contains 3 television commercials used during Hare's campaign for a 1986 Alabama election.

HARKIN, Tom. 6 videocassettes (3/4 in.).

Collection contains 5 television commercials from Harkin's 1980 and 1982 campaigns for U.S. Congress in District 5 of Iowa and 26 television spots from his 1984 campaign for U.S. Senate in Iowa. (Democratic Party).

HARPER. 1 sound tape reel (7 1/2 ips.).

Collection contains 4 radio commercials used during Dowd's campaign for a 1980 Supreme Court Judgeship election in Ohio. (Republican Party).

HARRIS, Claude. 4 videotapes (2 in.). 1 videocassette (3/4 in.). 24227159.

Collection contains 9 television commercials used during Harris' campaign for the 1986 congressional election in District 7 of Alabama.

HARRIS, David. 1 videotape (2 in.). 24227168.

Collection contains 1 television commercial used during Harris' 1982 campaign for a judgeship in Michigan.

HARRIS, Fred R. 1 film reel (16 mm.). 5 videotapes (2 in.). 21186267.

Collection contains 12 television commercials used during Harris' campaigns for the 1964 and 1966 U.S. senatorial elections in Oklahoma and 1976 presidential election. (Democratic Party).

HARRIS, Herbert. 1 sound tape reel (7 1/2 ips.).

Collection contains 1 radio commercial used during Harris' campaign for the 1982 congressional election in District 8 of Virginia. (Democratic Party).

HARRIS, Joe. 1 videocassette (3/4 in.).

Collection contains 1 television commercial used during Harris' 1986 campaign for Albany County Judge in New York.

HARRIS, Joe Frank. 4 videocassettes (3/4 in.).

Collection contains 9 television commercials used during Harris' 1982 campaign for Governor of Georgia. (Democratic Party).

HARRISON, William Henry. 1 film reel (16 mm.). 24227146.

Collection contains 12 television commercials used during Harrison's campaign for the 1968 congressional election in Wyoming. (Republican Party).

HARSHBARGER, Scott. 2 videocassettes (3/4 in.).

Collection contains 3 television commercials used during Harshbarger's 1986 campaign for District Attorney in Middlesex County, Massachusetts.

HART, Gary. 1936 -. 12 videocassettes (3/4 in.). 6 videotapes (2 in.). 1 sound tape reel (7 1/2 ips.). 21140053.

Collection contains 29 television commercials used during Hart's campaign for the 1980 U.S. senatorial election in Colorado, and 3 television commercials used during his re-election campaign. Includes 67 television and 2 radio commercials used during his campaign for the 1984 presidential election, and 7 television spots used in his 1988 presidential campaign. (Democratic Party).

HART, Phillip. 3 film reels (16 mm.). 24227177.

Collection contains 16 television commercials used during Hart's 1970 campaign for U.S. Senate in Michigan. (Democratic Party).

HART, Royal. 3 videotapes (2 in.). 21191478.

Collection contains 4 television commercials used during Hart's 1970 campaign for U.S. Congress, 5th District in Maryland. (Democratic Party).

HARTIGAN, Neil. 1 videotape (2 in.). 4 videocassettes (3/4 in.). 24227187.

Collection contains 1 television commercial used during Hartigan's 1982 campaign for Attorney General in Illinois. Includes 4 television commercials used during his 1986 campaign for Attorney General. (Democratic Party).

HARTKE, Vance. 13 sound tape reels (7 1/2 ips.). 5 videotapes (2 in.). 3 film reel (16 mm.). 1 videocassette (3/4 in.). 21175201.

Collection contains 1 television commercial used during Hartke's re-election campaign for the 1964 U.S. Senate, 25 television and 21 radio commercials used during his 1970 re-election campaign, and 4 television commercials used during his 1976 re-election campaign; all elections in Indiana. Also includes 37 radio commercials used during Hartke's 1972 campaign for President. (Democratic Party).

HARTNETT, Tommy. 1 videocassette (3/4 in.).

Collection contains 2 television commercials used during Hartnett's 1986 campaign for Lt. Governor in South Carolina. (Republican Party).

HASARA, Karen. 1 videocassette (3/4 in.).

Collection contains 1 television spot from Hasara's 1986 campaign for State Representative in Illinois. (Republican Party).

HASKELL, Floyd. 8 videocassette (3/4 in.).

Collection contains 19 television commercials used during Haskell's 1978 campaign in Colorado. (Democratic Party).

HATCH, Francis Whiting, Jr. 1925 -. 1 videocassette (3/4 in.). 2 sound tape reels (7 1/2 ips.). 22137720.

Collection contains 14 television and 3 radio commercials used during Hatch's 1978 gubernatorial campaign in Massachusetts. (Republican Party).

HATCH, Orrin. 1 videotape (2 in.). 1 videocassette (3/4 in.). 24227202.

Collection contains 16 television commercials used during Hatch's campaign for the 1982 U.S. Senate campaign in Vermont. (Republican Party).

HATCHADORIAN, Matt. 3 videocassettes (3/4 in.).

Collection contains 13 television spots from Hatchadorian's 1984 campaign for Congress in Ohio. (Republican Party).

HATCHER, Charles. 3 videocassettes (3/4 in.).

Collection contains 3 television commercials used during Hatcher's 1982 campaign for U.S. Congress in District 3 in Georgia. (Democratic Party).

HATCHER, Richard Gordon. 1 sound tape reel (7 1/2 ips).

Collection contains 1 radio commercial used during Hatcher's 1966 campaign for Mayor in Indiana.

HATFIELD, Mark O., 1922 -. 1 film reel (16 mm.). 1 sound tape reel (7 1/2 ips.). 1 videocassette (3/4 in.).

Collection contains 8 television commercials and 6 radio commercials used during Hatfield's 1972 campaign and 5 television commercials used during his 1984 campaign for U.S. Senate in Oregon. (Republican Party).

HATFIELD, Paul Gerhart. 1928 -. 1 sound tape reel (7 1/2 ips.). 3 videotapes (2 in.). 1979454.

Collection contains 4 radio commercials and 4 television commercials used during Hatfield's campaign for the 1978 U.S. senatorial election in Montana. (Democratic Party).

HATHAWAY, Richard. 1 videocassette (3/4 in.). 24227210.

Collection contains 1 television commercial used during Hathaway's 1982 campaign for a judgeship in Michigan.

HATHAWAY, Stanley K. 2 film reels (16 mm.). 21421485.

Collection contains 2 television commercials used during Hathaway's campaign for the 1966 gubernatorial election in Wyoming. (Republican Party).

HATHAWAY, William Dodd. 1924 -. 3 film reels (16 mm.). 214216200.

Collection contains 44 television commercials used during Hathaway's campaign for the 1972 and 1978 U.S. senatorial elections in Maine. (Democratic Party).

HAWKINS, Paula. 2 film reels (16 mm.). 26 videocassettes (3/4 in.). 24227222.

Collection contains 4 television commercials used during Hawkins' 1972 campaign for Public Service Commissioner in Florida and 16 television spots used during her 1980 campaign for U.S. Senate in Florida. Includes 74 television commercials used during her 1986 campaign for U.S. Senate. (Republican Party).

HAWKS, R. Jack. 1 videotape (2 in.). 21486407.

Collection contains 1 television commercial used during Hawks' campaign for the 1972 U.S. congressional election in North Carolina. (Republican Party).

HAYAKAWA, Samuel I. 1906 -. 1 sound tape reel (7 1/2 ips.). 2 film reels (16 mm.). 1 videocassette (3/4 in.). 21437395.

Collection contains 21 radio commercials and 8 television commercials used during Hayakawa's campaign for the 1976 U.S. senatorial election in California. (Republican Party).

HAYDEN, Andrew. 1 videocassette (3/4 in.).

Collection contains 2 television commercials used during Hayden's 1986 campaign for State Senator in District 23 of Alabama. (Democratic Party).

HAYDEN, Mike. 1 videocassette (3/4 in.).

Collection contains 13 television commercials used during Hayden's 1986 campaign for Governor of Kansas. (Republican Party).

HAYDEN, Tom. 1 film reel (16 mm.). 2 videotapes (2 in). 21437386.

Collection contains 1 television commercial used during Hayden's campaign for the 1972 U.S. senatorial election in California. Includes 9 television commercials used during his 1976 U.S. Senate campaign in California. (Democratic Party).

HAYES, Karen. 1 sound tape reel. (7 1/2 ips.).

Collection contains 1 radio commercial used during Hayes' 1982 campaign for local office in Nevada.

HAYES, Ken. 1 videocassette (3/4 in.).

Collection contains 4 television commercials from Hayes' 1984 campaign for State Senate in District 11 of Maine. (Democratic Party).

HAYES, Phillip Harold. 1 videotape (2 in.). 3 sound tape reels (7 1/2 ips.). 24227346.

Collection contains 2 television commercials and 7 radio spots used during Hayes' campaign for the 1976 U.S. Senate election in Indiana. (Democratic Party).

HAYFEN, Andy. 1 sound tape reel (7 1/2 ips.).

Collection contains 2 radio commercials used during Hayfen's campaign for the 1980 County Commissioner election in Nevada.

HAYNES, Barbara. 1 videocassette (3/4 in.).

Collection contains 1 television commercial used during Haynes' 1982 campaign for a judgeship in Tennessee.

HAYS, Brooks. 1 videotape (2 in.). 21315003.

Collection contains 1 television commercial used during Hays' campaign for the U.S. congressional election in North Carolina. (Democratic Party).

HAZLETT, Allan A., 1943 -. 1 videotape (2 in.). 21437437.

Collection contains 1 television commercial used during Hazlett's campaign for a 1972 judgeship in Kansas. (Republican Party).

HEADLEE, Richard. 2 videocassettes (3/4 in.). 24227357.

Collection contains 24 television commercials used during Headlee's campaign for the 1982 gubernatorial election in Michigan. (Republican Party).

HECHT, Clark. 1 sound tape reel. (7 1/2 ips.).

Collection contains 1 radio commercial used during Hecht's 1982 campaign for U.S. Senate in Nevada. (Republican Party).

HECKLER, Margaret. 1 videocassette (3/4 in.). 24227363.

Collection contains 5 television commercials used during Heckler's campaign for the 1982 congressional election in District 4 of Massachusetts. (Republican Party).

HEFTEL, Cecil. 2 videocassettes (3/4 in.).

Collection contains 30 television commercials used during Heftel's 1986 campaign for Governor of Hawaii. (Democratic Party).

HEGGEGAN, A. Owen. 1 sound tape reel (7 1/2 ips).

Collection contains 1 radio commercial used during Heggegan's 1984 campaign for Baltimore County Circuit Judge in Maryland.

HEIDEPRIEM, Scott. 1 videocassette (3/4 in.).

Collection contains 11 television commercials used during Heidepriem's 1986 campaign for Congressman At Large in South Dakota. (Republican Primary).

HEINZ, John P. 1 videotape (2 in.). 1 videocassette (3/4 in.). 24227376.

Collection contains 2 television commercials used during Heinz's campaign for the 1983 gubernatorial election in Pennsylvania. Includes 1 television appearance on "Meet the Press" in 1986. (Republican Party).

HEIRONIMUS, Dan. 1 videocassette (3/4 in.).

Collection contains 1 television commercial used during Heironimus' 1986 campaign for State Representative in Ohio. (Republican Party).

HELLIVIG, Maureen. 1 sound tape reel (7 1/2 ips).

Collection contains 1 radio commercial used during Hellivig's 1984 campaign for Cook County Board of Tax Appeals in Illinois. (Democratic Party).

HELMS, Jesse. 1 videotape (2 in.). 7 videocassettes (3/4 in.). 21268983.

Collection contains 1 television commercial used during Helms' 1972 campaign and 114 television spots for his 1984 re-election campaign for U.S. Senate in North Carolina. (Republican Party).

HELSTOSKI, Henry. 1 sound tape reel (7 1/2 ips).

Collection contains 1 radio commercial used during Helstoski's 1964 campaign for Congress in District 9 of New Jersy. (Democratic Party).

HENDON, Bill. 5 videocassettes (3/4 in.). 24227383.

Collection contains 19 television commercials used during Hendon's 1982 and 1984 campaigns for U.S. Congress in District 11 of North Carolina. Includes 2 television commercials used during his 1986 campaign for Congress in District 11. (Republican Party).

HENDRICKSEN, Margie. 1 videocassette (3/4 in.).

Collection contains 3 television commercials used during Hendricksen's 1984 campaign for U.S. Senate in Oregon. (Democratic Party).

HENIGAN, Maura. 2 videocassettes (3/4 in.).

Collection contains 2 television commercials used during Henigan's 1986 campaign for State Auditor in Massachusetts. (Democratic Party).

HENNIGAN, James W.. 8 sound tape reels (7 1/2 ips).

Collection contains 25 radio commercials used during Hennigan's 1964 campaign for Attorney General in Massachusetts. (Democratic Party).

HENRY, Paul. 1 videocassette (3/4 in.).

Collection contains 10 television spots used in Henry's 1984 campaign for U.S. Congress in District 5 of Michigan. (Republican Party).

HENRY, Bubba. 1 videocassette (3/4 in.).

Collection contains 16 television commercials from Henry's 1978 primary campaign for Governor of Louisiana. (Democratic Party).

HENRY, Robert. 2 videocassettes (3/4 in.).

Collection contains 5 television commercials used during Henry's 1986 campaign for Attorney General in Oklahoma. (Democratic Party).

HEPHERD, H. Joseph. 1 sound tape reel (7 1/2 ips.).

Collection contains 1 radio commercial used during Hepherd's 1972 campaign for State House in District 104 in Pennsylvania. (Republican Party).

HERBERT, Tom. 1 videotape (2 in.).

Collection contains 1 television commercial used during Herbert's campaign for the 1978 judicial election in Ohio.

HERRMANN, Karl. 1915 -. 1 film reel (16 mm.). 21979471.

Collection contains 3 television commercials used during Herrmann's 1972 campaign for State Insurance Commissioner in Washington. (Democratic Party).

HERSCHEL, Klein. 1 sound tape reel (7 1/2 ips.).

Collection contains 2 radio commercials used during Herschel's 1982 congressional campaign in District 1 in Connecticut. (Republican Party).

HERSCHLER, Ed. 1918 -. 2 film reels (16 mm.). 1 videocassette (3/4 in.). 21437341.

Collection contains 17 television commercials used during Herschler's campaign for the 1974 gubernatorial election in Wyoming. Includes 2 television commercials used during his 1982 re-election campaign. (Democratic Party).

HETRICK, Norm. 2 sound tape reels (7 1/2 ips.).

Collection contains 5 radio commercials used during Hetrick's campaign for the 1980 Dauphin County Commissioner election in Pennsylvania. (Republican Party).

HEWLETT, Steve. 1 videocassette (3/4 in.).

Collection contains 6 television commercials used during Hewlett's 1986 campaign for Public Service Commission in Tennessee. (Democratic Party).

HIBBARD, Henry "Hank". 2 film reels (16 mm.). 1 sound tape reel (7 1/2 ips.). 24227393.

Collection contains 3 television commercials and 8 radio spots used during Hibbard's campaign for the 1972 U.S. Senate election in Montana. (Republican Party).

HICKMAN, Darrell. 1 sound tape reel (7 1/2 ips.).

Collection contains 1 radio commercial used during Hickman's campaign for the 1972 judgeship election in Arkansas.

HICKS, Louise Day. 1 sound tape reel (7 1/2 ips).

Collection contains 1 radio commercial used during Hicks' 1971 campaign for Mayor of Boston, Massachusetts.

HILDEBRAND, Don. 1 videocassette (3/4 in.).

Collection contains 1 television commercial used during Hildebrand's campaign for a 1982 judicial election in Tennessee.

HILDRETH, Wilbur. 1 videotape (2 in.). 24227396.

Collection contains 1 television commercial used during Hildreth's 1972 campaign for Sheriff in Iowa. (Democratic Party).

HILER, John. 1 videocassette (3/4 in.).

Collection contains 2 television spot from Hiler's 1986 campaign for Congress in District 3 of Indiana. (Republican Party).

HILL, Jerry. 1 sound tape reel (7 1/2 ips.).

Collection contains 1 radio commercial used during Hill's 1980 campaign for Sheriff in Maricopa County in Arizona.

HILL, John L. 1923 -. 1 film reel (16 mm.). 21892541.

Collection contains 4 television commercials used during Hill's 1972 campaign for Attorney General in Texas. (Democratic Party).

HILL, Lou. 1 videocassette (3/4 in.).

Collection contains 1 television commercials used in Hill's 1975 campaign for Mayor of Philadelphia, Pennsylvania. (Democratic Party).

HILLENBRAND, John. 1 videocassette (3/4 in.).

Collection contains 1 television commercial used during Hillenbrand's 1980 campaign for Governor of Indiana. (Democratic Party).

HILLIS, Edward "Bud". 1 sound tape reel (7 1/2 ips).

Collection contains 1 radio commercial used during Hillis' 1970 campaign for Congress in District 5 of Indiana.

HIMELEIN, Larry. 1 videocassette (3/4 in.).

Collection contains 2 television commercials used during Himelein's 1986 campaign for Congress in District 34 of New York. (Democratic Party).

HINKLE, William. 1 sound tape reel (7 1/2 ips.).

Collection contains 3 radio commercials used during Hinkle's 1982 campaign for a judgeship in Maryland.

HIRST, Julius. 1 sound tape reel (7 1/2 ips).

Collection contains 1 radio commercial used during Hirst's 1968 campaign for Congress in Tennessee.

HIRST. 1 sound tape reel (7 1/2 ips).

Collection contains 1 radio commercial used during Hirst's 1971 campaign for the State Senate in Virginia.

HOBBINS, Barry. 1 videocassette (3/4 in.).

Collection contains 2 television commercials used during Hobbins' 1984 campaign for U.S. Congress in Maine. (Democratic Party).

HOBBY, Wilbur. 2 videotapes (2 in.). 21269372.

Collection contains 5 television commercials used during Hobby's 1972 campaign for Governor in North Carolina. (Democratic Party).

**HOBBY, William Pettus. 1932 -. 1 videotape (2 in.).
1 videocassette (3/4 in.). 21388352.**

Collection contains 6 television spots from Hobby's 1972 campaign for Lt. Governor in Texas and 2 television commercials from his 1982 re-election campaign for Lt. Governor. (Democratic Party).

HOCH, Nancy. 1 videocassette (3/4 in.).

Collection contains 2 television commercials used during Hoch's 1986 campaign for Governor of Nebraska. (Republican Party).

HOCHENDONER, Larry. 1 videocassette (3/4 in.). 24227505.

Collection contains 3 television commercials used during Hochendoner's campaign for the 1982 congressional election in District 17 of Pennsylvania. (Democratic Party).

HODGSON, Clayton. 1 videocassette (3/4 in.).

Collection contains 20 television commercials used during Hodgson's 1986 campaign for Congress in District 6 of Iowa. (Democratic Party).

HOEFFEL, Joe. 4 videocassette (3/4 in.).

Collection contains 5 television commercials used during Hoeffel's 1984 campaign for U.S. Congress in Pennsylvania. Includes 10 television commercials used during his 1986 campaign for Congress in District 13. (Republican Party).

HOFF, Phil. 1 film reel (16 mm.).

Collection contains 14 television commercials used during Hoff's 1970 campaign for U.S. Senate in Vermont. (Democratic Party).

HOFFER, George. 2 sound tape reels (7 1/2 ips.). 22198984.

Collection contains 12 radio commercials used during Hoffer's 1979 campaign for a juudgeship in Cumberland County, Pennsylvania. (Republican Party).

HOFFMAN, Robert. 1 videotape (2 in.). 24227409.

Collection contains 1 television commercial used during Hoffman's 1972 campaign for Attorney General in Kansas. (Republican Party).

HOFFNER, Buckshot. 1 videocassette (3/4 in.). 1 sound tape reel (7 1/2 ips.).

Collection contains 2 radio and 3 television commercials used in Hoffner's 1980 campaign for Commissioner of Agriculture in North Dakota. (Democratic Party).

HOGAN, Lawrence J. 1928 -. 1 sound tape reel (7 1/2 ips.). 2 film reels (16 mm.). 21930041.

Collection contains 3 radio and 7 television commercials used during Hogan's campaign for the 1972 U.S. congressional election in Maryland, 5th District,. (Republican Party).

HOGAN, Pat. 1 sound tape reel (7 1/2 ips.).

Collection contains 1 radio commercial used during Hogan's 1982 campaign for State House in Connecticut. (Democratic Party).

HOLCOMB, Terry. 3 videocassettes (3/4 in.).

Collection contains 3 television commercials used during Holcomb's 1986 campaign for Congress in District 5 of Tennessee. (Republican Party).

HOLEWINSKI, MIKE.   1 sound tape reel.   (7 1/2 ips.).

Collection contains 3 radio commercials used during Holewinski's 1983 campaign for local offices in Maryland. (Democratic Party).

HOLLAND, Iris K. 1920 -. 3 videotapes (2 in.). 21256323.

Collection contains 3 television commercials used during Holland's 1972 campaign for State Representative in Massachusetts, 7th District. (Republican Party).

HOLLAR, Jess. 1 sound tape reel (7 1/2 ips).

Collection contains 4 radio commercials used during Hollar's campaign for a state office in Missouri. (Republican Party).

HOLLINGS, Ernest F. "Fritz." 1922 -.   3 videocassettes (3/4 in.).

Collection contains 4 television commercials used during Hollings 1986 campaign for U.S. Senate in South Carolina. Also includes television spots from Hollings' 1984 primary campaign for President.   (Democratic Party).

HOLLOWAY, Clyde. 1 videocassette (3/4 in.).

Collection contains 1 television commercial used during Holloway's 1986 campaign for Congress in District 8 of Louisiana. (Republican Party).

HOLM, Hugh. 1 sound tape reel (7 1/2 ips).

Collection contains 3 radio commercials used during Holm's campaign for Mayor in Montana.

HOLMDAHL, Dewayne. 2 videotapes (2 in.). 1 videocassette (3/4 in.). 24227416.

Collection contains 6 television commercials used during Holmdahl's campaign for the 1986 State Senate election in California. (Republican Party).

HOLMES, John A, Jr. 6 videotapes (2 in.). 7 videocassettes (3/4 in.). 24227426.

Collection contains 22 television commercials used during Holmes' campaign for the 1986 congressional election in District 11 of Rhode Island. (Republican Party).

HOLMES. 1 sound tape reel (7 1/2 ips.).

Collection contains 4 radio commercials used during Holmes' 1980 campaign for Supreme Court Judge in Ohio. (Republican Party).

HOLSHOUSER, James E. 4 videotapes (2 in.). 21270245.

Contains seven television commercials used during Holshouser's 1972 campaign for Governor in North Carolina. (Republican Party).

HOLT, Majorie. 1 film reel (16 mm.). 24241668.

Collection contains 3 television commercials used during Holt's campaign for the 1972 congressional election in District 4 of Maryland. (Republican Party).

HOLTON, Linwood. 1 sound tape reel (7 1/2 ips).

Collection contains 1 radio commercial used during Holton's 1969 campaign for Governor of Iowa. (Republican Party).

HOLTZMAN, Elizabeth. 2 videocassettes (3/4 in.).

Collection contains 22 commercials from Holtzman's 1980 campaign for U.S. Senate in New York. (Democratic Party).

HOLTZMAN, Marc. 1 videocassette (3/4 in.).

Collection contains 1 television commercial used during Holtzman's 1986 campaign for Congress in District 11 of Pennsylvania. (Republican Party).

HOOKER, John Jay. 1 film reel (16 mm.). 24241680.

Collection contains 17 television commercials used during Hooker's campaign for the 1970 gubernatorial election in Indiana. Democratic Party.

HOOPER, Sheila. 2 videotapes (2 in.).

Collection contains 4 television commercials used during Hooper's 1980 campaign for State House in Illinois.

HOPPER, John. 1 sound tape reel (7 1/2 ips.).

Collection contains 3 radio commercials used during Hopper's campaign for the 1980 State Senate election in District 31 in Pennsylvania. (Republican Party).

HORN, Chuck. 1 videocassette (3/4 in.).

Collection contains 5 television commercials used during Horn's 1986 campaign for Governor of Ohio. (Republican Party).

HORNER, Henry. 1 sound tape reel (7 1/2 ips.). 24350576.

Collection contains 18 radio spots from Horner's 1936 campaign for Governor of Illinois.

HOSSLER, David. 1 videotape (2 in.). 24241690.

Collection contains 1 television commercial used during Hossler's 1986 campaign for a judgeship in Arizona.

HOWARD, Edward.   1 sound tape reel (7 1/2 ips.).

Collection contains 4 radio commercials used during Howard's campaign for the 1980 U.S. Senate election in Pennsylvania. (Republican Party).

HOWARD, Everett. 1 sound tape reel (7 1/2 ips.). 22155985.

Collection contains 4 radio commercials used during Howard's campaign for the 1972 Scott County supervisor election in Iowa. (Democratic Party).

HOWARD, Gene.   1 videocassette (3/4 in.).

Collection contains 1 television commercial used in Howard's 1980 primary campaign for U.S. Senate in Oklahoma.   (Democratic Party).

HOWARD, Jim. 1 videocassette (3/4 in.).

Collection contains 3 television commercials used during Howard's 1986 campaign for Congress in District 3 of New Jersy. (Democratic Party).

HOWELL, Henry E. 1920-. 1 film reel (16 mm.).   19 videotapes (2 in.). 21254614.

Collection contains 21 television commercials used during Howell's 1971 campaign for Lt. Governor and his 1973 campaign for Governor in Virginia. (Democratic Party).

HOWLETT, Michael J. 3 videotapes (2 in.). 2 film reels (16 mm.). 24241704.

Collection contains 10 television commercials used during Howlett's campaign for the 1972 State Senate election in Illinois. (Democratic Party).

HUBER, Sherry. 1 videocassette (3/4 in.).

Collection contains 21 television commercials used during Huber's 1986 campaign for Governor of Maine. (Independent)

HUDDLES, Gary.   1 sound tape reel (7 1/2 ips.).

Collection contains 3 radio commercials used during Huddles' campaign for the 1982 County Council election in Baltimore County in Maryland.

HUDDLESTON, Don. 1 videocassette (3/4 in.).

Collection contains 1 television commercials used during Huddleston's 1986 campaign for State Legislature in District 100 of Illinois.

HUDDLESTON, Walter D. 1 film reel (16 mm.) 4 videocassettes (3/4 in.). 24241711.

Collection contains 7 television commercials used during Huddleston's 1972 campaign and 30 from his 1984 campaign for U.S. Senate in Kentucky. (Democratic Party).

HUDDOCK, Bob. 1 videocassette (3/4 in.).

Collection contains 3 television commercials used during Huddock's 1984 campaign for U.S. Congress in Pennsylvania. (Republican Party).

HUDSON, George. 1 sound tape reel (7 1/2 ips).

Collection contains 1 radio commercial used during Hudson's 1984 campaign for Congress in Illinois. (Republican Party).

HUDSON, Tommy. 3 videocassette (3/4 in.).

Collection contains 24 television commercials used during Hudson's 1986 campaign for Congress in District 6 of Louisiana. (Democratic Party).

HUFF, Richard. 1 videocassette (3/4 in.).

Collection contains 30 television commercials used during Huff's 1980 campaign for U.S. Congress in District 2 of Arizona. (Republican Party).

HUGHES, Bill. 1 videocassette (3/4 in.).

Collection contains 2 television commercials used during Hughes' 1986 campaign for Congress in District 2 of New Jersy. (Democratic Party).

HUGHES, Harry. 5 videocassettes (3/4 in.). 2 sound tape reels (7 1/2 ips.).

Collection contains 15 television commercials from Hughes' 1978 campaign for Governor of Maryland, 3 radio commercials used during his 1982 gubernatorial election, and 6 radio commercials used during his 1980 campaign for Governor. Includes 5 television commercials used during his 1986 U.S. Senate election. (Democratic Party).

HUGHES, Scott. 1 videocassette (3/4 in.).

Collection contains 4 television commercials used during Hughes' 1986 campaign for Congress in District 5. (Democratic Party).

HUGHES, Therese. 1 sound tape reel (7 1/2 ips.).

Collection contains 1 radio commercial used during Hughes' 1982 campaign for State House. (Democratic Party).

HULLINGER, Arlo. 1 sound tape reel (7 1/2 ips.). 21979513.

Collection contains 2 radio commercials used during Hullinger's 1972 campaign for State Senate in Iowa, 47th District. (Democratic Party).

HUMPHREY, Gordon. 3 videocassettes (3/4 in.).

Collection contains 10 television commercials used during Humphrey's 1984 campaign for U.S. Senate in New Hampshire. (Republican Party).

HUMPHREY, Hubert H. 1911-1978. 15 film reels (16 mm.). 31 videotapes (2 in.). 2 sound tape reels (7 1/2 ips.). 3 video-cassettes (3/4 in.). 21145092.

Collection contains 4 television commercials used during Humphrey's campaign for the 1964 presidential election; 42 television and 1 radio commercial used in his 1968 presidential election; 34 television and 13 radio commercials used in his 1970 campaign

This ad for the 1968 Hubert Humphrey presidential campaign ridiculed Spiro Agnew's vice-presidential suitability.

for U.S. Senate in Minnesota; and 57 television spots from his 1972 presidential campaign. Also included is a documentary from his 1970 U.S. Senate campaign. (Democratic Party).

HUNT, James. 10 videocassettes (3/4 in.).

Collection contains 13 television commercials from Hunt's 1976 campaign for Governor of North Carolina, 4 spots from his 1980 campaign for Governor, and 92 television spots from his 1984 campaign for U.S. Senate in North Carolina. (Democratic Party).

HUNTER, Garry.   1 videocassette (3/4 in.).

Collection contains 1 television commercial used during Hunter's 1986 campaign for State Representative in Ohio. (Republican Party).

HUTCHINSON, Asa. 3 videocassette (3/4 in.).

Collection contains 5 television commercials used during Hutchinson's 1986 campaign for U.S. Senate in Arkansas. (Republican Party).

HUTCHINSON, Don.   1 videocassette (3/4 in.). 1 sound tape reel (7 1/2 ips.).

Collection contains 4 television spots used in Hutchinson's 1978 campaign in Baltimore County, Maryland. Includes 3 radio spots from a 1982 local campaign. (Democratic Party).

HUTCHINSON, Frank. 1 videocassette (3/4 in.).

Collection contains 2 television commercials used during Hutchinson's 1986 campaign for U.S. Senate in Hawaii. (Republican Party).

HYATT, Jerry.   1 sound tape reel (7 1/2 ips.).

Collection contains 1 radio commercial used during Hyatt's campaign for the 1982 House of Delegates election in District 15 in Maryland.

HYNES, Tom.   1 sound tape reel (7 1/2 ips.).

Collection contains 8 radio commercials used during Hynes' campaign for the 1982 County Assessor election in Cook County in Illinois. (Democratic Party).

INGRAM, John Randolph. 3 videotapes (2 in.). 21426508.

Contains five television commercials used during Ingram's campaign for the 1972 State Representative in North Carolina. (Democratic Party).

INHOFE, James. 1 videocassette (3/4 in.).

Collection contains 9 television commercials used during Inhofe's 1986 campaign for Congress in Oklahoma. (Republican Party).

INOUYE, Daniel. 1 videocassette (3/4 in.).

Collection contains 12 television commercials used during Inouye's 1986 campaign for Governor of Hawaii. (Democratic Party).

136

IRWIN, Mitch. 2 videocassettes (3/4 in.).

Collection contains 6 television commercials used during Irwin's 1986 campaign for State Senator in Michigan. (Democratic Party).

ISRAEL, Richard Jerome. 1930-. 3 videotapes (2 in.). 22186061.

Collection contains 3 television commercials used during Israel's 1974 campaign for Attorney General in Rhode Island. (Republican Party).

JACK, Larry. 1 sound tape reel (7 1/2 ips.).

Collection contains 1 radio commercial used during Jack's campaign for the 1980 State Representative election in Pennsylvania. (Democratic Party).

JACKSON, David. 1 videocassette (3/4 in.).

Collection contains 6 television commercials used during Jackson's 1986 campaign for Congress in District 15 of Ohio. (Democratic Party).

JACKSON, Henry M. 1912-1983. 2 film reels (16 mm.). and 12 videotapes (2 in.). 1 videocassette (3/ 4 in.). 21368935.

Collection contains 20 television commercials used during Jackson's campaigns for the 1972 and 1976 presidential elections. Also contains 6 television spots from his 1982 campaign for U.S. Senate in Washington. (Democratic Party).

JACKSON, Jesse. 1941-. 4 videocassettes (3/4 in.). 21140087.

Collection contains 10 television commercials used during Jackson's campaign for the 1988 presidential election. (Democratic Party).

JACKSON, Larry. 1 sound tape reel (7 1/2 ips).

Collection contains 2 radio commercials used during Jackson's campaign for a state office in Idaho.

JACKSON, Maynard. 1 film reel (16 mm.). 1 videotape (2 in.). 21492242.

Collection contains 3 television commercials used during Jackson's 1973 campaign for Mayor in Atlanta, Georgia.

JACOBS, Danny. 1 videocassette (3/4 in.).

Collection contains 1 television commercials used during Jacobs' 1986 campaign for U.S. Senate in Illinois. (Democratic Party).

JACOBS, Jeff. 4 videotapes (1 in.). 2 videocassette (3/4 in.). 24241718.

Collection contains 2 television commercials used during Jacobs' 1982 Cuyahoga County Recorder campaign and 12 television commercials used in his 1986 State Treasurer campaign in Ohio. (Republican Party).

JACOBSON, Leonard S.. 1 sound tape reel (7 1/2 ips).

Collection contains 1 radio commercial used during Jacobson's 1984 campaign for Baltimore County Circuit Judge in Maryland.

JACOBSON, Tom. 1 film reel (16 mm.). 24241727.

Collection contains 6 television commercials used during Jacobson's 1970 campaign for Attorney General in Wisconsin. (Democratic Party).

JAHNKE, Herb. 1 videotape (2 in.). 22256872.

Collection contains 1 television commercial used during Jahnke's campaign for the 1974 U.S. congressional election in Wisconsin. (American Independent Party).

JALOVEC, Rich. 1 sound tape reel (7 1/2 ips.).

Collection contains 4 radio commercials used during Jalovec's campaign for the 1980 congressional election in District 4 in Illinois. (Democratic Party).

JAMES, Forest Hood. 5 videotapes (2 in.). 24241737.

Collection contains 5 television commercials used during James' campaign for the 1986 gubernatorial election in Alabama. (Democratic Party).

JAMES, Jesse. 1904-1977. 1 videotape (2 in.). 21492319.

Collection contains 1 television commercial used during James' campaign for the 1972 State Treasurer election in Texas. (Democratic Party).

JANKLOW, William. 2 videocassettes (3/4 in.).

Collection contains 29 television commercials used during Janklow's 1982 campaign for U.S. Senate in South Dakota. (Republican Party).

JANKOWSKI, Harold S. 1 sound tape reel (7 1/2 ips.).

Collection contains 1 radio commercial used during Jankowski's campaign for the 1982 Clerk of the Circuit Court election.

JAROS, Mike. 1 videocassette (3/4 in.).

Collection contains 1 television commercials used during Jaros' 1986 campaign for State Representative in Minnesota.

JAVITS, Jacob K. 1904-. 1 film reel (16 mm.). 1 videocassette (3/4 in.). 21382850.

This campaign spot for Jacob Javits' 1980 Senate campaign in New York shows him hard at work.

Collection contains 4 television commercials used during Javits' 1962 campaign and 5 television spots from his 1980 campaign for U.S. Senate in New York. (Republican Party).

JEFFERSON, William. 1 videocassette (3/4 in.).

Collection contains 21 television commercials used during Jefferson's 1986 campaign for Mayor of New Orleans, Louisiana. (Democratic Party).

JENNARO, William. 3 videotapes (2 in.). 22185996.

Collection contains 1 television commercial used during Jennaro's 1970 campaign for a judgeship, and 2 television spots used in his 1972 judgeship campaign; both in Wisconsin. (Democratic Party).

JENNINGS, Dave. 1 videocassette (3/4 in.).

Collection contains 3 television commercials used during Jennings' 1986 campaign for Governor of Minnesota. (Republican Party).

JENNINGS, Renz. 1 videocassette (3/4 in.).

Collection contains 1 television commercial used during Jennings' 1986 campaign for Corporation Commissioner in Arizona. (Democratic Party).

JENRETTE, John W. 1 film reel (16 mm.). 21431626.

Collection contains 7 television commercials used during Jenrette's campaign for the 1974 U.S. congressional election in South Carolina, District 6. (Democratic Party).

JERNIGAN, George D. 1 videotape (2 in.). 24241746.

Collection contains 2 television commercials used during Jernigan's campaign for the 1976 Attorney General election in Arkansas.

JESPIN, Roger. 1 film reel (16 mm.). 3 videocassettes (3/4 in.). 24241758.

Collection contains 2 television commercials used during Jespin's 1970 campaign for Lt. Governor and 10 television spots from his 1984 campaign for U.S. Senate in Iowa. (Republican Party).

JEWETT, Doug. 2 videocassettes (3/4 in.). 24241764.

Collection contains 6 television commercials used during Jewett's campaign for the 1982 U.S. Senate election in Washington. (Republican Party).

JEWETT, Jack. 1 videotape (2 in.). 24245067.

Collection contains 2 television commercials used during Jewett's campaign for a 1986 Alabama election.

JOACHIM, Steve. 1 sound tape reel (7 1/2 ips.).

Collection contains 1 radio commercial used during Joachim's campaign for the 1982 congressional election in District 7 in Pennsylvania. (Republican Party).

JOHAAN, Sara Lee. 1 sound tape reel (7 1/2 ips.).

Collection contains 1 radio commercial used during Johaan's campaign for the 1982 State House election in Wisconsin. (Democratic Party).

JOHANNESON, Helgi. 1906-. 1 film reel (16 mm.). 1 sound tape reel. 21567316.

Collection contains 2 television commercials used during Johanneson's campaign for the 1972 Attorney General election in North Dakota. Includes 1 radio spot from her 1968 campaign for the same office. (Republican Party).

JOHANNESON, Kent. 2 videocassettes (3/4 in.).

Collection consists of 5 television spots from Johanneson's 1980 campaign for U.S. Senate in North Dakota. (Democratic Party).

JOHNS, Ken. 1 sound tape reel. (7 1/2 ips.).

Collection contains 3 radio commercials used during John's 1982 campaign for a judgeship in California.

JOHNSON, Charles 1 videocassette (3/4 in.).

Collection contains 1 television commercial used during Johnson's 1986 campaign for Congress in District 5 of Georgia. (Democratic Party).

JOHNSON, Harry. 2 videocassettes (3/4 in.).

Collection contains 4 television commercial used during Johnson's 1986 campaign for Governor of Florida. (Democratic Party).

JOHNSON, Jed. 1 videocassette (3/4 in.).

Collection contains 2 television commercials from Johnson's 1966 campaign for U.S. Congress from Oklahoma, District 6. (Democratic Party).

JOHNSON, Jim. 1 film reel (16 mm.). 24245075.

Collection contains 2 television commercials used during Johnson's campaign for Governor in Arizona. (Democratic Party).

JOHNSON, John Warren. 1929-. 1 videotape (2 in.). 21348101.

Collection contains two commercials used during Johnson's campaign for the 1974 gubernatorial election in Minnesota. (Republican Party).

JOHNSON, Kenneth L. 1 sound tape reel (7 1/2 ips.).

Collection contains 1 radio commercial used during Johnson's 1982 campaign for Supreme Bench Judgeship in Baltimore, Maryland.

JOHNSON, Lyndon B. 1908-1973. 10 film reels (16 mm.). 1 videotape (2 in.). 4 sound tape reels (3 3/4 in.). 1 sound tape reel (7 1/2 ips.). 21145134.

Collection contains 57 television and 16 radio commercials used during Johnson's campaign for the 1964 presidential election. (Democratic Party).

The "Daisy Girl" ad is a famous spot from Lyndon Johnson's 1964 presidential campaign.

In this 1964 spot Lyndon Johnson made fun of a Goldwater quip about "sawing off the Eastern seaboard."

JOHNSON, Nancy. 1 sound tape reel (7 1/2 ips.). 3 videocassettes (3/4 in.).

Collection contains 5 radio commercials used during Johnson's 1982 campaign for U.S. Congress in District 6 in Connecticut and 8 television spots from her 1982 and 1984 campaigns for the same office. Includes 3 television commercials used during her 1986 congressional campaign. (Republican Party).

JOHNSON, Roy. 1 videotape (2 in.).

Collection contains 1 television commercial used during Johnson's campaign for a 1986 Alabama election.

JOHNSON, Sven. 1 videocassette (3/4 in.).

Collection contains 1 television commercial used during Johnson's 1986 campaign for Congress in District 11 of Michigan. (Democratic Party).

JOHNSON, Tim. 3 videocassettes (3/4 in.).

Collection contains 14 television commercials used during Johson's 1986 campaign for Congress At Large in South Dakota. (Democratic Party).

JOHNSON, Wally. 1 videotape (2 in.).

Collection contains 1 television commercial used during Johnson's campaign for Mayor in Illinois.

142

JOHNSTON, Dan L. 1 videotape (2 in.). 24245084.

Collection contains 1 television commercial used during Johnston's campaign for the 1970 State House election in Iowa. (Democratic Party).

JOHNSTON, Fred. 1 sound tape reel (7 1/2 ips).

Collection contains 1 radio commercial used during Johnston's 1970 campaign for State Senate in Montana. (Democratic Party).

JOHNSTON, J. Bennettt. 2 videocassettes (3/4 in.).

Collection contains 6 television commercials used during Johnston's 1984 campaign for U.S. Senate in Louisiana. (Democratic Party).

JOHNSTON, Rod. 1 videocassette (3/4 in.). 24245088.

Collection contains 9 television commercials used during Johnston's campaign for the 1982 congressional election in District 5 of Wisconsin. (Republican Party).

JONES, Bill. 2 videotapes (2 in.). 24245098.

Collection contains 2 television commercials used during Jones' campaign for the 1986 State Senate election in Mississippi.

JONES, Fulton. 1 videocassette (3/4 in.). 24245102.

Collection contains 1 television spot from Jones' 1982 campaign for State House in District 64 of Michigan. (Democratic Party).

JONES, James R. 1939-. 1 film reel (16 mm.). 4 videocassette (3/4 in.). 21421269.

Collection contains 3 television commercials used during Jones' 1978 campaign for U.S. Congress in Oklahoma, 8 television spots from his 1982 re-election campaign, and 28 television spots from his 1984 re-election campaign. Includes 25 television commercials used during his 1986 campaign for U.S. Senate. (Democratic Party).

JONES, Richard R. 1910-. 1 film reel (16 mm.). 21474822.

Collection contains 5 commercials used during Jones' campaign for the 1974 gubernatorial election in Wyoming. (Republican Party).

JONES, Sandra. 1 videocassette (3/4 in.).

Collection contains 1 television commercial used during Jones' 1986 campaign for Milwaukee County Treasurer in Wisconsin. (Independent).

JONES, Sheila. 1 sound tape reel (7 1/2 ips.).

Collection contains 2 radio commercials used during Jones'
campaign for the 1982 congressional election in District 9 of
Illinois. (Anti-Drug Party).

JONES, Wayne. 1 videocassette (3/4 in.).

Collection contains 2 television commercials used during Jones'
1986 campaign for State Senate in Ohio. (Democratic Party).

**JORDAN, B. Everett. 1896-. 1 film reel (16 mm.). 1 videotape
(2 in.). 21276345.**

Collection contains 4 television commercials used during Jordan's
1972 campaign for U.S. Senate in North Carolina. (Democratic
Party).

JORDAN, Barbara. 1 videocassette (3/4 in.).

Collection contains 1 television commercial used during Jordan's
1986 broadcast supporting "People for the American Way".

JORDAN, Bob. 1 videocassette (3/4 in.).

Collection contains 2 television spots from Jordan's 1984
campaign for Lt. Governor of North Carolina. (Democratic Party).

JORDAN, Charles. 1 videocassette (3/4 in.). 1 videotape (2 in.).

Collection contains 1 television commercials used during Jordan's
1974 campaign for City Commissioner in Portland, Oregon.

JORDAN, Hamilton. 2 videocassettes (3/4 in.).

Collection contains 6 television commercials used during Jordan's
1986 campaign for U.S. Senate in Georgia. (Democratic Party).

JORDAN, Len B. 1899-. 1 film reel (16 mm.). 21369676.

Collection contains 10 television spots used during Jordan's 1966
campaign for U.S. Senate in Idaho. (Republican Party).

JORDAN, Lester. 1 sound tape reel (7 1/2 ips.).

Collection contains 1 radio commercial used during Jordan's
campaign for the 1980 State Legislature election in District 92
in Pennsylvania. (Republican Party).

JOYNER, Conrad. 1 videocassette (3/4 in.).

Collection contains 5 television commercials used during Joyner's
1982 campaign for U.S. Congress in Arizona. (Republican Party).

144

JUDGE, Thomas L. 12 videotapes (2 in.). 1 videocassette (3/4 in.). 3 film reels (16 mm.). 21287285.

Collection contains 35 television commercials used during Judge's 1972 campaign for Governor in Montana. Includes 12 television spots used in his 1976 re-election campaign and 5 television spots from his 1980 re-election campaign. (Democratic Party).

JUNKINS, Lowell. 3 videocassettes (3/4 in.).

Collection contains 24 television commercials used during Junkins' 1986 campaign for Governor of Iowa. (Democratic Party).

KAMM, Robert. 1 videotape (2 in.). 24367960.

Collection contains 7 television commercials used during Kamm's 1970 campaign for U.S. Senate in Oklahoma. (Republican Party).

KAMMER, Kerry. 1 videocassette (3/4 in.). 24245111.

Collection contains 5 television spots from Kammer's campaign for the 1982 gubernatorial election in Michigan. (Democratic Party).

KANJORSKI, Paul. 1 videocassette (3/4 in.).

Collection contains 2 television commercials used during Kanjorski's 1984 campaign for U.S. Congress in Pennsylvania.

KANNER, Richard. 2 videotapes (2 in.). 21511275.

Collection contains 5 television commercials used during Kanner's campaign for a 1974 judgeship in Florida. (Independent Party).

This frame was taken from one of Marcy Kaptur's spots used in her 1986 congressional campaign in Ohio.

KAPTUR, Marcy. 4 videotapes (1 in.). 2 videocassettes (3//4 in.). 24245116.

Collection contains 10 television commercials from Kaptur's 1984 campaign for U.S. Congress in Ohio and 11 television commercials used during her re-election campaign. Includes 7 television commercials used during her 1986 campaign for Congress. (Democratic Party).

KARABIAN, Walter. 1938-. 2 film reels (16 mm.). 21567358.

Collection contains 2 television commercials used during Karabian's 1974 campaign for Secretary of State in California. (Democratic Party).

KARIOTIS, George. 6 videocassettes (3/4 in.).

Collection contains 28 television spots from Kariotis' 1986 campaign for Governor of Massachusetts. (Republican Party).

KARP, Ron. 1 sound tape reel (7 1/2 ips.).

Collection contains 1 radio commercial used during Karp's campaign for the 1982 State House election in Virginia.

KASSEBAUM, Nancy Landon. 1 videocassette (3/4 in.). 1 sound tape reel (7 1/2 ips).

Collection contains 16 television spots from Kassebaum's 1978 campaign for U.S. Senate in Kansas. Includes 1 radio commercial used during her 1984 re-election campaign. (Republican Party).

KASTEN, Robert W. 1942-. 3 videotapes (2 in.). 10 videocassettes (3/4 in.). 22164909.

Collection contains 3 television spots from Kasten's campaign for the 1974 U.S. congressional election in Wisconsin, 9th District. Also includes 11 television spots from his 1980 campaign for U.S. Senate in Wisconsin. Includes 36 television commercials used during his 1986 campaign for U.S. Senate. (Republican Party).

KASTENMEIER, Robert. 1924 -.   2 videocassettes (3/4 in.).

Collection contains 16 television commercials used during Kastenmeier's 1986 campaign for Congress in District 2 of Wisconsin. (Democratic Party).

KAUFFMAN, Bruce W. 1 sound tape reel (7 1/2 ips). 21986909.

Collection contains 4 radio commercials used during Kauffman's 1979 campaign for Supreme Court in Pennsylvania.

KAUFMAN, George. 1 sound tape reel (7 1/2 ips.). 22226382.

Collection contains 3 radio commercials used during Kaufman's 1979 campaign City Treasurer in Harrisburg, Pennsylvania.

KAVANAUGH, Sean P.. 1 videocassette (3/4 in.).

Collection contains 2 television commercials used during Kavanaugh's 1986 campaign for Wayne County Circuit Court Judge in Michigan.

KAVNER, Sam. 1 sound tape reel. (7 1/2 ips.).

Collection contains 1 radio commercial used during Kavner's 1982 campaign for U.S. Senate in Nevada. (Republican Party).

KAVOUKLIS, Mike. 1 videocassette (3/4 in.).

Collection contains 2 television commercials used during Kavouklis' 1984 campaign for U.S. Congress in District 7 of Florida. (Republican Party).

KAY, Morris. 1 videotape (2 in.). 21244045.

Collection contains 2 television commercials used during Kay's campaign for the 1972 gubernatorial election in Kansas. (Republican Party).

KAZEN, Abraham, Jr. 1 videocassette (3/4 in.).

Collection contains 1 television commercial used during Kazen's 1982 campaign for U.S. Congress in Texas. (Democratic Party).

KEAN, Tom. 2 videocassettes (3/4 in.). 1 sound tape reel (7 1/2 ips.).

Collection consists of 2 television commercials from Kean's 1977 campaign for Governor of New Jersey and 19 television commercials and 2 radio spots from his 1981 Governor's campaign.

KEANE, James. 1 videocassette (3/4 in.).

Collection contains 1 television commercial used during Keane's campaign for Congress in District 31 in New York. (Democratic Party).

KEATING, Frank. 1 videocassette (3/4 in.).

Collection contains 2 television commercials used during Keating's 1984 campaign for U.S. Congress in District 1 of Oklahoma. (Republican Party).

KEATING, Anton. 1 videocassette (3/4 in.).

Collection consists of 1 television commercial for Keating's 1978 campaign for Baltimore County State's Attorney in Maryland. (Democratic Party).

KEATING, Barbara. 1 film reel (16 mm.). 21498978.

Collection contains 2 television commercials used during Keating's campaign for the 1974 U.S. senatorial election in New York. (Conservative party).

KEATON, David.   1 sound tape reel.   (7 1/2 ips.).

Collection contains 1 radio commercial used during Keaton's 1982 campaign for local election in Nevada.

KECK, James. 1 videocassette (3/4 in.). 24245124.

Collection contains 4 television commercials used during Keck's campaign for the 1982 U.S. Senate election in Nebraska. (Republican Party).

KEFAUVER, ESTES. 1 film reel (16 mm.). 24367977.

Collection contains 1 television commercial used during Kefauver's campaign for the 1960 presidential campaign.

KELLEY, Frank J. 1 videotape (2 in.). 3 videocassette (3/4 in.). 21287314.

Collection contains 1 television commercials used during Kelley's 1972 campaign for the U.S. Senate and 5 television spots from his 1982 campaign for Attorney General in Michigan. Includes 5 television commercials used during his 1986 campaign for Attorney General.

KELLEY, George. 1 film reel (16 mm.). 24244938.

Collection contains 2 television commercials used during Kelley's campaign for the 1970 congressional election in District 5 of Tennessee. (Republican Party).

KELLEY, Harry.   2 sound tape reels (7 1/2 ips.).

Collection contains 4 radio commercials used during Kelley's campaign for the 1982 gubernatorial election in Maryland. (Democratic Party).

KELLEY, Peter Stephen. 1940-. 1 videotape (2 in.). 21741098.

Collection contains 1 television commercial used during Kelley's campaign for the 1974 gubernatorial election in Maine. (Democratic Party).

KELLY, John F.   1 sound tape reel (7 1/2 ips.).

Collection contains 1 radio commercial used during Kelly's campaign for the 1982 Clerk of the Circuit Court election in Baltimore in Maryland.

KELLY, Margaret. 1 videocassette (3/4 in.).

Collection contains 2 television commercials used during Kelly's 1986 campaign for State Auditor in Missouri. (Republican Party).

KELLY, Richard. 1 videotape (2 in.). 24244951.

Collection contains 3 television commercials used during Kelly's campaign for the 1976 congressional election in Florida.

KELLY, Vance. 1 sound tape reel (7 1/2 ips.).

Collection contains 5 radio commercials used during Kelly's campaign for the 1982 State Senate election in District 14 in New Hampshire. (Republican Party).

KEMP, Jack. 4 videocassettes (3/4 in.). 21368909.

Collection contains 14 television commercials used during Kemp's campaign for the presidential election of 1988. Includes 4 television commercials used during his 1986 campaign for Congress in District 31 of New York. (Republican Party).

KENDRICK, Bill. 1 videocassette (3/4 in.). 24244961.

Collection contains 1 television commercial used during Kendrick's 1982 campaign for Superintendent of Public Instruction in Oregon.

KENNEDY, Edward Moore. 1932-. 2 sound tape reels (7 1/2 ips.). and 3 film reel (16 mm.). 1 videotape (2 in.). 19 videocassettes (3/4 in.). 21416221.

Collection contains 15 radio commercials used during Kennedy's campaign for the 1962 U.S. senatorial election, 6 television commercials used in his 1970 re-election campaign, 7 television commercials used in his 1976 re-election campaign, and 7 television commercials used in his 1982 re-election campaign; all in Massachusetts. In-cludes 1 documentary and 62 television commercials from Kennedy's primary campaigns for the 1980 presidential election. (Democratic Party).

KENNEDY, John Fitzgerald. 1917-1963. 5 videocassettes (3/4 in.). 5 film reels (16 mm.). 21140077.

Collection contains 103 items and television commercials used during Kennedy's campaign for the 1960 presidential election. Also includes copies of the 1960 presidential television debates. (Democratic Party).

KENNEDY, Joseph, III. . 6 videocassettes (3/4 in.).

Collection contains 15 television commercials used during Kennedy's 1986 campaign for Congress in District 8 of Massachusetts. (Democratic Party).

This family shot was part of John Kennedy's 1960 presidential campaign ads.

KENNEDY, Robert F. 1925-1968. 8 film reels (16 mm.). 1 videocassette (3/4 in.). 1 videotape (2 in.). 21186248.

Collection contains 3 television commercials used during Kennedy's 1964 campaign for U.S. Senate in New York. Includes 20 television commercials used during his campaign for the 1968 presidential election. (Democratic Party).

KENNEDY, Walter Lawrence. 1920-. 1 film reel (16 mm.). 21474842.

Collection contains 6 television commercials used during Kennedy's campaign for the 1974 gubernatorial election in Vermont. (Republican Party).

KENNELLY, Barbara. 2 sound tape reels (7 1/2 ips.). 5 videocassettes (3/4 in.).

Collection contains 2 radio commercials used during Kennelly's 1982 congressional campaign in District 1 of Connecticut and 6 television spots from her 1984 re-election campaign. Includes 5 television commercials used during his 1986 campaign for Congress in District 1. (Democratic Party).

KENNEY, Jack. 1 sound tape reel (7 1/2 ips.).

Collection contains 1 radio commercial used during Kenney's 1982 campaign for U.S. Senate in Nevada. (Republican Party).

KEPPER, Morie. 1 videotape (2 in.). 24244967.

Collection contains 1 television commercial used during Kepper's campaign for a 1986 Mississippi election.

KERNAN, Tom. 1 videocassette (3/4 in.).

Collection contains 3 television commercials used during Kernan's 1986 campaign for Baltimore County Executive in Maryland. (Democratic Party).

KERR, Robert S. 1896-1963. 3 videocassettes (3/4 in.). 22137708.

Collection contains 1 television commercial and 1 television interview used during Kerr's campaign for the 1954 U.S. Senate seat in Oklahoma, and 1 television interview used in his 1960 re-election campaign. Includes a 1962 interview with the CBS news. (Democratic Party).

KERR, Robert, S., Jr. 3 videocassettes (3/4 in.).

Collection contains 6 television commercials from Kerr's 1980 primary campaign for U.S. Senate in Oklahoma. (Democratic Party).

KERR, Robert S., III.. 2 videocassettes (3/4 in.).

Collection contains 4 television commercials used during his 1986 campaign for Lt. Governor of Oklahoma. (Democratic Party).

KERREY, Bob. 2 videocassettes (3/4 in.). 24244972.

Collection contains 16 television commercials used during Kerrey's campaign for the 1982 gubernatorial election in Nebraska. (Democratic Party).

KERRY, John. 5 videocassettes (3/4 in.).

Collection contains 13 television commercials used during Kerry's 1984 campaign for U.S. Senate in Massachusetts. (Democratic Party).

KERRY, John. 1 sound tape reel (7 1/2 ips.).

Collection contains 1 radio commercial used during Kerry's campaign for the 1982 congressional election in District 1 in Maine. (Democratic Party).

KERTULA, Jalmar. 1 videocassette (3/4 in.).

Collection contains 2 television commercials used during Kertula's campaign for U.S. Senate in Alaska. (Independent Party).

KESSLER, Bill. 1 videocassette (3/4 in.).

Collection contains 4 television commercials used during Kessler's City Councilman campaign in Oklahoma City in 1965.

KESSLER, Fred. 1 videocassette (3/4 in.). 24244985.

Collection contains 1 television commercial used during Kessler's campaign for the 1982 congressional election in Wisconsin. (Democratic Party).

KIDD, Bill. 1 film reel (16 mm.). 21499020.

Collection contains 14 television commercials used during Kidd's campaign for the 1972 U.S. congressional election in Wyoming. (Republican Party).

KIDWELL, Wayne. 1 videotape (2 in.). 24244994.

Collection contains 4 television commercials used during Kidwell's campaign for the 1972 congressional election in District 1 of Idaho. (Republican Party).

KILBANE, James P. 1 sound tape reel (7 1/2 ips.).

Collection contains 1 radio commercial used during Kilbane's 1980 campaign for a judgeship in Cuyahoga County, Ohio.

KILLIAN, Robert. 1 videocassette (3/4 in.).

Collection contains 6 television commercials from Killian's 1978 campaign for Governor of Connecticut. (Democratic Party).

KIMBALL, Richard. 8 videotapes (2 in.). 3 videocassettes (3/4 in.). 24245000.

Collection contains 15 television commercials used during Kimball's campaign for the 1986 U.S. Senate election in Arizona. (Democratic Party).

KINDNESS, Tom. 3 videotapes (2 in.). 3 videocassettes (3/4 in.). 24245005.

Collection contains 15 television spots from Kindness' 1986 campaign for U.S. Senate in Ohio. (Republican Party).

KING, Edward. 1 videocassette (3/4 in.). 24245011.

Collection contains 5 television commercials used during King's campaign for the 1982 gubernatorial election in Massachusetts. (Democratic Party).

KING, Leigh. 1 sound tape reel. (7 1/2 ips.).

Collection contains 1 radio commercial used during King's 1982 campaign for State Senate in District 5 in Nevada. (Democratic Party).

KING, Mel. 3 videocassettes (3/4 in.).

Collection contains 1 television commercial used during King's 1983 campaign for Mayor in Boston, Massachusetts. Also includes 2 television commercials used during his 1986 campaign for Congress in District 8 of Massachusetts. (Democratic Party).

KING, R.J. 1913-. 1 videotape (2 in.). 21276413.

Collection contains 7 television commercials used during King's 1972 campaign for Governor in Missouri. (Republican Party).

KINLEY, George. 1 videocassette (3/4 in.).

Collection contains 6 television commercials used during Kinley's 1986 campaign for Governor in Iowa. (Democratic Party).

KINNEY, David B. 1921-. 1 film reel (16 mm.). 21887774.

Collection contains 1 television commercial used during Kinney's 1968 campaign for U.S. Congress in Virginia. (Democratic Party).

KINTNER, Janet. 1 sound tape reel. (7 1/2 ips.).

Collection contains 8 radio commercials used during Kintner's 1982 campaign for a judgeship in California.

KIRBY, Russell. 1 videotape (2 in.). 24243347.

Collection contains 3 television commercials used during Kirby's campaign for the 1976 congressional election in District 2 of North Carolina.

KIRK, Claude R. 1926-. 2 videotapes (2 in.). 1 film reel (16 mm.). 21244001.

Collection contains 5 television commercials used during Kirk's campaign for the 1970 gubernatorial election in Florida. (Republican Party).

KIRKWOOD, Charles. 1 videocassette (3/4 in.).

Collection contains 1 television commercials used during Kirkwood's 1986 campaign for State Senate in Pennsylvania. (Republican Party).

KIRSCHT, Robert. 1 videocassette (3/4 in.).

Collection contains 1 television commercial used during Kirscht's 1986 campaign for Governor of Colorado. (Republican Party).

KISNER, Gerald. 1 videotape (2 in.).

Collection contains 1 television commercial used during Kisner's campaign for the 1979 clerk election in Ohio.

KISSILER. 1 sound tape reel (7 1/2 ips.).

Collection contains 2 radio commercials used during Kissiler's campaign for the 1972 State House election in Pennsylvania.

KISSINGER, Henry. 1 videotape (2 in.).

Collection contains 1 television documentary from Bill Moyer's Journal International Report: "A Conversation with Henry Kissinger." (WNET--New York).

KLAMM, Bill. 1 sound tape reel (7 1/2 ips.).

Collection contains 1 radio commercial used during Klamm's 1982 campaign for Sheriff of Milwaukee County in Wisconsin.

KLAUDER, Jim. 1 videocassette (3/4 in.).

Collection contains 3 television commercials used during Klauder's 1984 campaign for U.S. Congress in District 2 of Washington. (Republican Party).

KLECZKA, Jerry. 1 videocassette (3/4 in.).

Collection contains 2 television commercials used during Kleczka's 1984 campaign for U.S. Congress in District 4 of Wisconsin. (Democratic Party).

KLEIN, Carl. 1 sound tape reel (7 1/2 ips.).

Collection contains 2 radio commercials used during Klein's campaign for the 1982 County Sanitary District Trustee election in Cook County.

KLEIN, Joe. 1 sound tape reel (7 1/2 ips.).

Collection contains 5 radio commercials used during Klein's campaign for the 1980 State Representative election in District 103 in Pennsylvania. (Republican Party).

KLENK, Bill. 1 videocassette (3/4 in.).

Collection contains 2 television commercials for Klenk's campaign for Mayor of Philadelphia, Pennsylvania.

KLEPPE, Thomas S. 1919-. 1 film reel (16 mm.). 21358345.

Collection contains 1 television commercial used during Kleppe's campaign for the 1970 U.S. senatorial election in North Dakota. (Republican Party).

KLUCZYNSKI, Melanie. 1 sound tape reel (7 1/2 ips.).

Collection contains 3 radio commercials used during Kluczynski's campaign for the 1980 congressional election in District 4 in Illinois. (Democratic Party).

KLUNZINGER, Thomas Edward, 1944-. 1 film reel (16 mm.). 22245555.

Collection contains 1 television commercial used during Klunzinger's campaign for the 1970 U.S. congressional election in Michigan, 17th District. (Republican Party).

KNEIP, Richard F. 1933-1987. 1 film reel (16 mm.). 21431709.

Collection contains 8 television commercials used during Kneip's campaign for the 1974 gubernatorial election in South Dakota. (Democratic Party).

KNEPPER, Jim. 1 sound tape reel (7 1/2 ips.).

Collection contains 2 radio commercials used during Knepper's campaign for the 1980 State Auditor General election in Pennsylvania. (Republican Party).

KNIGHT, Bob. 2 videocassettes (3/4 in.).

Collection contains 9 television commercials used during Knight's 1986 campaign for Congress in District 4 of Kansas. (Republican Party).

KNORR, Gene. 2 videotapes (2 in.).

Collection contains 5 television commercials used during Knorr's campaign for the 1982 U.S. senatorial election in North Dakota. (Republican Party).

KNORR, John. 1 videocassette (3/4 in.).

Collection contains 3 television commercials used during Knorr's 1986 campaign for State Senate in District 37 of Michigan. (Republican Party).

KNOWL, Richard. 1 sound tape reel (7 1/2 ips.).

Collection contains 1 radio commercial used during Knowl's campaign for the 1972 congressional election in Pennsylvania. (Democratic Party).

KNOWLES, Warren. 1 film reel (16 mm.). 24367988.

Collection contains 12 television commercials used during Knowles' campaign for the 1968 gubernatorial election in Wisconsin. (Republican Party).

KOCH, Edward I. 4 videocassettes (3/4 in.). 24243357.

Collection contains 17 television commercials used during Koch's primary campaign for the 1982 gubernatorial election in New York. (Democratic Party).

KOEHLER, Judy. 3 videotapes (2 in.). 24243365.

Collection contains 6 television commercials used during Koehler's campaign for the 1984 U.S. Senate election in Illinois. (Republican Party).

KOERBER, Jerry. 1 sound tape reel (7 1/2 ips.).

Collection contains 5 radio commercials used during Koerber's campaign for the 1982 State House election in Iowa.

KOHLER, Terry J. 3 videotapes (2 in.). 1 videocassette (3/4 in.). 24243374.

Collection contains 6 television commercials used during Kohler's 1980 campaign for the U.S. Senate and 10 television commercials used during his 1982 gubernatorial election in Wisconsin. (Republican Party).

KOLBE, Jim. 2 videocassettes (3/4 in.).

Collection contains 9 television commercials used during Kolbe's 1982 campaign for U.S. Congress in Arizona. (Republican Party).

KOLTER, Joe. 1 videocassette (3/4 in.).

Collection contains 1 television commercial used during Kolter's 1984 campaign for U.S. Congress in Pennsylvania. (Democratic Party).

KOSTEL, George. 1 film reel (16 mm.). 24243381.

Collection contains 5 television commercials used during Kostel's 1971 campaign for Lt. Governor in Virginia. (Republican Party).

KOSTMAYER, Peter H. 3 sound tape reels (7 1/2 ips.). 2 videocassettes (3/4 in.). 22186048.

Collection contains 2 television commercials used during Kostmayer's 1978 campaign, 1 radio spot from his 1980 campaign, 7 radio commercials from his 1982 campaign, and 6 television spots from his 1984 re-election campaign for U.S. Congress in District 8 of Pennsylvania. (Democratic Party).

KOTTKE, Virginia, 1 videotape (2 in.). 22256862.

Collection contains 1 television commercial used during Kottke's 1972 campaign for State Assembly in Wisconsin.

KOZUBOWSKI, Walter. 1 sound tape reel. (7 1/2 ips.).

Collection contains 1 radio commercial used during Kozubowski's 1983 campaign for local offices in Illinois. (Democratic Party).

KRAKOWSKI, Jerome. 1 videotape (2 in.).

Collection contains 2 television commercials used during Krakowski's campaign for the 1979 clerk election in Ohio. (Democratic Party).

KRAMER, Pat. 1 sound tape reel (7 1/2 ips.).

Collection contains 13 radio commercials used during Kramer's campaign for the 1981 gubernatorial election in New Jersey. (Republican Party).

KRAMER, Barbara. 1 sound tape reel. (7 1/2 ips.).

Collection contains 2 radio commercials used during Kramer's 1982 campaign for State House in District 34 in Maryland. (Democratic Party).

KRITTIKOS, Stephan J. 1 videotape (2 in.). 22441606.

Collection contains 1 television commercial used during Krittikos' campaign for the 1972 judgeship election in Kansas.

KRUEGER, Bob. 4 videocassettes (3/4 in.).

Collection consists of 12 television commercials from Krueger's 1974 congressional campaign, 2 television commercials from his 1976 congressional campaign, and 7 television commercials from his 1978 U.S. Senate campaign in Texas. Also contains 14 television spots from his 1984 primary campaign for U.S. Senate. (Democratic Party).

KRUPANSKY, Blanche. 1 videocassette (3/4 in.). 24243391.

Collection contains 1 television commercial used during Krupansky's 1982 campaign for a judgeship in Ohio. (Republican Party).

KRUPSAK, Mary Anne. 1 film reel (16 mm.). 1 videocassette (3/4 in.). 21437328.

Collection contains 1 television commercials used during Krupsak's 1974 campaign for Lt. Governor and 6 television commercials from her 1978 gubernatorial campaign in New York. (Democratic Party).

KUCHARSKI, Ed. 3 videotapes (2 in.). 24243402.

Collection contains 5 television commercials used during Kucharski's 1972 campaign for Secretary of State in Illinois. (Republican Party).

KUCHEL, Thomas H. 1 film reel (16 mm.). 21421527.

Collection contains 1 television commercials used during Kuchel's 1968 campaign for U.S. Senate in California. (Republican Party).

In this 1972 Illinois campaign, Ed Kucharski appears in a television spot featuring youngsters.

KUCINICH, Dennis. 4 videotapes (2 in.).

Collection contains 10 television commercials used during Kucinich's 1979 campaign for Mayor in Ohio. (Democratic Party).

KUEHLE, Harold. 1 videotape (2 in.). 24243411.

Collection contains 1 television commercial used during Kuehle's 1972 campaign for Secretary of State in Missouri. (Republican Party).

KULL, Bart. 1 videocassette (3/4 in.).

Collection contains 6 television commercials from Kull's 1980 campaign for U.S. Congress in District 1 of Minnesota. (Republican Party).

KULONGSKI, Ted. 3 videocassettes (3/4 in.). 24243425.

Collection contains 14 television spots from Kulongoski's 1980 campaign for U.S. Senate and 22 television commercials used during his 1982 campaign for Governor in Oregon. (Democratic Party).

KUNIN, Madeleine. 5 videocassettes (3/4 in.).

Collection contains 5 television commercials used during Kunin's campaign for the 1982 gubernatorial election in Vermont and 4 television spots from her 1984 campaign for Governor. (Democratic Party).

This spot was used in Madeleine Kunin's gubernatorial campaign in Vermont.

KURTZ, Walter. 2 videocassettes (3/4 in.).

Collection contains 7 television commercials used during Kurtz's campaign for the 1982 judgeship election in District 5 of Tennessee. (Democratic Party).

KUSHELL, Bob. 1 sound tape reel. (7 1/2 ips.).

Collection contains 1 radio commercial used during Kushell's 1982 campaign for Lt. Governor in Nevada. (Democratic Party).

KUSPER, Stanley. 1 sound tape reel (7 1/2 ips.).

Collection contains 2 radio commercials used during Kusper's campaign for the 1982 County Clerk election in Cook County in Illinois. (Democratic Party).

KYL, John. 4 videotapes (2 in.). 24243430.

Collection contains 7 television commercials used during Kyl's campaign for the 1972 congressional election in District 4 of Iowa. (Republican Party).

LA FALCE, John. 1 sound tape reel (7 1/2 ips.).

Collection contains 1 radio commercial used during La Falce's campaign for the 1982 gubernatorial election in Wisconsin. (Republican Party).

LA ROUCHE, Lyndon H. 15 videocassettes (3/4 in.). 4 videotapes (2 in.). 21175190.

Collection contains 24 television commercials used during La Rouche's campaign for the 1980, 1984, and 1988 presidential elections. Also includes some longer television programs and specials on La Rouche. (Democratic Party).

LAFAVER, Jon Fetherolf, 1935-. 1 sound tape reel (7 1/2 ips.). 21984402.

Collection contains 2 radio commercials used during Lafaver's 1979 campaign for a judgeship in Pennsylvania, Cumberland County. (Republican Party).

LAFFEY, Jane. 1 sound tape reel (7 1/2 ips.).

Collection contains 1 radio commercial used during Laffey's campaign for the 1980 State Representative election in Pennsylvania. (Republican Party).

LAFOLLETTE, Bronson. 1 film reel (16 mm.).

Collection contains 1 television commercial used during LaFollette's campaign for the 1968 gubernatorial election in Wisconsin. (Democratic Party).

LAIRD, Mel. 1 film reel (16 mm.). 24367925.

Collection contains 1 television commercial used during Laird's campaign for the 1968 congressional election in Wisconsin. (Republican Party).

LAKIAN, John. 1 videocassette (3/4 in.). 24253380.

Collection contains 2 television commercials used during Lakian's campaign for the 1982 gubernatorial election in Massachusetts. (Republican Party).

LAMBERT, Al. 1 sound tape reel (7 1/2 ips.).

Collection contains 2 radio commercials used during Lambert's campaign for the 1982 State Senate election in District 9 in New Hampshire. (Republican Party).

LAMKIN, Robert B. 1 videotape (2 in.). 1 film reel (16 mm.). 24253390.

Collection contains 6 television commercials used during Lamkin's campaign for the 1972 congressional election in District 22 of Illinois. (Republican Party).

LAMONT, Peg. 1 videocassette (3/4 in.).

Collection contains 2 television commercials from Lamont's 1984 campaign for State Senate in South Dakota.

LAMSON, Bob. 1 videotape (1 in.). 1 videocassette (3/4 in.). 24253399.

Collection contains 2 television commercials used during Lamson's campaign for the 1984 congressional election in District 8 of Washington. (Democratic Party).

LANCE, Bert. 1931-. 1 film reel (16 mm.). 21538662.

Collection contains 9 television commercials used during Lance's 1974 campaign for Governor in Georgia. (Democratic Party).

LANCE, Bill. 1 sound tape reel (7 1/2 ips.).

Collection contains 1 radio commercial used during Lance's campaign for the 1972 State Senate election in Pennsylvania. (Republican Party).

LANDES, Irwin. 1 videocassette (3/4 in.).

Collection contains 2 television commercials from Landes' 1977 campaign for local office in Nassau County, New York. (Democratic Party).

LANE, Ed. 1 videocassette (3/4 in.).

Collection contains 4 television commercials from Lane's 1977 campaign for Attorney General in Virginia. (Democratic Party).

LANGEN, Odin. 1913-1976. 4 film reels (16 mm.).   1 videotape (2 in.). 21348150.

Collection contains 11 television commercials used during Langen's campaigns for the 1962 U.S. congressional election in Minnesota, District 7. Includes 2 television commercials used during his campaign for the 1970 congressional election in Minnesota. (Republican Party).

LANGRELL, James. 1 sound tape reel (7 1/2 ips.).

Collection contains 3 radio commercials used during Langrell's campaign for a 1982 judgeship in Maryland.

LANKFORD, George Allen. 1 film reel (16 mm.). 21538651.

Collection contains 1 television commercial used during Lankford's campaign for the 1974 gubernatorial election in Georgia. (Republican Party).

LAOS, Roy. 1 videocassette (3/4 in.).

Collection contains 5 television commercials used during Laos' 1982 campaign for U.S. Congress in Arizona. (Republican Party).

LARSEN, Richard F. 1 film reel (16 mm.). 1 videotape (2 in.). 1 sound tape reel (7 1/2 ips). 21567377.

Collection contains 2 television commercials used during Larsen's campaign for the 1972 gubernatorial election in North Dakota. Includes 1 radio commercial used during his 1968 campaign for Lt. Governor. (Republican Party).

LASHLEE, John. 1 videocassette (3/4 in.).

Collection contains 1 television commercial used during Lashlee's campaign for the 1982 Criminal Court Clerk in Tennessee.

LATTA, Del. 1 videocassette (3/4 in.).

Collection contains 3 television commercials used during Latta's 1984 campaign for U.S. Congress in District 5 of Ohio. (Republican Party).

LAURITA, Joseph. 1 film reel (16 mm.). 21474829.

Collection contains 9 television commercials used during Laurita's campaign for the 1974 U.S. congressional election in West Virginia, District 1. (Republican Party).

LAUSMANN, Jerry. 1 sound tape reel (7 1/2 ips.). 22137684.

Collection contains 4 radio commercials used during Lausmann's campaign for the 1978 U.S. congressional election in Oregon. (Republican party).

LAUSTEN, Dave. 1 videocassette (3/4 in.).

Collection contains 6 television commercials used during Lausten's 1984 campaign for State Senate in South Dakota. (Democratic Party).

LAUTENBERG, Frank. 8 videocassettes (3/4 in.). 1 sound tape reel (7 1/2 ips.).

Collection contains 23 television and 10 radio commercials used during Lautenberg's 1982 campaign for U.S. Senate in New Jersey. (Democratic Party).

LAVNER, Peggy. 1 sound tape reel. (7 1/2 ips.).

Collection contains 2 radio commercials used during Lavner's 1982 campaign for Congress in Nevada. (Republican Party).

LAWLER, Bruce. 2 videocassettes (3/4 in.).

Collection contains 4 television commercials used during Lawler's 1984 campaign for Attorney General in Vermont. (Democratic Party).

LAWTHER, Robert. 1 videocassette (3/4 in.). 24253406.

Collection contains 1 television commercial used during Lawther's campaign for a 1982 judgeship in Ohio.

LAXALT, Paul. 1 videocassette (3/4 in.). 1 sound tape reel (7 1/2 ips.).

Collection contains 7 television spots and 4 radio spots from Laxalt's 1980 campaign for U.S. Senate from Nevada. (Republican Party).

LAYNG, John. 1 videotape (2 in.).

Collection contains 1 television commercial used during Layng's campaign for a 1978 judicial election.

LEACH, Robert E. 1 videotape (2 in.). 21567364.

Collection contains 1 television commercial used during Leach's 1972 campaign for Supreme Court Judge in Ohio.

LEAHY, Patrick J. 3 videocassettes (3/4 in.).

Collection contains 6 television commercials from Leahy's 1974 campaign for U.S. Senate in Vermont and 5 television spots from his 1980 re-election campaign. (Democratic Party).

LEAR, John. 1 sound tape reel (7 1/2 ips.).

Collection contains 2 radio commercials used during Lear's campaign for the 1980 State Senate election in Nevada. (Republican Party).

LEBOUTILLIER, John. 1 videotape (2 in.). 1 videocassette (3/4 in.).

Collection contains 4 television commercials used during LeBoutillier's campaign for the 1980 congressional election in New York. (Republican Party).

LECHNER, Ina. 1 sound tape reel (7 1/2 ips.).

Collection contains 2 radio commercials used during Lechner's campaign for the 1982 congressional election in District 10 in Virginia. (Democratic Party).

LEDBETTER, Steward. 3 videocassettes (3/4 in.).

Collection contains 14 television spots from Ledbetter's 1980 campaign for U.S. Senate and 7 television commercials from his 1982 U.S. Senate campaign in Vermont. (Republican Party).

LEE, Blair. 1 videocassette (3/4 in.).

Collection contains 11 television commercials from Lee's 1978 campaign for Governor of Maryland. Some spots also feature Lt. Governor candidate Steny Hoyer. (Democratic Party).

LEE, Howard Nathaniel. 1 videotape (2 in.). 1 sound tape reel (7 1/2 ips.). 24253411.

Collection contains 6 television commercials used during Lee's campaign for the 1976 Lt. gubernatorial election in North Carolina. Also contains 5 radio spots from his 1972 campaign for Congress in District 4. (Democratic Party).

LEHR, George Warwick. 1937-. 1 film reel (16 mm.). 21437356.

Collection contains 7 commercials used during Lehr's 1974 campaign for State Assembly in Missouri. (Democratic Party).

LEHRMAN, Lew. 4 videocassettes (3/4 in.). 1 sound tape reel (7 1/2 ips.).

Collection contains 37 television commercials and 4 radio spots used during Lehrman's campaign for the 1982 gubernatorial election in New York. (Republican Party).

LEMUCCHI, Tim. 1 film reel (16 mm.).

Collection contains 10 television commercials used during Lemucchi's campaign for the 1972 congressional campaign in California. (Democratic Party).

LENAHAN, Jude. 1 videocassette (3/4 in.).

Collection contains 1 television commercial used during Lenahan's campaign for a 1982 judgeship in Tennessee.

LENS, Sidney. 1 sound tape reel (7 1/2 ips.).

Collection contains 3 radio commercials used during Lens' campaign for the 1980 U.S. Senate election in Illinois. (Citizens Party).

LENT, Burkley. 1 sound tape reel (7 1/2 ips.).

Collection contains 10 radio commercials used during Lent's campaign for a 1972 election in Oregon.

LEONARD, Jerry. 1 film reel (16 mm.).

Collection contains 1 television commercial used during Leonard's campaign for the 1968 U.S. senatorial election in Wisconsin. (Republican Party).

LEONARD, Tom. 3 videotapes (2 in.).

Collection contains 4 television commercials used during Leonard's 1979 campaign for Comptroller in Pennsylvania.

LEONHARDT, Frank. 1 videotape (2 in.). 24253417.

Collection contains 1 television commercial used during Leonhardt's campaign for the 1972 local election in Polk County, Iowa. (Democratic Party).

LETENDRE, Andre E. 1937-. 2 film reels. (16 mm.). 21920858.

Collection contains 2 commercials used during LeTendre's campaign for the 1970 U.S. congressional election in Wisconsin in District 7. (Democratic Party).

LEVIN, Carl, 1934-. 1 film reel (16 mm.). 12 videocassettes (3/4 in.). 21511158.

Collection contains 1 television commercial used during Levin's campaign for the 1973 local election, 18 television commercials from his 1978 campaign, and 12 commercials from his 1984 re-election campaign for U.S. Senate in Michigan. (Democratic Party).

This cost comparison was made in a 1986 senatorial campaign spot by Carl Levin of Michigan.

LEVIN, Charles L., 1926-. 2 videotapes (2 in.). 1 sound tape reel (7 1/2 in.). 21426493.

Collection contains 2 television commercials and 1 radio spot used during Levin's campaign for the 1972 judgeship election in Michigan.

LEVIN, Sander M. 3 film reel (16 mm.). 21421289.

Collection contains 13 commercials used during Levin's campaign for the 1970 gubernatorial election in Michigan. (Democratic Party.)

LEVITAS, Elliott, . 1 film reel (16 mm.). 2 videocassettes (3/4 in.). 21486390.

Collection contains 2 television commercials used during Levitas' 1976 campaign for U.S. Congress in Georgia. Also includes 3 television spots from his 1980 campaign and 2 television spots from his 1984 campaign for the same office. (Democratic Party).

LEVITT, Arthur. 1 film reel (16 mm.).

Collection contains 2 television commercials used during Levitt campaign for a 1970 state office election in New York. (Democratic Party).

LEVITT, Myron. 1 sound tape reel. (7 1/2 ips.).

Collection contains 1 radio commercial used during Levitt's 1982 campaign for Governor in Nevada.

LEWIS, Andrew Lindsay. 1931-. 1 film reel (16 mm.). 21474857.

Collection contains 5 television commercials used during Lewis' campaign for the 1974 gubernatorial election in Pennsylvania. (Republican Party).

LEWIS, George. 1 videocassette (3/4 in.).

Collection contains 1 television spot from Lewis' 1980 campaign for State Senate in District 48 of Illinois. (Democratic Party).

LEWIS, Rich. 1 sound tape reel (7 1/2 ips.).

Collection contains 10 radio spots from Lewis' 1979 campaign for District Attorney in Pennsylvania. (Republican Party).

LIACOURAS, Peter. 1 sound tape reel (7 1/2 ips.).

Collection contains 1 radio spot from Liacouras' 1980 campaign for U.S. Senate in Pennsylvania. (Democratic Party).

LICHT, Frank. 2 sound tape reels (7 1/2 ips.). 2 film reels (16 mm.). 21421217.

Collection contains 7 radio commercials used during Licht's campaign for the 1968 gubernatorial election in Rhode Island. Includes 22 television commercials used during his 1970 re-election campaign. (Democratic Party).

LIEBERMAN, Joe. 1 videocassette (3/4 in.). 2 sound tape reels (7 1/2 ips.).

Collection contains 4 television spots and 16 radio commercials used during Lieberman's campaigns for Attorney General in Connecticut. (Democratic Party).

LIEN, Chuck. 2 film reels (16 mm.). 21631167.

Collection contains 5 television commercials used during Lien's campaign for the 1972 U.S. senatorial election in South Dakota. (Republican Party.)

LIGHTFOOT, Jim. 3 videocassettes (3/4 in.).

Collection contains 6 television commercials used during Lightfoot's 1984 campaign for U.S. Congress in District 5 of Iowa. (Republican Party).

LIGHTHIZER, Jim. 1 sound tape reel (7 1/2 ips.).

Collection contains 1 radio commercial used during Lighthizer's campaign for the 1982 County Executive election in Maryland.

LIND, Gloria. 1 videotape (2 in.). 24253422.

Collection contains 1 television commercial used during Lind's campaign for a 1986 election in Illinois.

LINDLEY, George. 1 videotape (2 in.).

Collection contains 1 television commercial used during Lindley's campaign for a 1978 judicial election in Oklahoma.

LINDSAY, John V. 4 videotapes (2 in.). 1 videocassette (3/4 in.). 24253431.

Collection contains 5 television commercials from Lindsay's campaign for Mayor of New York City and 6 television commercials used during Lindsay's 1972 campaign for the presidency. (Democratic Party).

LINK, Arthur A. 3 film reels (16 mm.). 4 videotapes (2 in.). 2 videocassettes (3/4 in.). 21498943.

Collection contains 16 television commercials used during Link's campaign for the 1972 gubernatorial election in North Dakota. Includes 13 television commercials used in his 1976 re-election campaign and 2 television spots from his 1980 re-election campaign. (Democratic Party).

LINK, Art. 1 sound tape reel (7 1/2 ips.).

Collection contains 18 radio commercials used during Link's campaign for the 1972 gubernatorial election in North Dakota. (Democratic Party).

LIPPITT, Tom. 1 sound tape reel (7 1/2 ips.).

Collection contains 4 radio commercials used during Lippitt's campaign for the 1980 congressional election in District 22 in Ohio. (Democratic Party).

LISHMAN, Helen. 1 videocassette (3/4 in.).

Collection contains 3 television commercials used during Lishman's fictional campaign for the 1983 Mayoral election in Chicago, Illinois.

LIST, Robert. 1 videotape (2 in.). 21368972.

Collection contains 3 television commercials from List's 1974 state Attorney General campaign in Nevada (Republican Party).

LITTON, Jerry Lon. 1937-1976. 5 videotapes (2 in.). 21270299.

Collection contains 4 television commercials used during Litton's 1972 campaign for U.S. Congress in Missouri, 6th District. Includes 6 television commercials used during his campaign for the 1976 U.S. Senate election in Missouri. (Democratic Party).

LLOYD, Jim. 1 sound tape reel (7 1/2 ips.).

Collection contains 5 radio commercials used during Lloyd's campaign for the 1980 congressional election in District 35 in California. (Democratic Party).

LOCK, Joshua. 1 sound tape reel (7 1/2 ips). 22441615.

Collection contains 7 radio commercials used during Lock's 1979 campaign for District Attorney in Dauphin County, Pennsylvania.

LODGE, Henry Cabot. 3 videocassettes (3/4 in.).

Collection contains a series of 9 television spots featuring Lodge as part of the 1960 presidential campaign in which Lodge was Nixon's vice-presidential candidate. (Republican Party).

LOMBARDINO, Frank. 1 videotape (2 in.). 21498922.

Collection contains 1 television commercial used during Lombardino's campaign in 1972 for state representative in Texas.

LONG, Bruce.   1 videocassette (3/4 in.).

Collection contains 2 television commercials used during Long's 1984 campaign for U.S. Congress in Oregon's 4th District. (Republican Party).

LONG, Clarence.   2 sound tape reels (7 1/2 ips.).

Collection contains 13 radio commercials used during Long's 1982 campaign and 1 radio spot from his 1984 campaign for U.S. Congress in District 2 of Maryland.   (Democratic Party).

LONG, Russell B.   1 videotape (2 in.). 2 videocassettes (3/4 in.).   22199013.

Collection includes 17 television commercial used during Long's 1980 U.S. Senate campaign in Louisiana (Democratic Party).

LONGSTRETH, Thatcher. 1 film reel (16 mm.). 24253436.

Collection contains 7 television commercials used during Longstreth's campaign for the 1972 Mayoral election in Philadelphia, Pennsylvania. (Republican Party).

LORBER, Richard. 1 videotape (2 in.). 24253442.

Collection contains 3 television commercials used during Lorber's campaign for the 1976 U.S. Senate election in Rhode Island. (Democratic Party).

LORENZ, Frances.   1 sound tape reel (7 1/2 ips.).

Collection contains 1 radio commercial used during Lorenz's campaign for the 1980 State Supreme Court Justice election in Illinois.   (Democratic Party).

LOTTO, Myron P. 2 videotapes (2 in.). 24243441.

Collection contains 2 television commercials used during Lotto's campaign for the 1972 congressional election in Wisconsin.

LOUNSBERRY, Robert.   2 sound tape reels (7 1/2 ips).   22226358.

Collection contains 8 radio commercials used during Lounsberry's 1972 campaign for Secretary of Agriculture in Iowa (Republican Party).

LOUSMA, Jack. 8 videocassettes (3/4 in.).

Collection contains 31 television commercials used during Lousma's 1984 campaign for U.S. Senate in Michigan.   (Republican Party).

LOWE, Bruce. 2 videotapes (2 in.).

Collection contains 2 television commercials used during Lowe's 1979 campaign for a judgeship in Wisconsin.

LOWERY, Bill. 1 sound tape reel. (7 1/2 ips.).

Collection contains 2 radio commercials used during Lowery's 1982 congressional campaign in District 41 of California. (Republican Party).

LOWRY, Mike. 3 videocassettes (3/4 in.).

Collection contains 2 television commercials from Lowry's 1978 campaign for Congress in District 7 and 23 television commercials used during his 1983 campaign for the U.S. Senate in Washington. (Democratic Party).

LUCEY, Patrick J. 1918--. 2 film reels (16 mm.). 3 videotapes (2 in.). 1 sound tape reel (7 1/2 ips.). 21437373.

Collection contains 19 television and 1 radio commercials from Lucey's 1970 gubernatorial election in Wisconsin. Includes 14 television commercials used during his 1974 re-election campaign. (Democratic Party).

LUDLOW, Willis H. 1 sound tape reel (7 1/2 ips). 21920923.

Collection contains 3 radio commercials used during Ludlow's 1972 U.S. congressional election in Idaho, 2nd District (Democratic Party).

**LUGAR, Richard.
3 videotapes (2 in.).
2 videocassettes
(3/4 in.). 22441578.**

Collection contains 1 television commercial used during Lugar's campaign for the 1974 U.S. Senate election in Indiana. Includes 4 television spots used during his campaign for the 1976 U.S. Senate election in Indiana. Also contains 30 television spots from Lugar's 1982 campaign for U.S. Senate in Indiana. (Republican Party).

This frame comes from a Richard Lugar campaign spot used in the 1982 Senate campaign in Indiana.

LUKEN, Thomas. 2 videotapes (2 in.). 21348142.

Collection contains of 5 television commercials used during Luken's 1974 U.S. congressional campaign in Ohio (Democratic Party).

LUKENS, Donald. 1 film reel (16 mm.). 24367943.

Collection contains 1 television commercial used during Lukens' campaign for the 1970 gubernatorial election in Ohio. (Republican Party).

LUNDINE, Stan. 2 videocassettes (3/4 in.).

Collection contains 4 television spots from Lundine's 1976 campaign, 3 television spots from his 1982 campaign, and 6 spots from his 1984 campaign for Congress in District 34 of New York. (Democratic Party).

LYBARGER, Len. 1 sound tape reel (7 1/2 ips.).

Collection contains 1 radio commercial used during Lybarger's campaign for the 1980 Judgeship of Common Pleas election in Cuyahoga County, Ohio.

LYMAN, Howard. 1 videocassette (3/4 in.).

Collection contains 5 television commercials used during Lyman's 1982 campaign for U.S. Congress in Montana. (Democratic Party).

LYMAN, James. 1 sound tape reel. (7 1/2 ips.).

Collection contains 1 radio commercial used during Lyman's 1982 congressional campaign in Nevada. (Republican Party).

LYNCH, John. 1 sound tape reel (7 1/2 ips.).

Collection contains 1 radio commercial used during Lynch's campaign for the 1972 State Senate election.

MACBRIDE, Roger Les. 1 videotape (2 in.). 1 videocassette (3/4 in.).

Collection contains 3 television commercials used during MacBride's campaign for the 1976 presidential election. (Libertarian Party).

MACDONALD, Kathleen. 1 videocassette (3/4 in.).

Collection contains 2 television commercials used during MacDonald's 1986 campaign for Wayne County Circuit Court in Detroit, Michigan.

MACGREGOR, Clark, 1922-. 1 film reel (16 mm.). 21567325.

Collection contains 1 television commercial used during MacGregor's 1970 campaign for U.S. Senate in Minnesota. (Republican Party).

MACKAY, Richard.   1 sound tape reel (7 1/2 ips.).

Collection contains 1 radio commercial used during Mackay's campaign for the 1980 County Engineer election in Ohio. (Democratic Party).

MACKOUL, Walter Ernest. 1936-. 1 videotape (2 in.). 21421299.

Collection contains 1 television commercial used during Mackoul's 1974 campaign for a judgeship in Florida. (Democratic Party).

MACPHAIL, John Arch. 1924-. 1 sound tape reel (7 1/2 ips.). 21984425.

Collection contains of 1 radio commercial used during MacPhail's 1979 campaign for Commonwealth Court in Pennsylvania.

MACY, Bob.   2 videocassettes (3/4 in.).

Collection contains 7 television commercials used during Macy's 1982 campaign for District Attorney in Oklahoma City, Oklahoma.

MADDOX, Lester. 1915-. 1 film reel (16 mm.). 21511145.

Collection contains of 12 television commercials used during Maddox's campaign for the 1974 gubernatorial election in Georgia. (Democratic Party).

MADDOX, Bob.   1 sound tape reel (7 1/2 ips.).

Collection contains 1 radio commercial used during Maddox's campaign for the 1972 State House election in Georgia.

MADIGAN, Edward R. 2 videotapes (2 in.).   24257353.

Collection contains 7 television commercials used during Madigan's campaign for the 1972 congressional election in District 21 of Illinois. (Republican Party).

MADSON, Steve.   1 sound tape reel (7 1/2 ips.).

Collection contains 1 radio commercial used during Madson's campaign for the 1982 County Sheriff election in Iowa.

MAGNUSON, Warren Grant. 1905-. 2 film reels (16 mm.). 4 videocassettes (3/4 in.). 21421538.

Collection contains 2 television commercials used during Magnuson's campaign for the 1968 U.S. Senatorial election in Washington and 12 television spots for his unsuccessful re-election campaign in 1980. (Democratic Party).

MAHAFEY, Mary Anne. 1 sound tape reel. (7 1/2 ips.).

Collection contains 3 radio commercials used during Mahafey's 1982 congressional campaign in Michigan.

MAHER, Jim. 1 videocassette (3/4 in.).

Collection contains 1 television commercial used during Maher's 1984 campaign for U.S. Senate in Kansas. (Democratic Party).

MAHER, Richard M. 2 film reels (16 mm.). 21492248.

Collection contains of 4 television commercials used during Maher's campaigns for 1974 and 1976 judgeships in Michigan.

MAHNIC, Frank. 1 videocassette (3/4 in.).

Collection contains 1 television commercial used during Mahnic's 1984 campaign for State Senate in Ohio. (Democratic Party).

MAHON, Don. 1 sound tape reel (7 1/2 ips.). 21930061.

Collection contains of 1 radio commercial used during Mahon's campaign for the 1970 U.S. congressional election in Iowa. (Republican Party).

MAHONEY, Jim. 2 videotapes (2 in.).

Collection contains 2 television commercials used during Mahoney's 1972 campaign for Auditor in Iowa. (Democratic Party).

MAIER, Henry W.,1918-. 1 film reel (16 mm.). 21499007.

Collection contains 6 television commercials used during Maier's campaign for the 1972 Mayoral election in Wisconsin. (Democratic Party).

MAILLARD, William. 1 film reel (16 mm.).

Collection contains 1 television commercial used during Maillard's campaign for the 1972 congressional election in District 6 of California. (Republican Party).

MALAGA, Robert S. 1 videocassette (3/4 in.). 24257368.

Collection contains 1 television commercial used during Malaga's 1982 campaign for a judgeship in Ohio.

MALOY, Dick. 1 videotape (2 in.). 21920828.

Collection contains 1 television commercial available from Maloy's 1972 campaign for State Senate in Florida. (Republican Party).

MANDEL, Marvin. 1920-. 4 film reels (16 mm.). 1 videotape (2 in.). 21243976.

Collection contains 12 television commercials used during Mandel's campaign for the 1970 gubernatorial election in Maryland. (Democratic Party).

MANIAN, Victor. 2 videotape (2 in.). 21421319.

Collection contains 1 television commercial used during Manian's campaign for a 1972 judgeship amd 1 television commercial used during his 1975 campaign for Circuit Court Judge of Branch B; both elections in Wisconsin.

MANMILLER, Joe. 1 sound tape reel (7 1/2 ips.).

Collection contains 1 radio commercial used during Manmiller's campaign for the 1980 State House election in Pennsylvania. (Republican Party).

MANNING, Brince. 1 sound tape reel (7 1/2 ips.).

Collection contains 2 radio commercials used during Manning's campaign for a 1972 local office in Georgia. (Republican Party).

MANSFIELD, Mike. 1903-. 2 film reels (16 mm.). 21382841.

Collection contains 4 commercials used during Mansfield's 1964 campaign for U.S. Senate in Montana. (Democratic Party).

MARCUS, Sidney. 1 videocassette (3/4 in.).

Collection contains 5 television commercials from Marcus' 1981 campaign for Mayor of Atlanta, Georgia.

MARIANE, Sunny. 1 sound tape reel. (7 1/2 ips.).

Collection contains 5 radio commercials used during Mariane's 1982 campaign for State House in District 75 of California. (Republican Party).

MARIANO, Joe. 1 sound tape reel. (7 1/2 ips.).

Collection contains 1 radio spot from Mariano's 1982 campaign for State House in District 9 in Maryland. (Democratic Party).

MARINO, Michael. 1 videocassette (3/4 in.).

Collection contains 4 television commercials used during Marino's 1982 campaign for U.S. Congress in Pennsylvania. (Republican Party).

MARITAS, Paul. 1 videocassettes (3/4 in.).

Collection contains 1 television commercial used during Maritas' campaign for a 1982 city office in Vermont. (Democratic Party).

MARKEY, Ed. 1 videocassette (3/4 in.).

Collection contains 1 commercial from Markey's 1976 congressional campaign in District 7 of Massachusetts. (Democratic Party).

MARKUS. 1 videocassette (3/4 in.). 24257378.

Collection contains 3 television commercials used during Markus' 1082 campaign for a judgeship in Ohio.

MARRIOTT, Dan. 1 videocassette (3/4 in.).

Collection contains 22 television commercials used during 1982 campaign for U.S. Congress in Utah. (Republican Party).

MARSHALL, Murray. 1 sound tape reel (7 1/2 ips.).

Collection contains 6 radio commercials from Marshall's 1964 campaign for Attorney General in Montana. (Republican Party).

MARSHALL, Tim. 1 sound tape reel (7 1/2 ips.).

Collection contains 3 radio commercials used during Marshall's campaign for the 1980 State Senate election in Ohio.

MARSTON, David. 1 videotape (2 in.). 1 videocassette (3/4 in.).

Collection contains 1 television commercial used during Marston's campaign for the 1978 gubernatorial election in Pennsylvania and 2 television spots from his 1979 campaign for Mayor of Philadelphia. (Republican Party).

MARTIN, Bill. 1 videocassette (3/4 in.).

Collection contains 1 television commercial used during Martin's 1986 campaign for State Representative in Michigan. (Republican Party).

MARTIN, Crawford C. 1 film reel (16 mm.). 1 sound tape reel (7 1/2 ips.). 22186001.

Collection contains 4 radio spots and 1 television spot used in Martin's campaigns for Attorney General in Texas. (Democratic Party).

MARTIN, David. 1 videocassette (3/4 in.).

Collection contains 3 television commercials used during Martin's campaign for the 1982 congressional election in District 26 of New York. (Republican Party).

MARTIN, James G., 1935-. 6 videotapes (2 in.). 5 videocassettes (3/4 in.). 21269060.

Collection contains six television commercials used during Martin's campaign for the 1972 U.S. congressional election in North Carolina, 9th District. Also contains 17 television commercials from his 1984 campaign for Governor of North Carolina. (Republican Party).

MARTIN, Lynn. 1 videotape (1 in.). 1 videocassette (1/2 in.). 24257390.

Collection contains 3 television commercials used during Martin's campaign for the 1986 congressional election in District 16 of Illinois. (Republican Party).

MARTINEZ, Bob. 6 videocassettes (3/4 in. & 1/2 in.).

Collection contains 9 television commercials used during Martinez's 1986 campaign for Governor of Florida. (Republican Party).

MASON, Randy. 2 videocassettes (3/4 in.).

Collection contains 4 television commercials used during Mason's 1986 campaign for State Representative in District 46 of Michigan.

MASON, Tony. 6 videotapes (2 in.). 3 videocassettes (3/4 in.). 24257405.

Collection contains 10 television commercials used during Mason's campaign for the 1986 gubernatorial election in Arizona. (Democratic Party).

MASSELL, Sam. 4 videotapes (2 in.). 22164921.

Collection contains 4 television commercials used during Massell's campaign for the 1973 Mayoral election in Atlanta, Georgia. (Democratic Party).

MASTEN, Jeff. 1 videocassette (3/4 in.).

Collection contains 2 television commercials used during Masten's 1986 campaign for Attorney General of South Dakota. (Democratic Party).

MATHESON, Scott. 1 videocassette (3/4 in.).

Collection contains 7 television spots from Matheson's 1980 campaign for Governor of Utah. (Democratic Party).

MATHIAS, Charles McC (Charles McCurdy). 1922-. 1 film reel (16 mm.). 3 videocassettes (3/4 in.). 21421517.

Collection contains 1 television commercial used during Mathias' campaign for the 1968 U.S. Senatorial election in Maryland and 8 television spots from his 1980 primary campaign for U.S. Senate in Maryland. (Republican Party).

MATHIEU, Tom. 1 videocassette (3/4 in.).

Collection contains 4 television commercials used during Mathieu's 1984 campaign for State Representative in Michigan. (Democratic Party).

MATHIS, Dawson. 1 videocassette (3/4 in.).

Collection contains 2 television spots from Mathis' 1980 campaign for U.S. Senate in Georgia. (Democratic Party).

MATHIS, Ralph. 1 sound tape reel (7 1/2 ips.).

Collection contains 1 radio commercial used during Mathis' campaign for the State Senate in District 21 in Iowa. (Democratic Party).

MATTHEWS, Bob. 1 film reel (16 mm.). 24257413.

Collection contains 2 television commercials used during Matthews' 1967 campaign for Lt. Governor in Kentucky. (Democratic Party).

MATTINGLY, Mack. 12 videocassettes (3/4 in.).

Collection contains 5 television spots from Mattingly's 1980 campaign for U.S. Senate in Georgia. Also contains 22 television spots from his 1986 campaign for the same office. (Republican Party).

MATTOX, Jim. 3 videocassettes (3/4 in.). 1 sound tape reel (7 1/2 ips.).

Collection contains 5 television spots from Mattox's 1980 campaign for U.S. Congress in District 5 of Texas and 1 radio commercial and 1 television commercial used during his 1982 campaign for Attorney General of Texas. Also includes 4 television spots from his 1986 re-election campaign for Attorney General. (Democratic Party).

MAY, Steve. 1 sound tape reel (7 1/2 ips.).

Collection contains 11 radio commercials used during May's campaign for the 1980 State Senate election in District 53 in New York. (Republican Party).

MCATEE, Charles D. 1 videotape (2 in.). 21244009.

Collection contains of 1 television commercial used during McAtee's campaign for the 1972 U.S. congressional election in Kansas.

MCBRAYER, Terry. 5 videocassettes (3/4 in.).

Collection contains 21 television commercials from McBrayer's 1979 primary campaign for Governor of Kentucky. (Democratic Party).

MCBRIDE, Roger. 1 videocassette (3/4 in.).

Collection contains 2 television commercials from McBride's 1976 campaign for President. (Libertarian Party).

MCCAFFREY, James. 1 videotape (2 in.). 24257436.

Collection contains 1 television commercial used during McCaffrey's campaign for the 1976 state election in District 28 of Massachusetts.

MCCAIN, John. 7 videotapes (2 in.). 13 videocassette (3/4 in. & 1/2 in.). 24257423.

Collection contains 28 television commercials used during McCain's 1986 campaign for the U.S. Senate, 9 television commercials from his 1982 and 1984 campaigns, and 20 television spots from his 1986 campaign for U.S. Congress in Arizona. (Republican Party).

MCCALL, Tom. 1 film reel (16 mm.).

Collection contains 10 television commercials used during McCall's 1970 campaign for Governor in Oregon. (Republican Party).

MCCALLUM, Scott. 1 videotape (2 in.).

Collection contains 2 television spots used during McCallum's 1982 campaign for U.S. Senate in Wisconsin. (Republican Party).

MCCARNEY, Robert P. 1 film reel (16 mm.). 21726626.

The collection contains of 4 television commercials used during McCarney's campaign for the 1972 gubernatorial election in North Dakota. (Republican Party).

MCCARTHY, Eugene J. 1916-. 3 videotapes (2 in.). 1 videocassette (3/4 in.). 22186017.

Collection contains 6 television commercials from McCarthy's 1968 presidential campaign and 3 television commercials from his 1972 presidential campaign. (Democratic Party).

MCCLASKEY, Paul. 1 sound tape reel (7 1/2 ips.).

Collection contains 7 radio commercials used during McClaskey's campaign for the 1972 presidential election. (New Hampshire Primary). (Republican Party).

MCCLELLAN, John. 1 film reel (16 mm.). 24257447.

Collection contains 6 television spots from McClellan's 1972 campaign for U.S. Senate in Arkansas. (Democratic Party).

MCCLELLAN, Jack. 1 sound tape reel (7 1/2 ips.).

Collection contains 4 radio commercials used during McClellan's campaign for a 1972 judgeship in Oregon.

MCCLERKIN, Hayes C. (Hayes Candor), 1931-. 1 videotape (2 in.). 21248131.

Collection contains 5 television commercials used during McClerkin's campaign for the 1970 gubernatorial election in Arkansas. (Democratic Party).

MCCLOSKEY, Frank. 2 videocassettes (3/4 in.).

Collection contains 8 television commercials used during McCloskey's 1986 campaign for U.S. Congress in District 8 of Indiana. (Democratic Party).

MCCLOSKEY, Paul N. 1927-. 6 videotapes (2 in.). 21256345.

Collection contains 10 television commercials used during McCloskey's campaigns for the 1972 presidential election and 1974 congressional election, 12th District, in California. (Republican Party).

MCCLOSKY, PETE. 1 videotape (2 in.). 24367898.

Collection contains 10 television commercials used during McCloskey's campaign for the 1982 U.S. Senate election in California. (Republican Party).

MCCLURE, James A. 2 sound tapes (7 1/2 ips.). 4 videotapes (2 in.). 2 videocassettes (3/4 in.). 21930030.

Collection contains 8 television and 7 radio commercials used during McClure's 1972 U.S. Senate election, includes 7 television and 5 radio commercials used during McClure's 1978 U.S. Senate re-election campaign in Idaho. Also contains 7 television spots from his 1984 campaign for U.S. Senate. (Republican Party).

MCCOLL, BILL. 1 videotape (2 in.).

Collection contains 4 television commercials used during McColl's campaign for the 1982 congressional election in District 43 of California. (Republican Party).

MCCOLLISTER, John Y. 1 film reel (16 mm.). 2 videotapes (2 in.). 21492273.

Collection contains 20 television commercials used during McCollister's 1976 campaign for U.S. Senate in Nebraska. (Republican Party).

MCCONNELL, Mitch. 2 videotapes (2 in.). 10 videocassettes (3/4 in.).

Collection contains 3 television commercials from McConnell's 1977 campaign for County Executive Judge in Jefferson County, Kentucky, and 9 commercials from McConnell's 1984 campaign for U.S. Senate in Kentucky. (Republican Party).

MCCORKEL, Frank. 2 sound tape reels (7 1/2 ips.).

Collection contains 3 radio commercials used during McCorkel's campaign for a state office in Pennsylvania. (Republican Party).

MCCORMACK, Ellen , 1926-. 1 film reel (16 mm.). 1 videotape (2 in.). 21368926.

Collection contains 2 television commercials on film reel and 3 television commercials on videotape used during McCormack's campaign for the 1976 presidential election. (Democratic Party).

MCCORMACK, Tim. 1 videocassette (3/4 in.). 24257455.

Collection contains 2 television commercials used during McCormack's campaign for the 1982 auditor election in Ohio. (Democratic Party).

MCCOY, Carol. 1 videocassette (3/4 in.).

Collection contains 1 television commercial used during McCoy's campaign for the 1982 judgeship election in circuit 5 of Tennessee.

MCCREADY, Connie. 1 videocassette (3/4 in.). 1 sound tape reel (7 1/2 ips.).

Collection contains 6 radio spots from McCready's 1970 campaign for local office in Oregon and 3 television spots from his 1980 campaign for Mayor of Portland, Oregon.

MCCURDY, Dave. 2 videocassettes (1/2 in. & 3/4 in.).

Collection contains 2 television commercials used during McCurdy's 1982 campaign for U.S. Congress in Oklahoma. (Democratic Party).

MCDANIEL, Roger. 2 videocassettes (3/4 in.). 24260673.

Collection contains 2 television commercials used during McDaniel's campaign for the 1982 U.S. Senate election in Wyoming. (Democratic Party).

MCDERMOTT, Jim. 1 videocassette (3/4 in.).

Collection contains 2 television commercials used during McDermott's 1984 campaign for Governor of Washington. (Democratic Party).

MCDONALD, Kathy. 2 videocassettes (3/4 in.).

Collection contains 10 television commercials used during McDonald's campaign for the 1983 congressional election in District 7 of Georgia. (Democratic Party).

MCDONNA, Joseph. 1 sound tape reel (3 3/4 ips.).

Collection contains 1 radio spot from McDonna's 1964 campaign for Circuit Court Clerk. (Democratic Party).

MCELROY, Tom. 1 film reel (16 mm.). 21887817.

Collection contains 9 television commercials used during McElroy's campaign for the 1972 gubernatorial election in Texas. (Republican Party).

MCFARLAND, Ruth. 3 videocassettes (3/4 in.). 24260678.

Collection contains 8 television commercials used during McFarland's 1982 and 1984 campaigns for U.S. Congress in District 5 of Oregon. (Democratic Party).

MCFAUL, Gerald T. 1 videocassette (3/4 in.). 24260684.

Collection contains 3 television commercials used during McFaul's campaign for the 1982 Cuyahoga county commissioner in Ohio. (Democratic Party).

MCGEE, Gale W. (Gale William), 1915-. 4 film reels (16 mm.). 21416071.

Collection contains 25 television commercials used during McGee's 1970 and 1976 campaigns for U.S. Senate in Wyoming. (Democratic Party).

MCGOVERN, George S. (George Stanley), 1922-. 19 sound reels (7 1/2 ips.), 12 videocassettes (3/4 in.), 8 sound tape reels (3 3/4 ips), 24 videotapes (2 in.). 4 film reels (16 mm.). 21256376.

Collection contains 116 television and 64 radio commercials used during McGovern's campaign for the 1972 presidential campaign. Includes 14 television and 18 radio commercials used in his campaign for the 1974 U.S. Senate election in South Dakota and 70 television spots from his unsuccessful 1980 Senate re-election campaign. Includes 30-minute television biography from 1980 campaign. (Democratic Party).

This frame comes from the identification slide of a 1972 George McGovern presidential ad.

MCGRATH, Ray. 1 videocassette (3/4 in.).

Collection contains 1 television commercial used during McGrath's 1984 campaign for U.S. Congress in New York. (Republican Party).

MCGREGOR, Jackie. 5 videocassettes (3/4 in. & 1/2 in.).

Collection contains 1 television commercial used during McGregor's 1984 campaign and 4 television spots from his 1986 campaign for U.S. Congress in Michigan. (Republican Party).

MCGREGOR, Tom. 1 videocassette (3/4 in.).

Collection contains 1 television commercial used during McGregor's campaign for the U.S. Senate election in Vermont. (Democratic Party).

MCGUIRE, Frank. 1 videocassette (3/4 in.).

Collection contains 27 television commercials from McGuire's 1979 campaign for County Executive in Erie County, New York. (Democratic Party).

MCGUIRK, Harry. 1 sound tape reel (7 1/2 ips.).

Collection contains 3 radio commercials used during McGuirk's campaign for the 1982 gubernatorial election in Maryland. (Democratic Party).

MCHARD, Sam. 4 videocassettes (3/4 in. & 1/2 in.).

Collection contains 5 television commercials used during McHard's 1986 campaign for U.S. Congress in Illinois, 17th District. (Republican Party).

MCHUGH, Matt. 1 videocassette (3/4 in.).

Collection contains 6 television commercials used during McHugh's 1986 campaign for U.S. Congress in District 28 of New York. (Democratic Party).

MCINERNEY, Gary. 1 videocassette (3/4 in.).

Collection contains 4 television commercials used during McInerney's 1984 campaign for U.S. Congress in Michigan. (Democratic Party).

MCINTEE, Rick. 3 videocassettes (3/4 in.).

Collection contains 2 television commercials used during McIntee's 1984 campaign and 5 television spots from his 1986 campaign for U.S. Congress. (Republican Party).

MCINTYRE, Richard. 1 videotape (1 in.). 5 videocassette (3/4 in. & 1/2 in.). 24260699.

Collection contains 13 television commercials used during McIntyre's 1984 and 1986 campaigns for U.S. Congress in District 8 of Indiana. (Republican Party).

MCKAY, Gunn. 1 videocassette (3/4 in.).

Collection contains 6 television commercials used during McKay's 1986 primary campaign for Governor of Maine. (Republican Party).

MCKAY, Brian. 1 sound tape reel. (7 1/2 ips.).

Collection contains 1 radio commercial used during McKay's 1982 campaign for Attorney General in Nevada.

MCKELLIPS, Roger. 7 videocassettes (3/4 in.).

Collection contains 21 television commercial from McKellips' 1978 campaign for Governor of South Dakota. (Democratic Party).

MCKERNAN, John. 9 videocassettes (3/4 in. & 1/2 in.). 1 sound tape reel (7 1/2 ips.).

Collection contains 8 television commercials used during McKernan's 1982 campaign for U.S. Congress in Maine and 10 radio spots from his 1984 campaign for the same office. Also includes 27 television spots from his 1986 campaign for Governor of Maine. (Republican Party).

MCKERNIN, John. 1 sound tape reel (7 1/2 ips.).

Collection contains 1 radio commercial used during McKernin's campaign for the 1982 congressional election in District 1 in Maine. (Republican Party).

MCKINNEY, Stu. 1 videocassette (1/2 in.).

Collection contains 1 television commercial used during McKinney's 1986 campaign for U.S. Congress in Connecticut. (Republican Party).

MCKNIGHT, Tommy. 1 videocassette (3/4 in.).

Collection contains 1 television spot from McKnight's 1982 campaign for Governor in Tennessee. (Democratic Party).

MCLANE, Susan. 1 sound tape reel (7 1/2 ips.).

Collection contains 3 radio commercials used during McLane's campaign for the 1982 State Senate election in New Hampshire. (Republican Party).

MCLAUGHLIN, John J. 1 sound tape reel (7 1/2 ips.).

Collection contains 6 radio spots from McLaughlin's 1966 campaign for Railroad and Public Services Commissioner in Montana. (Democratic Party).

MCLEROY, Mark. 1 videocassette (3/4 in.).

Collection contains 3 television commercials used during McLeRoy's 1986 campaign for State Representative in Illinois. (Republican Party).

MCMANAMON, Joe.   1 sound tape reel (7 1/2 ips.).

Collection contains 1 radio commercial used during McManamon's campaign for the 1980 Judgeship of Common Pleas election in Cuyahoga County, Ohio.

This 1986 Henry McMaster's spot from the south Carolina senatorial race criticized Fritz Hollings for "globetrotting."

MCMASTER, Henry. 6 videocassettes (3/4 in. & 1/2 in.).

Collection contains 6 television commercials used during McMaster's 1986 campaign for U.S. Senate in South Carolina. (Republican Party).

MCMILLAN, George. 6 videotapes (2 in.).

Collection contains 6 television commercials used during McMillan's campaign for the 1986 gubernatorial election in Alabama. (Democratic Party).

MCMILLEN, Tom.   2 videocassettes (3/4 in.).

Collection contains 3 television spot from McMillen's 1986 campaign for Congress in Maryland. (Democratic Party).

MCNAMARA, Ed. 2 videocassettes (3/4 in.).   24260703.

Collection contains 8 television spots from McNamara's 1982 campaign for local office in Michigan. (Democratic Party).

MCNARY, Gene. 1 videotape (2 in.). 1 videocassette (3/4 in.). 21276448.

Collection contains 1 television spot used during McNary's 1972 campaign for Governor and 11 television spots from his 1980 campaign for U.S. Senate in Missouri. (Republican Party).

MCNULTY, Jim.   2 videocassettes (3/4 in.).

Collection contains 13 television commercials used during McNulty's 1982 campaign and 1 television spot from his 1984 campaign for U.S. Congress in District 5 of Arizona. (Democratic Party).

MCQUADE, Dennis. 1 videocassette (3/4 in.).

Collection contains 4 television spots from McQuade's 1980 campaign for U.S. Congress in District 5 of California. (Republican Party).

MCRIGHT, Frank. 2 videocassettes (3/4 in.).

Collection contains 15 television commercials used during McRight's 1984 campaign for U.S. Congress in Alabama. (Democratic Party).

MCWHERTER, Ned Ray. 5 videocassettes (3/4 in.).

Collection contains 21 television commercials used during McWherter's 1986 campaign for Governor of Tennessee. (Democratic Party).

MECHAM, Evan. 7 videotapes (2 in.). 5 videocassettes (3/4 in.). 24260707.

Collection contains 8 television commercials from Mecham's 1982 campaign and 7 television commercials from his 1986 campaign for Governor of Arizona.

MEEKER, Tony. 1 videocassette (3/4 in.).

Collection contains 5 television commercials used during Meeker's 1986 campaign for U.S. Congress in Oregon. (Republican Party).

MELCHER, John. 2 film reels (16 mm.). 10 videocassettes (3/4 in.). 1 sound tape reel (7 1/2 ips). 24260878.

Collection contains 3 radio commercials from Melcher's 1966 campaign, 1 television commercial from his 1970 campaign, and 5 television commercials from his 1972 campaign; all for U.S. Congress in District 2 of Montana. Includes 22 television spots from his 1982 campaign for U.S. Senate in Montana. Also includes a series of NCPAC anti-Melcher commercials used in the 1982 campaign. (Democratic Party).

MERDES, Ed. 5 videocassettes (3/4 in.).

Collection contains 15 television commercials from Merdes' 1978 campaign for Governor of Alaska. (Democratic Party).

MERLINO, Joe. 1 sound tape reel (7 1/2 ips.).

Collection contains 5 radio commercials used during Merlino's campaign for the 1981 gubernatorial election in New Jersey. (Democratic Party).

MERLO, John. 1 videotape (2 in.). 1 videocassette (3/4 in.). 21486437.

Collection contains 3 television commercials used during Merlo's 1974 campaign for Lt. Governor of California. (Democratic Party).

MERRELL, Norman. 1 videocassette (3/4 in.).

Collection contains 2 television commercials used during Merrell's 1984 primary campaign for Governor of Missouri. (Democratic Party).

MESKILL, Thomas J. 2 sound tape reels (7 1/2 ips.). 21930000.

Collection contains 11 radio commercials used during Meskill's 1970 campaign for Governor in Connecticut. (Republican Party).

METCALF, Lee. 1911-1978. 2 film reels (16 mm.). 21369693.

Collection contains 29 television commercials used during Metcalf's campaign for the 1966 U.S. Senatorial election in Montana. Includes 12 television commercials used in his 1972 re-election campaign. (Democratic Party).

METZENBAUM, Howard M. 2 film reels (16 mm.). 6 videocassettes (3/4 in.). 1 videotape (2 in.). 1 sound tape reel (7 1/2 ips.). 21431642.

Collection contains 7 television commercials and 4 radio spots used during Metzenbaum's 1974 campaign for U.S. Senate in Ohio. Includes 3 television commercials used during his successful 1976 campaign for U.S. Senate in Ohio and 8 television commercials used in his 1982 re-election campaign. (Democratic Party).

MEZVINSKY, Edward M. 1 sound tape reel (7 1/2 ips.). 2 videocassettes (3/4 in.). 21930006.

Collection contains 15 radio commercials used during Mezvinsky's campaign for the 1972 U.S. congressional election and 7 television commercials from his 1976 congressional campaign, District 1 in Iowa. (Democratic Party).

MICA, Dan. 1 videocassette (3/4 in.).

Collection contains 12 television commercials used during Mica's 1986 campaign for U.S. Congress in District 14 of Florida. (Democratic Party).

MICHAELSON, Julius "Julie" C. 2 videocassettes (3/4 in.).

Collection contains 3 television commercials used during Michaelson's 1982 campaign for U.S. Senate in Rhode Island. (Democratic Party).

MICHEL, Robert H.   1 videocassette (3/4 in.).

Collection contains 1 television commercial used during Michel's 1982 campaign for U.S. Congress in Illinois. (Republican Party).

MICKELSON, George.   3 videocassettes (3/4 in. & 1/2 in.).

Collection contains 33 television commercials used during Mickelson's 1986 campaign for Governor of South Dakota. (Republican Party).

MIDONICK, Millard L. 1 sound tape reel (7 1/2 ips.). 21920873.

Collection contains 8 radio commercials used during Midonick's 1971 campaign for a judgeship in New York. (Democratic Party).

**MIKULSKI, Barbara.
2 sound tape reels
(7 1/2 ips.).
3 videocassettes
(3/4 in.).**

Collection contains 4 radio spots from Mikulski's 1982 campaign and 6 radio spots from her 1984 campaign for U.S. Congress in Maryland. Also contains 15 television spots from her 1986 campaign for the same office and a C-SPAN segment with media producer Bob Shrum showing and discussing the 1986 spots. (Democratic Party).

This spot was used in Barbara Milkulski's 1986 senatorial campaign in Maryland.

MILES, Stephen L.   1 sound tape reel (7 1/2 ips.).

Collection contains 1 radio commercial used during Miles' campaign for the 1982 Supreme Bench Judgeship election in Maryland.

MILLER, Dave.   1 sound tape reel (7 1/2 ips.).

Collection contains 2 radio commercials used during Miller's campaign for the 1980 State Representative election in District 88 in Pennsylvania. (Republican Party).

MILLER, Dean.   1 sound tape reel (7 1/2 ips.).

Collection contains 2 radio spots from Miller's 1968 campaign for State Tax Commissioner in North Dakota.   (Republican Party).

MILLER, Harold O. 1 videotape (2 in.). 21892576.

Collection contains 6 television commercials used during Miller's 1970 U.S. congressional election in Virginia. (Democratic Party).

MILLER, Jack R. (Jack Richard). 1916-. 3 film reel (16 mm.). 1 videotape (2 in.). 1 sound tape reel (7 1/2 ips.).   21421335.

Collection contains 1 television commercial used during Miller's campaign for the 1966 U.S. Senatorial election in Iowa. Includes 11 television commercials and 12 radio spots used during his 1972 re-election campaign. (Republican Party).

MILLER, John.   3 videocassettes (3/4 in.).

Collection contains 14 television spots from Miller's 1984 campaign for U.S. Congress in Washington and 9 television spots from the 1986 race for the same office.   (Republican Party).

MILLER, Kevin.   1 sound tape reel (7 1/2 ips.).

Collection contains 6 radio spots from Miller's 1982 campaign for Congress in District 6 in Virginia.   (Republican Party).

MILLER, Terry.   1 videocassette (3/4 in.).

Collection contains 4 television commercials used during Miller's 1982 campaign for Governor of Alaska.   (Republican Party).

MILLER, Thomas J. (Thomas John). 1944-. 1 sound tape reel (7 1/2 ips.). 1 videocassette (3/4 in.).   21979495.

Collection contains 3 radio commercials used during Miller's 1974 campaign for Attorney General and 2 television spots from his 1978 campaign and 1 television spot from his 1986 campaign for Attorney General in Iowa. (Democratic Party).

MILLER, Vern. 1 videotape (2 in.).   24260713.

Collection contains 1 television commercial used during Miller's 1972 campaign for Attorney General in Kansas. (Democratic Party).

MILLER, Zel. 1932-. 3 videocassettes (3/4 in.).   1 sound tape reel (7 1/2 ips.). 21920882.

Collection contains 2 radio spots from Miller's 1974 campaign for Governor in Georgia and 12 television spots from Miller's 1980 campaign for U.S. Senate. (Democratic Party).

MILLIKEN, John.   1 videocassette (3/4 in.).

Collection contains 4 television commercials used during Milliken's 1986 campaign for U.S. Congress in District 10 of Virginia. (Democratic Party).

MILLIKEN, William G. 1922-.   3 film reels (16 mm.). 5 videotapes (2 in.). 1 videocassette (3/4 in.).   21369956.

Collection contains 11 television commercials used during Milliken's 1970 campaign for Governor. Includes 26 television commercials used in his 1974 re-election campaign and 20 television commercials from his 1978 gubernatorial campaign; all elections in Michigan. (Republican Party).

MINK, Patsy.   1 videocassette (3/4 in.).

Collection contains 10 television commercials used during Mink's 1986 campaign for Governor of Hawaii. (Democratic Party).

MINNICK, Jack.   1 sound tape reel (7 1/2 ips.).

Collection contains 4 radio commercials used during Minnick's campaign for the 1980 Dauphin County Commissioner election in Pennsylvania. (Republican Party).

MINNICK, Bill.   1 sound tape reel (7 1/2 ips.).

Collection contains 1 radio commercial used during Minnick's 1972 campaign for Congress in District 105 in Pennsylvania.

MINSHALL, Bill. 1 film reel (16 mm.).

Collection contains 7 television commercials used during Minshall's campaign for the 1970 congressional election in District 23 of Ohio. (Republican Party).

MINTZ, Mel.   1 sound tape reel (7 1/2 ips.).

Collection contains 2 radio commercials used during Mintz's 1982 campaign for City Council in Baltimore in Maryland.

MITCHELL, Ed.   1 videocassette (3/4 in.).

Collection contains 2 television spots from Mitchell's 1980 primary campaign for Congress in Pennsylvania. (Democratic Party).

MITCHELL, Elizabeth "Libby."   2 videocassettes (3/4 in.).

Collection contains 8 television commercials used during Mitchell's 1984 campaign for U.S. Senate in Maine. (Democratic Party).

MITCHELL, Freemen D.   1 sound tape reel (7 1/2 ips.).

Collection contains 1 radio commercial used during Mitchell's 1972 campaign for a judgeship in Georgia.

MITCHELL, George.   1 sound tape reel (7 1/2 ips.).

Collection contains 1 radio commercial used during Mitchell's campaign for the 1982 U.S. Senate election in Maine.   (Democratic Party).

MITCHELL, Parrin J. 1922 -.   1 sound tape reel (7 1/2 ips.).

Collection contains 2 radio spots from Mitchell's 1982 campaign and 1 radio spot from his 1984 campaign for U.S. Congress in District 7 of Maryland.   (Democratic Party).

MITCHEM, Hinton. 3 videotapes (2 in.).   24260725.

Collection contains 21 television commercials used during Mitchem's 1986 campaign for Lt. Governor in Alabama. (Democratic Party).

MITTERRAND, François.   3 videocassettes (3/4 in.).

Collection contains the television debate between Mitterrand and Valerie Giscard d'Estaing in the 1981 presidential campaign in France.   (Socialist Party).

MIZE, Chester L. 1917-. 4 videotapes (2 in.). 21248146.

Collection contains 4 television commercials used during Mize' campaign for the 1970 U.S. congressional election in Kansas. (Republican Party).

MOAKLEY, John Joseph. 3 videotapes (2 in.). 21244014.

Collection contains 3 television commercials used during Moakley's campaign for the 1972 U.S. congressional election in Massachusetts. (Independent Party).

MOCHARY, Mary.   2 videocassettes (3/4 in.).

Collection contains 5 television commercials used during Mochary's 1984 campaign for U.S. Senate in New Jersey. (Republican Party).

MOFFETT, Toby. 2 videocassettes (3/4 in.).. 1 sound tape reel (7 1/2 ips.).

Collection contains 6 television commercials and 5 radio commercials used during Moffett's 1982 campaign for U.S. Senate in Connecticut. (Democratic Party).

MOLLOHAN, Alan. 2 videocassettes (3/4 in.).

Collection contains 7 television commercials used during Mollohan's 1984 campaign for U.S. Congress in District 1 of West Virginia. (Democratic Party).

This commercial was used by Toby Moffett in Connecticut.

MONDALE, Walter F. 1928-. 25 videocassettes (3/4 in.). 2 film reels (16 mm.). 2 sound tape reels (3 3/4 ips.). 27 videotapes (2 in.). 21368955.

Collection contains 18 television commercials and 13 radio commercials used during Mondale's campaign for the 1972 U.S. Senate election in Minnesota. Includes 89 television commercials used during his 1984 presidential campaign. Includes his acceptance speech for vice-president at the Democratic National Convention in 1980. (Democratic Party).

MONIER, Bob. 1 sound tape reel (7 1/2 ips.).

Collection contains 17 radio commercials used during Monier's 1982 campaign for Governor in New Hampshire. (Republican Party).

MONRONEY, A.S. Mike. 1902-. 3 videotapes (2 in.). 21186338.

Collection contains 10 television commercials used during Monroney's 1968 campaign for U.S. Senate in Oklahoma. (Democratic Party).

MONTGOMERY, Wayne. 1 film reel (16 mm.). 1 sound tape reel (7 1/2 ips.). 21741158.

Collection contains 4 television commercials used during Montgomery's 1962 campaign for U.S. Congress in Montana and 4 radio spots from his 1968 campaign for the same office. (Republican Party).

MOODY, Blair, Jr. 1 videocassette (3/4 in.). 24260885.

Collection contains 2 television commercials used during Moody's 1982 campaign for a judgeship in Michigan.

MOODY, Jim. 1 sound tape reel (7 1/2 ips.).

Collection contains 6 radio commercials used during Moody's campaign for the 1982 congressional election in District 5 in Wisconsin. (Democratic Party).

MOORE, Arch A. 3 film reels (16 mm.2). 1 videocassette (3/4 in.). 21369713.

Collection contains 19 television commercials used during Moore's campaign for the 1972 gubernatorial election in West Virginia and 8 television spots from his 1980 campaign for Governor. (Republican Party).

MOORE, Dennis. 2 videocassettes (3/4 in.).

Collection contains 3 television commercials used during Moore's 1986 campaign for Attorney General of Kansas. (Democratic Party).

MOORE, Donald Page. 1 film reel (16 mm.). 24263276.

Collection contains 1 television commercial used during Moore's 1972 campaign for Attorney General in Illinois. (Democratic Party).

MOORE, Ed. 1 videocassette (3/4 in.).

Collection contains 2 television commercials used during Moore's 1982 campaign for U.S. Congress in District 6 of Oklahoma. (Republican Party).

MOORE, Henson. 13 videocassettes (3/4 in. & 1/2 in.).

Collection contains 51 television commercials used during Moore's 1986 campaign for U.S. Senate in Louisiana. (Republican Party).

MOORE, Preston J. (Preston Jay). 3 videotapes (2 in.). 21256337.

Collection contains 5 television commercials used during Moore's campaign for the 1966 gubernatorial election in Oklahoma. (Democratic Party).

MOORE, Schmitt. 1 videotape (2 in.). 24260923.

Collection contains 1 television commercial used during Moore's campaign for a 1986 school related election in Alabama.

MOORE, Warfield. 1 film reel (16 mm.). 24260918.

Collection contains 1 television commercial used during Moore's 1972 campaign for a judgeship in Michigan.

MOORHEAD, Carlos. 1 sound tape reel (7 1/2 ips.).

Collection contains 1 radio commercial used during Moorhead's campaign for the 1980 congressional election in District 22 in California. (Republican Party).

MOORISON, Clarence Christopher. 1939-. 1 sound tape reel (7 1/2 ips.). 22198953.

Collection contains 5 radio commercials used during Morrison's 1979 campaign for a judgeship in Dauphin County, Pennsylvania. (Republican Party).

MORAN, John. 1 sound tape reel. (7 1/2 ips.).

Collection contains 1 radio commercial used during Moran's 1982 campaign for a local office in Nevada.

MORELLA, Connie. 4 videocassettes (3/4 in. & 1/2 in.).

Collection contains 8 television commercials used during Morella's 1986 campaign for U.S. Congress in District 8 of Maryland. (Republican Party).

MORGAN, P.J. 1 videotape (2 in.). 21191447.

Collection contains 2 television commercials used during Morgan's campaign for the 1969 City Council in Nebraska. (Republican Party).

MORGAN, Robert Burren. 1925-. 2 film reels (16 mm.) and 1 videotape (2 in.). 21274745.

Collection contains 31 television commercials used during Morgan's campaign for Attorney General election and for U.S. Senate in North Carolina. (Democratic Party).

MORRIS, Bill. 1 sound tape reel (7 1/2 ips.).

Collection contains 1 radio spot from Morris' campaign for Mayor of Memphis.

MORRIS, Melanie. 1 videocassette (3/4 in.).

Collection contains 1 television commercial used during Morris' campaign for the 1982 County Clerk election in Tennessee.

MORRIS, Vern.   1 sound tape reel (7 1/2 ips.).

Collection contains 3 radio commercials from Morris' campaign for local office in Idaho.

MORRIS, William Shelton. 1919-. 2 videotapes (2 in.). 21416184.

Collection contains 17 television commercials used during Morris' campaign for the 1972 gubernatorial election in Missouri. (Democratic Party).

MORRISON, Bruce.   7 videocassette (3/4 in.).

Collection contains 5 television commercials used during Morrison's 1982 campaign, 12 television spots from his 1984 campaign, and 7 television spots from his 1986 campaign for U.S. Congress in District 3 of Connecticut.   (Democratic Party).

MORSE, Wayne L. (Wayne Lyman), 1900-1974.   2 film reels (16 mm.). 2 sound tape reels (3 3/4 & 7 1/2 ips.).   21416008.

Collection contains 2 television commercials and 53 radio spots used during Morse's 1968 campaign for U.S. Senate in Oregon. (Democratic Party).

MORTON, Warren. 1 videocassette (3/4 in.).   24263287.

Collection contains 3 television commercial used during Morton's campaign for the 1982 gubernatorial election in Wyoming. (Republican Party).

MOSEE, Dan. 1 videocassette (3/4 in.). 24260926.

Collection contains 2 television commercials used during Mosee's 1982 campaign for Metropolitan Service District Executive in Oregon.

MOSER, William R. 1 videotape (2 in.).

Collection contains 1 television commercial used during Moser's 1980 campaign for a judgeship in Wisconsin.

MOSHOFSKY, Bill. 2 videocassettes (3/4 in.).   24260929.

Collection contains 10 television commercials used during Moshofsky's 1982 and 7 television spots from his 1984 campaign for U.S. Congress in District 1 of Oregon. (Republican Party).

MOSS, Frank.   1 sound tape reel (7 1/2 ips.).

Collection contains 34 radio spots from Moss' 1970 campaign for U.S. Senate in Utah.   (Democratic Party).

MOSS, John E. (John Emerson), 1915-. 1 videotape (2 in.). 1 videocassette (3/4 in.). 22226299.

Collection contains 4 television commercials used during Moss' 1972 campaign for the U.S. congressional in District 3 in California. (Democratic Party).

MOTTL, Ron, Sr. 1 videocassette (3/4 in.).

Collection contains 2 television commercials used during Mottl's 1984 campaign for State Senate in Ohio. (Democratic Party).

MOTTL, Ron, Jr. 1 sound tape reel (7 1/2 ips.).

Collection contains 1 radio commercial used during Mottl's campaign for the 1980 State Senate election in Ohio. (Democratic Party).

MOUNTAIN, Barbara. 3 videotapes (2 in.). 24260933.

Collection contains 4 television commercials used during Mountain's campaign for a 1986 judgeship in Alabama.

MOWERY, Jean. 1 videocassette (3/4 in.). 24260936.

Collection contains 1 television commercial used during Mowery's campaign for the 1982 congressional election in District 16 of Pennsylvania. (Democratic Party).

MOYER, Thomas. 3 videotapes (1 in.). 24260938.

Collection contains 6 television commercials used during Moyer's campaign for a 1986 judgeship in Ohio. (Republican Party).

MOYLAN, Charles E. 1 videotape (2 in.). 21348134.

Collection contains 1 television commercial used during Moylan's campaign for the 1966 Baltimore City State's Attorney in Maryland.

MOYNIHAN, Daniel Patrick. 4 videotapes (2 in.). 1 videocassette (3/4 in.). 24260941.

Collection contains 5 television commercials used during Moynihan's 1976 campaign and 12 television spots from his 1982 campaign for U.S. Senate in New York. (Democratic Party).

MULCAHEY, Richard Thomas. 1935-. 2 videotape (2 in.). 22245577.

Collection contains 5 television commercials used during Mulcahey's 1978 re-election campaign for State Representative in Illinois. (Democratic Party).

MURKOWSKI, Frank. 1 videocassette (1/2 in.).

Collection contains
1 television commer-
cial used during
Murkowski's 1986
campaign for U.S.
Senate in Arkansas.
(Republican Party).

**MURPHY, Dan. 2
videocassettes (3/4
in.).**

Collection contains 2
television commercials
used during Murphy's
1986 primary campaign
for Governor of
Michigan. (Republican
Party).

Frank Murkowski utilized this spot in his 1986 Senate campaign in Arkansas.

MURPHY, Evelyn. 4 videocassettes (3/4 in.). 24280863.

Collection contains 1 television commercial from Murphy's 1982
campaign for Lt. Governor in Massachusetts and 2 television spots
from her 1986 campaign for the same office. (Democratic Party).

MURPHY, George. 1902-. 2 videotapes (2 in.). 21248153.

Collection contains 6 television commercials used during Murphy's
1970 campaign for U.S. Senate in California. (Republican Party).

MURPHY, Jim. 1 sound tape reel (7 1/2 ips.).

Collection contains 1 radio spot from Murphy's campaign for
Secretary of Agriculture in Iowa. (Democratic Party).

MURPHY, Robert. 1 videocassette (3/4 in.).

Collection contains 1 television commercial used during Murphy's
1982 campaign for a judgeship in Tennessee.

MURPHY, William H. 1 sound tape reel. (7 1/2 ips.).

Collection contains 2 radio commercials used during Goslee's 1983
campaign for Mayor in Maryland. (Democratic Party).

MURRAY, Walter J. 1 film reel (16 mm.). 24280872.

Collection contains 1 television commercial used during Murray's
campaign for a 1972 judgeship election in Michigan.

MURRAY, William Gordon. 1903-. 2 film reels (16 mm.). 21416113.

Collection contains 2 television commercials used during Murray's 1966 campaign for Governor in Iowa. (Republican Party).

MUSKIE, Edmund S. 1914-. 4 film reels (16 mm.). 44 videotapes (2 in.). 1 videocassette (3/4 in.). 1 sound tape reel (7 1/2 ips.). 21369716.

Collection contains 14 television commercials used during Muskie's re-election 1970 campaign for U.S. Senate in Maine and 16 television commercials used in his 1976 re-election campaign. Includes 70 television commercials used in his campaign for the 1972 presidential election (includes the primary and Muskie as the vice-presidential candidate under Humphrey). (Democratic Party).

MUTZ, John. 1 videocassette (3/4 in.).

Collection contains 3 television commercials used during Mutz's 1984 campaign for Lt. Governor of Indiana. (Republican Party).

MYERS, Robert. 1 sound tape reel (7 1/2 ips.).

Collection contains 5 radio spots from Myers' 1979 campaign for a judgeship in Cumberland County. (Democratic Party).

MYERS, Dave. 1 sound tape reel (7 1/2 ips.).

Collection contains 1 radio spot from Myers' 1979 campaign for State Assemblyman in Pennsylvania. (Democratic Party).

MYLANDER, Elwood. 1 sound tape reel (7 1/2 ips.).

Collection contains 1 radio spot from Mylander's campaign for local office in Idaho.

MYSE, Gordon. 1 videotape (2 in.). 22441647.

Collection contains 2 television commercials used during Myse' campaign for the 1983 Supreme Court election in Wisconsin.

NAHRA, Joseph. 2 videocassettes (3/4 in.). 24280879.

Collection contains 7 television spots from Nahra's 1980 campaign for U.S. Congress in District 22 and 1 television commercial used during his 1982 campaign a judgeship in Ohio. (Republican Party).

NANCE, Edward. 1 videocassette (3/4 in.). 24280889.

Collection contains 1 television commercial used during Nance's campaign for a 1982 judgeship in Michigan.

NEAL, Joe. 1 film reel (16 mm.). 21892548.

Collection contains 3 television commercials used during Neal's campaign for the 1972 U.S. congressional election in West Virginia. (Republican Party).

NEAL, Steve. 1 videocassette (3/4 in.).

Collection contains 2 television commercials used during Neal's 1986 campaign for U.S. Congress in District 5 of North Carolina. (Democratic Party).

NEALL, Bob. 3 videocassettes (3/4 in.).

Collection contains 2 television commercials used during Neall's 1986 campaign for U.S. Congress in District 4 of Maryland. (Republican Party).

NEDERLANDER, Robert E. 1933-. 1 film reel (16 mm.). 21474888.

Collection contains 1 television commercial used during Neder- lander's campaign for the 1976 State Representative election in Michigan. (Democratic Party).

NEFF, Richard. 1 sound tape reel (7 1/2 ips.).

Collection contains 3 radio commercials used during Neff's campaign for the 1980 Cuyahoga County Engineer election in Ohio. (Democratic Party).

NEIL, Ben. 1 sound tape reel. (7 1/2 ips.).

Collection contains 1 radio commercial used during Neil's 1982 campaign for local office in Maryland. (Democratic Party).

NELSON, Gaylord Anton. 1916-. 6 videotapes (2 in.) and 1 film reel (16 mm.). 4 videocassettes (3/4 in.). 21416256.

Collection contains 40 television commercials used during Nelson's 1968, 1974, and 1980 campaigns for U.S. Senate in Wisconsin. (Democratic Party).

NESBITT, Charles R. 1921-. 2 videotapes (2 in.). 21319751.

Collection contains 8 television commercials used during Nesbitt's 1972 campaign for U.S. Senate in Oklahoma. (Democratic Party).

NEU, Arthur A. (Arthur Alan). 1933-. 1 sound tape reel (7 1/2 ips.).

Collection contains 1 radio commercial used during Neu's 1972 campaign for Lt. Governor in Iowa. (Republican Party).

NEVIN, Richard.   1 sound tape reel (7 1/2 ips).

Collection contains 6 radio spots from Nevin's 1970 campaign for state office in California.

NEVIUS, Jack. 1 film reel (16 mm.).   24280903.

Collection contains 3 television commercials used during Nevius' 1972 campaign for U.S. Congress in the District of Columbia.

NEWMAN, Don Melvin. 1923-.   5 videotapes (2 in.).   21175207.

Collection contains 5 television commercials used during Newman's campaign for the 1970 U.S. congressional election, District 3, in Indiana. (Republican Party).

NICHOLAS, Jeff.   1 sound tape reel (7 1/2 ips.).

Collection contains 1 radio commercial used during Nicholas' 1982 campaign for State House in Iowa.   (Republican Party).

NICHOLS, Bill.   1 videocassette (3/4 in.).

Collection contains 2 television spots from Nichols' 1986 campaign for Congress in Alabama.   (Democratic Party).

NICHOLS, John Francis. 1918-.   2 film reels (16 mm.). 21538677.

Collection contains 7 television commercials used during Nichols' 1973 campaign for Mayor in Detroit, Michigan.

NICHOLSON, George. 1 videotape (2 in.).   1 videocassette (3/4 in.).

Collection contains 1 television commercial used during Nicholson's 1982 campaign and 2 television spots from his 1986 campaign for Attorney General in California.   (Republican Party).

NICKINELLO, Lou. 1 videocassette (3/4 in.).   24280915.

Collection contains 1 television commercial used during Nickinello's 1982 campaign for Lt. Governor in Massachusetts. (Democratic Party).

NICKLES, Don. 4 videotapes (2 in.). 8 videocassette (3/4 in.). 24367885.

Collection contains 15 television commercials used during Nickles' campaign for the 1980 U.S. Senate election in Oklahoma and 23 television commercials from his 1986 re-election campaign for the same office.   Also includes 1 television spot supporting Nickles produced by the Fund for a Conservative Majority. (Republican Party).

NIELSON, Howard. 1 videocassette (3/4 in.).

Collection contains 3 television commercials used during Nielson's 1982 campaign for U.S. Congress in District 3 of Utah. (Republican Party).

NIGH, Bill. 1 videocassette (3/4 in.).

Collection contains 3 television commercials used during Nigh's 1974 campaign for Corporation Commissioner in Oklahoma.

NIGH, George. 1927-. 6 videotape (2 in.). 2 videocassette (3/4 in.). 1 sound tape reel (7 1/2 ips.). 21892559.

Collection contains 13 television commercials and 12 radio commercials used during Nigh's campaign for the 1978 gubernatorial election in Oklahoma and 19 television commercials used in his 1982 re-election campaign. (Democratic Party).

NIXON, Richard M. (Richard Milhouse). 1913-. 15 film reels (16 mm.), 15 videocassettes (3/4 in.). 4 videotapes (2 in.). 1 sound tape reel (3/4 ips.). 21276366.

Collection contains 1 television item used during Nixon's campaign for the 1952 vice-presidential position with Eisenhower, 57 television commercials used during Nixon's campaign for the 1960 presidential election, 8 television commercials used during his campaign for the 1962 gubernatorial election in California, 76 television commercials used in his campaign for the 1968 presiden-

Nixon spoke directly to the people in spots like this one from his 1960 presidential campaign.

tial election, and 40 television and 3 radio commercials used in his 1972 re-election campaign. The collection also includes a series of 9 television spots from the 1960 campaign which featured Henry Cabot Lodge as the vice-presidential nominee. The archive also holds copies of the 1952 "Checkers" speech and the 1960 presidential debates between Kennedy and Nixon. (Republican Party).

NOBLE, Ed.   2 videocassettes (3/4 in.).

Collection contains 16 television commercials used in Noble's 1980 primary campaign for U.S. Senate in Oklahoma.   (Democratic Party).

NOEL, Phillip W. 2 film reels (16 mm.). 21431722.

Collection contains 11 television commercials used during Noel's campaign for the 1974 gubernatorial election in Rhode Island. (Democratic Party).

NORLAND, Lowell.   1 videocassette (3/4 in.).

Collection contains 6 television commercials used during Norland's 1986 primary campaign for U.S. Congress in District 3 of Iowa.   (Democratic Party).

NORQUIST, John.   1 videocassette (3/4 in.).

Collection contains 2 television commercials used during Norquist's 1986 campaign in Wisconsin.   (Democratic Party).

NORRIS, Wayne.   1 videocassette (3/4 in.).

Collection contains 1 television commercial used during Norris' 1986 campaign for U.S. Congress in California.

NORTH, Ernie.   1 videocassette (3/4 in.).

Collection contains 1 television commercial used during North's 1986 campaign for State Senate in Michigan.   (Republican Party).

NORTH, Steve. 1 videocassette (3/4 in.).

Collection contains 6 television commercials used during North's campaign for the 1982 District Attorney election in Tennessee.

NORTHERN, Eugene E. 1906-.   1 sound tape reel (7 1/2 ips.). 21929993.

Collection contains 9 television commercials used during Northern's campaign for the 1968 U.S. congressional election in Missouri. (Republican Party).

NORTON, Mike.   1 videocassette (3/4 in.).

Collection contains 1 television commercial used during Norton's 1986 campaign for U.S. Congress in District 2 of Colorado. (Republican Party).

202

NUNN, Louie B. 2 film reels (16 mm.). 24280931.

Collection contains 9 television commercials used during Nunn's campaign for the 1967 gubernatorial election and 16 television commercials used during Nunn's campaign for the U.S. Senate election in Kentucky. (Republican Party).

O'BRIEN, Annabelle Clement. 1 videocassette (3/4 in.).

Collection contains 2 television commercials used during O'Brien's 1982 primary campaign for Governor of Tennessee. (Democratic Party).

O'BRIEN, Billy. 2 videotapes (2 in.).

Collection contains 4 television spots from O'Brien's 1976 campaign for Congress in District 4 of Texas. (Democratic Party).

O'BRIEN, Buch. 1 videocassette (3/4 in.).

Collection contains 3 television commercials used during O'Brien's 1986 campaign for U.S. Congress in District 2 of Montana. (Democratic Party).

O'BRIEN, Ed. 1 videotape (2 in.). 21921194.

Collection consists of 1 television commercial used during O'Brien's campaign for the 1972 Governor's counselor election in Massachusetts. (Democratic Party).

O'BRIEN, George. 1 sound tape reel. (7 1/2 ips.).

Collection contains 5 radio commercials from O'Brien's 1982 campaign for Congress in District 4 in Illinois. (Republican Party).

O'CALLAGHAN, Mike. 1 videotape (2 in.). 21348121.

Collection contains 6 television commercials used during O'Callaghan's campaign for the 1974 gubernatorial election in Nevada. (Democratic Party).

O'CONNELL, Jack. 2 videotapes (1 in.). 3 videocassettes (3/4 in.). 24280938.

Collection contains 2 television commercials used during O'Connell's campaign for a 1986 California election. Also includes 8 television spots from his 1984 campaign for Assemblyman in California. (Democratic Party).

O'CONNOR, Frank Daniel, 1909- . 1 film reel (16 mm.). 21479133.
Collection consists of 1 television commercial used during O'Connor's campaign for the 1966 gubernatorial election in New York. (Democratic Party).

O'CONNOR, Mike. 1 videocassette (3/4 in.).
Collection contains 1 television spot for O'Connor's 1980 campaign for State Senate in Minnesota.

O'CONNOR, Sandra Day, 1930- . 1 videotape (2 in.). 1 sound tape reel (7 1/2 ips.). 21369724.
Collection contains 1 television commercial used during O'Connor's 1974 campaign General Attorney election in Maryland. Also includes 1 radio spot for her 1982 campaign. (Republican Party).

O'DONNELL, Terrence. 1 videotape (2 in.).
Collection contains 1 television commercial used during O'Donnell's campaign for a 1978 judgeship in Ohio.

O'DWYER, Paul. 7 videotapes (2 in.). 10 sound tape reels (7 1/2 ips.).
Collection contains 7 television spots and 10 radio spots from O'Dwyer's campaigns for state office in New York.

O'FLYNN, James. 1 sound tape reel (7 1/2 ips.).
Collection contains 1 radio commercial used during O'Flynn's campaign for the 1982 County Sheriff election in Hillsboro County, New Hampshire. (Republican Party).

O'HARA, James G. 3 videotapes (2 in.). 24280954.
Collection contains 5 television commercials used during O'Hara's campaign for the 1976 U.S. Senate election in Michigan. (Democratic Party).

O'KONSKI, Alvin E. (Alvin Edward), 1904-1987. 2 videotapes (2 in.). 22164901.
Collection contains 2 television commercials used during O'Konski's campaign for the 1972 U.S. congressional election in the 10th District, in Wisconsin. (Republican Party).

O'MALLEY, Thomas D. 2 videotapes (2 in.). 21479066.
Collection contains 3 television spots from O'Malley's 1970 campaign for State Treasurer in Florida. (Democratic Party).

O'NEAL, Dave. 4 videotapes (2 in.). 5 videocassettes (3/4 in.). 1 sound tape reel (7 1/2 ips). 2436784B.
Collection contains 17 television and 7 radio commercials used during O'Neal's campaign for the 1980 U.S. Senate election in Illinois. (Republican Party)

O'NEILL, Cathy. 1 videocassette (3/4 in.).
Collection contains 9 television commercials used during O'Neill's 1974 campaign for Secretary of State in California. (Democratic Party).

O'NEILL, Tom. 1 videotape (2 in.).
Collection contains 1 television spot from O'Neill's 1978 campaign for Lt. Governor in Massachusetts. (Democratic Party).

O'NEILL, William. 5 videocassettes (3/4 in.).
Collection contains 15 television commercials used during O'Neill's 1982 campaign for Governor of Connecticut and 26 television commercials from his 1986 re-election campaign for the same office. (Democratic Party).

O'ROURKE, Andrew. 2 videocassettes (3/4 in.).
Collection contains 13 television spots from O'Rourke's 1986 campaign for Governor of New York. (Republican Party).

O'ROURKE, John. 1 videocassette (3/4 in.).
Collection contains 4 television commercials from O'Rourke's 1986 campaign for local office in Baltimore, Maryland.

OBERSTAR, Jim. 1 videocassette (3/4 in.).
Collection contains 4 television commercials used during Oberstar's 1986 campaign for U.S. Congress in District 8 of Minnesota. (Democratic Party).

OBEY, David R. 2 film reels (16 mm.). 1 videocassette (3/4 in.). 2141608l.
Collection contains television commercials used during Obey's campaigns for the 1970, 1976, and 1980 U.S. congressional elections in Wisconsin. (Democratic Party).

OGILVIE, Richard. 2 film reels (16 mm.). 2428094J.
Collection contains 21 television commercials used during Ogilvie's campaign for the 1972 gubernatorial election in Illinois. (Republican Party).

OLIN, Jim.   1 videocassette (3/4 in.).
Collection contains 5 television commercials used during Olin's 1984 campaign for U.S. Congress in District 6 of Virginia and 1 television spot from his 1986 re-election campaign to the same office.   (Democratic Party).

OLIN, Jim.   1 sound tape reel (7 1/2 ips.).
Collection contains 5 radio commercials used during Olin's campaign for the 1982 congressional election in District 6 in Virginia.   (Democratic Party).

OLSEN, Arnold.   1 film reel (16 mm.).
Collection contains 3 television spots from Olsen's 1970 campaign for U.S. Congress in District 1 of Montana.   (Democratic Party).

OLSEN, Leslie O.   1 sound tape reel (7 1/2 ips.).   2216864.
Collection contains 8 radio commercials used during Olsen's campaign for the 1970 U.S. congressional election in Missouri.   (Republican Party).

OLSON, Alan.   1 sound tape reel (7 1/2 ips.).
Collection contains 1 radio commercial used during Olson's campaign for the 1972 Attorney General election in North Dakota.   (Republican Party).

OLSON, Jack B..   24 videotapes (2 in.).   2428059.
Collection contains 24 television commercials used during Olson's campaign for the 1970 gubernatorial election in Wisconsin.   (Republican Party).

OLSON, Tom.   1 videotape (2 in.).
Collection contains 1 television commercial used during Olson's campaign for 1980 County Auditor in Illinois.

Jack Olson hoped appearing with President Nixon would help his election chances in this spot from the 1970 Wisconsin gubernatorial race.

OLVER, John Walter. 1936-. 1 videotape (2 in.). 21254547.

Collection contains 1 television spot from Olver's 1972 campaign for State Senate in Massachusetts. (Democratic Party).

OMDAHL, Lloyd B. 2 videotapes (2 in.). 24253376.

Collection contains 2 television commercials used during Omdahl's campaign for the 1976 congressional election in North Dakota. (Democratic Party).

ORLINSKY, Walter. 1 videocassette (3/4 in.).

Collection contains 1 television commercial used for Orlinsky's 1978 campaign for Governor of Maryland. (Democratic Party).

ORR, Robert. 1 sound tape reel (7 1/2 ips.).

Collection contains 6 radio commercials used during Orr's campaign for the 1980 gubernatorial election in Indiana. (Republican Party).

ORR, Bob. 3 videocassettes (3/4 in.).

Collection contains 20 television spots from Orr's 1980 campaign for Governor of Indiana and 3 television commercials from his 1984 re-election campaign. (Republican Party).

ORR, Kay. 4 videocassettes (3/4 in.).

Collection contains 19 television commercials used during Orr's 1986 campaign for Governor of Nebraska. (Republican Party).

OSTER, Jon. 1 videocassette (3/4 in.).

Collection contains 1 commercial used during Oster's 1978 campaign for Attorney General of Maryland. (Democratic Party).

OTTERBACHER, John Robert. 1942-. 1 videotape (2 in.). 21270303.

Collection contains 1 television commercial used during Otterbacher's 1972 campaign for State Senate in Michigan. (Democratic Party).

OWEN, David Carroll. 2 videotapes (2 in.). 21248139.

Collection contains 2 television commercials used during Owen's 1972 campaign for Lt. Governor in Kansas. (Republican Party).

OWENS, Jack. 1 videocassette (3/4 in.).

Collection contains 5 television commercials used during Owens' 1986 campaign for Sheriff in Shelby County, Tennessee.

OWENS, Wayne.   1 videocassette (3/4 in.).

Collection contains 10 television commercials used during Owens' 1986 campaign for U.S. Congress in District 2 of Vermont. (Democratic Party).

PACJIK, Steve.   2 videocassettes (3/4 in.).

Collection contains 15 television commercials used during Pacjik's 1986 campaign for Governor of Florida.   (Democratic Party).

PACKARD, George. 1 videotape (2 in.). 24281937.

Collection contains 1 television commercial used during Packard's campaign for the 1976 U.S. Senate election in Pennsylvania.

PACKWOOD, Robert.   9 videocassettes (3/4 in.).

Collection contains 12 television commercials used during Packwood's 1974 and 1980 campaigns for U.S. Senate in Oregon. Also includes 23 television spots from his 1986 re-election campaign for the same office.   (Republican Party).

PALLADERO, Don.   1 videotape (2 in.).

Collection contains 1 television spot from Palladero's campaign for U.S. Congress in District 116 of Florida.   (Democratic Party).

PALLADINO, Madaline. 1924-. 1 sound tape reel (7 1/2 ips.). 22446435.

Collection contains 3 radio commercials used during Palladino's 1979 campaign for a judgeship in Pennsylvania.

PALMER, Chuck.   1 sound tape reel (7 1/2 ips.).

Collection contains 2 radio commercials from Palmer's campaign for State Representative in Idaho.   (Republican Party).

PALMER, Lu.   1 sound tape reel.   (7 1/2 ips.).

Collection contains 1 radio commercial used during Palmer's 1983 congressional campaign in District 1 in Illinois. (Democratic Party).

PANETTA, Leon.   3 videocassettes (3/4 in.).

Collection contains 4 television commercials used by Panetta in his 1978 campaign and 7 television spots used in his 1984 campaign for U.S. Congress in District 16 of California. (Democratic Party).

PAPPAS, Pete. 1927-. 1 sound tape reel (7 1/2 ips.). 22155917.

Collection contains 2 radio commercials used during Pappas'
campaign for the 1972 State Representative election in Illinois.
(Republican Party).

PARINNO, Frank M. 1 videotape (2 in.).   24281963.

Collection contains 1 television commercial used during Parinno's
campaign for the 1978 State Senate election in Illinois.

PARKER, Barry. 1 sound tape reel (7 1/2 ips.).

Collection contains 1 radio commercial used during Parker's
campaign for the 1981 gubernatorial election in New Jersey.
(Republican Party).

PARKER, George. 1 film reel (16 mm.).   24281950.

Collection contains 2 television commercials used during Parker's
campaign for the 1972 State Treasurer election in Missouri.
(Republican Party).

PARKER, Kathleen. 1 sound tape reel (7 1/2 ips.).

Collection contains 3 radio commercials used during Parker's
campaign for a 1982 local office election in Cook County,
Illinois.

PARKER, Mary Evelyn. 1 videocassette (3/4 in.).

Collection contains 2 television spots from Parker's 1980
campaign for State Treasurer in Louisiana. (Democratic Party).

PARRIS, Stanford E. 1929-. 2 videocassettes (3/4 in.). 22226348.

Collection contains 14 television commercials used during Parris'
1980 and 1982 campaigns for U.S. Congress in the 8th District, in
Virginia. (Republican Party).

PARRISH, Clarence. 3 videotapes (2 in.).

Collection contains 2 television commercials used during
Parrish's 1979 campaign for Circuit Court Judge in Branch 34 of
Wisconsin. Includes 1 television commercial used in Parrish's
1981 judicial election in Wisconsin.

PARROT, James. 1 sound tape reel (7 1/2 ips.).

Collection contains 3 radio commercials used during Parrot's 1982
campaign for Supreme Bench Judge in Baltimore, Maryland.

PASCAL, Robert. 1 sound tape reel (7 1/2 ips.).

Collection contains 3 radio commercials used during Pascal's campaign for the 1982 gubernatorial election in Maryland. (Republican Party).

PASTORE, John O. (John Orlando), 1907-. 6 videotapes (2 in.). 21186309.

Collection contains 11 television commercials used during Pastore's 1970 campaign for U.S. Senate in Rhode Island. (Democratic Party).

PATCHETT, Randy. 3 videocassettes (3/4 in.).

Collection contains 2 television commercials used during Patchett's 1984 campaign for U.S. Congress in Illinois and 3 television commercials from his 1986 campaign for the same office. (Republican Party).

PATSQUORIS, Nick. 1 sound tape reel (7 1/2 ips.). 22256852.

Collection contains 2 radio commercials used during Patsquoris' 1978 campaign for Supervisor in Los Angeles, California.

PATTERSON, Brooks. 2 videocassettes (3/4 in.). 24281975.

Collection contains 15 television commercials used during Patterson's campaign for the 1982 gubernatorial election in Michigan. (Republican Party).

PATTERSON, Liz. 1 videocassette (3/4 in.).

Collection contains 8 television commercials used during Patterson's 1986 campaign for U.S. Congress in District 4 of South Carolina. (Democratic Party).

PAUKEN, Tom. 1 videocassette (3/4 in.).

Collection contains 1 television commercial for Pauken's 1980 campaign for U.S. Congress in District 5 of Texas. (Republican Party).

PAULIE, Ruth. 1 sound tape reel (7 1/2 ips).

Collection contains 2 radio spots from Paulie's campaign for local office in Idaho.

PAULUS, Norma.   3 videocassettes (3/4 in. & 1/2 in.).

Collection contains 18 television commercials used during Paulus' 1986 campaign for Governor of Oregon. (Republican Party).

PAXTON, Floyd. 1 videocassette (3/4 in.).

Collection contains 2 television commercials used during Paxton's 1974 campaign for Congress in District 4 of Washington. (Republican Party).

This spot was used by Norma Paulus in her 1986 campaign for Governor of Oregon.

PEACE, Steve. 1 videotape (1 in.).   24281988.

Collection contains 1 television commercial used during Peace's campaign for the 1986 State House election in California.

PEARCY, Noble.   3 videotapes (2 in.). 1 sound tape reel (7 1/2 ips.).   21421255.

Collection contains 2 radio commercials and 3 television commercials used during Pearcy's 1970 campaign for County Prosecutor's in Indiana. (Republican Party).

PEARSON, James. 1 videotape (2 in.).   24281995.

Collection contains 3 television commercials used during Pearson's campaign for the 1972 U.S. Senate election in Kansas. (Republican Party).

PEASE, Don. 1 videocassette (3/4 in.).

Collection contains 3 television commercials used during Pease's 1986 campaign for U.S. Congress in Ohio. (Democratic Party).

PECK, Carey. 1 sound tape reel (7 1/2 ips.).

Collection contains 1 radio commercial used during Peck's campaign for the 1980 congressional election in District 27 in California. (Democratic Party).

PELL, Claiborne, 1918-. 2 film reels (16 mm.). 1 videocassette (3/4 in.). 215387400.

Collection contains 9 television commercials used during Pell's 1972 campaign for U.S. Senate in Rhode Island. Also contains 2 television spots from his 1984 re-election campaign. (Democratic Party).

PENDELL, George. 1 videotape (2 in.). 22441635.

Collection contains 2 television commercials used during Pendell's campaign for the 1974 associate District judgeship election in Oklahoma.

PENNY, Tim. 1 videocassette (3/4 in.).

Collection contains 3 television commercials used during Penny's 1984 campaign for U.S. Congress in Minnesota.

PEPINIO, Leo. 1 sound tape reel (7 1/2 ips.).

Collection contains 7 radio commercials used during Pepinio's 1982 campaign for State Senate District 18 in New Hampshire. (Republican Party).

PERCY, Charles H. 1919-. 1 sound tape reel (7 1/2 ips.). 2 film reels (16 mm.). 16 videotapes (2 in.). 9 videocassettes (3/4 in.). 21382676.

Collection contains 1 television commercial used during Percy's 1964 gubernatorial campaign, 7 television commercials used during his campaign for the 1972 U.S. Senate election, 26 television and 9 radio commercials used in his 1978 re-election campaign, 17 television commercials used in his 1984 re-election campaign; all in Illinois. Also includes a series of anti-Percy commercials sponsored by Michael Goland in the 1984 U.S. Senate campaign. (Republican Party).

Charles Percy used this spot in his 1972 U.S. Senate campaign in Illinois.

PERKINS, Carl "Chris" C.   1 videocassette (3/4 in.).

Collection contains 4 television commercials used during Perkins' 1986 campaign for U.S. Congress in District 7 of Kentucky. (Democratic Party).

PERKINS, Jane. 2 videotapes (2 in.).   24282005.

Collection contains 3 television commercials used during Perkins' campaign for a 1984 Pennsylvania election.

PERPICH, Rudy.   3 videocassettes (3/4 in.).

Collection contains 18 television commercials used during Perpich's 1986 campaign for Governor of Minnesota.   (Democratic Party).

PERRY, Buddy. 1 videocassette (3/4 in.).

Collection contains 1 television commercial used during Perry's campaign for the 1982 congressional election in District 4 of Tennessee. (Democratic Party).

PETERS, Jack. 1 videotape (2 in.).

Collection contains 2 television commercials used during Peters' campaign for a congressional election in New York.

PETERSON, Collin.   1 videocassette (3/4 in.).

Collection contains 5 television commercials used during Peterson's 1984 campaign for U.S. Congress in Minnesota.

PETERSON, Donald O. 1925-. 1 film reel (16 mm.). 21887780.

Collection contains 1 television commercial used during Peterson's campaign for the 1970 gubernatorial election in Wisconsin.   (Democratic Party).

PETERSON, John Charles. 1948-. 4 videotapes (2 in.). 22186006.

Collection contains 11 television commercials used during Peterson's campaign for the 1974 U.S. congressional election in District 2 of Kansas. (Republican Party).

PETERSON, Wallace C. 1 videotape (2 in.). 1 sound tape reel (7 1/2 ips.).   21486449.

Collection contains 3 television and 3 radio commercials used during Peterson's 1972 campaign for U.S. Senate in Nebraska. (Democratic Party).

PETRI, Thomas. 1 videotape (2 in.).

Collection contains 6 television commercials used during Petri's campaign for the 1980 congressional election in District 6 of Wisconsin. (Republican Party).

PFEIFFER, Paul. 1 videotape (1 in.). 2 videocassettes (3/4 in.). 24282019.

Collection contains 18 television commercials used during Pfeiffer's campaign for the 1982 U.S. Senate race and 3 television commercials used during his 1986 gubernatorial campaign in Ohio. (Republican Party).

PHELPS, William C. 1 videotape (2 in.). 24282032.

Collection contains 4 television commercials used during Phelps' 1976 campaign for Lt. Governor in Missouri. (Republican Party).

PHILBRICK, Ed. 1 sound tape reel (7 1/2 ips.).

Collection contains 1 radio commercial used during Philbrick's campaign for the 1982 County Sheriff election in New Hampshire. (Republican Party).

PHILLIPS, Bill. 1 sound tape reel (7 1/2 ips.).

Collection contains 2 radio commercials used during Phillips' campaign for the 1980 congressional election in District 3 in Pennsylvania. (Republican Party).

PHILLIPS, Channing. 1 film reel (16 mm.). 24282045.

Collection contains 2 television commercials used during Phillips' campaign for the 1972 congressional election in the District of Columbia.

PHILLIPS, John. 1 videocassette (3/4 in.).

Collection contains 1 television commercial used during Phillips' 1982 campaign for U.S. Congress in Connecticut. (Democratic Party).

PHILLIPS, Vel R. 1924-. 1 sound tape reel (7 1/2 ips.). 7 videotapes (2 in.). 22044360.

Collection contains 5 radio and 5 television commercials used during Phillips' 1972 campaign for a judgeship in Wisconsin. Also includes 4 television spots from his 1978 campaign for Secretary of State in Wisconsin. (Democratic Party).

PIACENTINI, John.   1 videocassette (3/4 in.).

Collection contains 1 commercials used during Piacentini's 1974 congressional campaign in District 3 of Oregon.   (Republican Party).

PICA, John, Jr.   1 sound tape reel (7 1/2 ips.).

Collection contains 1 radio commercial used during Pica's campaign for the 1982 State Senate election in Maryland. (Democratic Party).

PICCOLA, Jeff.   1 sound tape reel (7 1/2 ips.).

Collection contains 4 radio commercials used during Piccola's campaign for the 1980 State Representative election in District 104 in Pennsylvania.   (Republican Party).

PICKETT, Owen.   1 videocassette (3/4 in.).

Collection contains 9 television commercials used during Pickett's 1986 campaign for U.S. Congress in District 2 of Virginia.   (Democratic Party).

PICKLE, Jake.   5 videocassettes (3/4 in.).

Collection contains 10 television commercials used during Pickle's 1986 campaign for U.S. Congress in District 10 of Texas. (Democratic Party).

PIERCE, Edward. 1 videocassette (3/4 in.).   24282057.

Collection contains 9 television commercials used during Pierce's campaign for the 1982 gubernatorial election in Michigan. (Democratic Party).

PLAWECKI, Dave. 1 videocassettes (3/4 in.).   24282696.

Collection contains 10 television commercials used during Plawecki's campaign for the 1982 gubernatorial election in Michigan. (Democratic Party).

PODLES, Elinore.   1 sound tape reel (7 1/2 ips.).

Collection contains 2 radio commercials used during Podles' campaign for the 1982 State Senate election in District 16 in New Hampshire.   (Republican Party).

POFFENBAGRER, John.   1 videocassette (3/4 in.).

Collection contains 1 television commercial for Poffenbagrer's 1980 campaign for State Senate in West Virginia.

POIRER, Peter. 2 sound tape reels (7 1/2 ips.).

Collection contains 7 radio commercials used during Poirer's campaign for the 1982 Governor's Executive Council election in New Hampshire. (Democratic Party).

POLLINA, Anthony. 1 videocassette (3/4 in.).

Collection contains 1 television commercial used during Pollina's 1984 campaign for U.S. Congress in Vermont. (Democratic Party).

POMARO, Nicholas. 1 sound tape reel (7 1/2 ips.).

Collection contains 2 radio commercials used during Pomaro's campaign for the 1982 Associate Judgeship election in Cook County in Illinois.

POOLER, Rosemary. 1 videocassette (3/4 in.).

Collection contains 6 television commercials used during Pooler's 1986 campaign for U.S. Congress in District 27 of New York. (Democratic Party).

POPE, Larry. 1 sound tape reel (7 1/2 ips.).

Collection contains 3 radio commercials used during Pope's campaign for the 1982 Lieutenant Governor election in Iowa. (Republican Party).

PORTER, John Edward. 3 sound tape reels. (7 1/2 ips.).

Collection contains 14 radio commercials used during Porter's campaigns for U.S. Congress in District 10 in Illinois. (Republican Party).

POSTON, Ralph R. 1923-. 2 videotapes (2 in.). 21479076.

Collection contains 2 television commercials used during Poston's campaign for the 1972 and 1974 state senatorial elections in Florida. (Democratic Party).

POTTER, B. Andrew. 1 videocassette (3/4 in.).

Collection contains 1 television commercial from Potter's 1972 campaign for Corporation Commission in Oklahoma. (Democratic Party).

POTTS, Hugh. 4 videotapes (2 in.). 1 sound tape reel (7 1/2 ips.). 24282697.

Collection contains 12 television commercials and 4 radio spots used during Pott's campaign for the 1972 congressional election in District 2 of Mississippi.

POWELL, Kenneth.   1 videocassette (3/4 in.).

Collection contains 1 television commercial used during Powell's 1986 campaign for U.S. Congress in Virginia's 3rd District. (Democratic Party).

POWELL, Wesley.   1 sound tape reel (7 1/2 ips.).

Collection contains 1 radio spot from Powell's campaign for U.S. Senate in New Hampshire.

POWER, Phil.   2 videocassettes (3/4 in.).

Collection consists of 15 television commercial from Power's 1978 primary campaign for U.S. Senate in Michigan.   (Democratic Party).

POWERS, Walter W. 1 videotape (2 in.). 21567354.

Collection contains 4 television commercials used during Powers' campaign for the 1974 State Representative election, District 5, in California. (Democratic Party).

PRESSLER, Larry.   6 videocassettes (3/4 in.).

Collection contains 23 television commercials used during Pressler's 1984 campaign for U.S. Senate in South Dakota.   (Republican Party).

PRESSMAN, Hyman.   1 sound tape reel. (7 1/2 ips.).

Collection contains 1 radio commercials used during Pressman's 1983 campaign for local office in Maryland. (Democratic Party).

PREYER, Richardson.   1 videocassette (3/4 in.).

Collection contains 2 television spots from Preyer's 1980 campaign for U.S. Congress in District 6 of North Carolina.

PRICE, David.   1 videocassette (3/4 in.).

Collection contains 9 television commercials used during Price's 1986 campaign for U.S. Congress in District 4 of North Carolina. (Democratic Party).

PRICE, Bill.   1 videocassette (3/4 in.).

Collection contains several television commercials used during Price's 1990 campaign for Governor of Oklahoma.   (Republican Party).

PRIVETT, Rex. 1924-. 2 videotape (2 in.). 1 sound tape reel (7 1/2 ips.). 21319759.

Collection contains 5 television commercials and 1 radio spot used during Privett's 1972 campaign for Corporation Commissioner in Oklahoma. (Democratic Party).

PROUTY, Winston. 1 film reel (16 mm.).

Collection contains 8 television spots from Prouty's 1970 campaign for U.S. Senate in Vermont. (Republican Party).

PROXMIRE, William. 4 film reels (16 mm.). 21358332.

Collection contains 74 television commercials used during Proxmire's 1964 and 1970 campaigns for U.S. Senate in Wisconsin. (Democratic Party).

PRYOR, David. 3 videotapes (2 in.). 1 film reel (16 mm.). 1 videocassette (3/4 in.). 1 sound tape reel (7 1/2 ips.). 21314995.

Collection contains 5 television spots from Pryor's campaign for the 1972 U.S. congressional election, 9 radio spots used in the 1982 primary campaign for U.S. Senate, 6 television spots used in his 1974 gubernatorial election, and 3 television spots from his 1976 gubernatorial re-election campaign. Includes 15 television spots from his 1984 campaign for U.S. Senator. All elections were held in Arkansas. (Democratic Party).

PURCELL, Fran. 2 videotapes (2 in.).

Collection contains 2 television commercials from Purcell's 1977 campaign for local office in New York. (Republican Party).

QUAYLE, Dan. 10 videocassettes (3/4 in.& 1/2 in.). 1 sound tape reel (7 1/2 ips.).

Collection contains 11 television commercials and 11 radio spots from Quayle's 1980 campaign for U.S. Senate in Indiana and 8 television spots from his 1986 re-election campaign for the same office. (Republican Party).

QUIE, Albert. 1 videocassette (3/4 in.).

Collection contains 4 commercials from Quie's 1978 campaign for Governor of Minnesota. (Republican Party).

QUIGG, J.T. 1 videocassette (3/4 in.). 24282703.

Collection contains 3 television commercials used during Quigg's campaign for the 1982 congressional election in District 3 of Washington. (Republican Party).

QUILLEN, Bill.   1 videocassette (3/4 in.).

Collection contains 5 television commercials used during Quillen's 1984 campaign for Governor of Delaware.   (Democratic Party).

QUINLAN, John Michael. 1935-.   1 videotape (2 in.). 21416345.

Collection contains 1 television commercial used during Quinlan's campaign for the 1974 Secretary of State election in Massachusetts. (Republican Party).

QUINN, Bob.   6 videotapes (2 in.).

Collection contains 6 television spots from Quinn's 1976 campaign for U.S. Congress in District 1 of Virginia.   (Democratic Party).

QUINN, Pat.   1 sound tape reel (7 1/2 ips.).

Collection contains 2 radio commercials used during Quinn's campaign for the 1982 Board of Tax Appeals election in Cook County in Illinois.   (Democratic Party).

QUINN, Robert H. 1 videotape (2 in.). 21426462.

Collection contains 1 television commercial used during Quinn's 1974 campaign for Governor in Massachusetts. (Democratic Party).

RABY, Al.   1 sound tape reel. (7 1/2 ips.).

Collection contains 1 radio commercial used during Raby's 1983 campaign for Congress in District 1 in Illinois. (Democratic Party).

RAFFERTY, Max. 1 film reel (16 mm.).

Collection contains 6 television commercials used during Rafferty's campaign for the 1968 U.S. Senate election in California.   (Republican Party).

RAINS, Omar L. 3 videotapes (2 in.). 2 videocassettes (3/4 in.).

Collection contains 3 television commercials used during Rains' 1982 campaign for Attorney General in California.   (Democratic Party).

RAMOS, Hilario. 1 videotape (2 in.). 21479103.

Collection contains 1 television commercial used during Ramos' 1974 campaign for State Senate in Florida. (Democratic Party).

RAMPTON, Calvin L.   1 sound tape reel (7 1/2 ips.).

Collection contains 12 radio commercials used during Rampton's campaign for the 1972 gubernatorial election in Utah.

RAMSAY, Patricia Smith.   2 videocassettes (3/4 in.).

Collection contains 7 television commercials used during Ramsay's 1984 campaign for U.S. Congress in California.   (Republican Party).

RAMSEY, Jack.   1 sound tape reel (7 1/2 ips.).

Collection contains 1 radio commercial from Ramsey's campaign for Shelby County Commissioner in Arizona.

RAMSEY, Richard Ralph. 1940-.   1 sound tape reel (7 1/2 ips.). 22256902.

Collection contains 2 radio commercials used during Ramsey's campaign for the 1972 state senatorial election in Iowa. (Republican Party).

RANDA, Rudolph. 1 videotape (2 in.).

Collection contains 1 television commercial used during Randa's campaign for a 1979 judgeship in Wisconsin.

RANDOLPH, Jennings. 1 videotape (2 in.). 1 sound tape reel (7 1/2 ips.).   24282707.

Collection contains 2 television commercials and 10 radio spots used during Randolph's campaign for the 1972 U.S. Senate election in West Virginia. (Democratic Party).

RASHID, James.   1 sound tape reel.   (7 1/2 ips.).

Collection contains 1 radio commercial used during Rashid's 1982 campaign for State Senate in Michigan.

RATCHFORD, William. 1 sound tape reel (7 1/2 ips.).

Collection contains 3 radio commercials used during Ratchford's 1982 congressional campaign in District 5 in Connecticut. (Democratic Party).

RAVENEL, Charles D. 1 videotape (2 in.). 1 videocassette (3/4 in.).   22198937.

Collection contains 22 television commercials used during Ravenel's campaign for the 1974 gubernatorial election in South Carolina. (Democratic Party).

RAVITZ, Mel. 1 sound tape reel. (7 1/2 ips.).

Collection contains 1 radio commercial used during Ravitz's 1982 campaign for local office in Michigan.

RAVOSA, Tony. 1 videotape (2 in.). 21486460.

Collection contains 11 television commercials used during Ravosa's 1972 campaign for Governor's Council Committee in Massachusetts.

RAWLINGS, George. 1 film reel (16 mm.). 24282710.

Collection contains 5 television commercials used during Rawlings' campaign for the 1970 U.S. Senate election in Virginia. (Democratic Party).

RAY, Richard. 1 videocassette (3/4 in.).

Collection contains 12 television commercials used during Ray's 1984 campaign for Governor of Georgia. (Democratic Party).

RAY, Robert D. 1928-. 2 sound tape reels (7 1/2 ips.). 3 film reel (16 mm.). 2 videotapes (2 in.). 1 videocassette (3/4 in.). 21416046.

Collection contains 7 television commercials and 9 radio commercials used during Ray's 1970 campaign for Governor of Iowa, 10 television and 3 radio commercials used in his 1972 re-election campaign, and 10 television commercials used in his 1978 gubernatorial campaign. (Republican Party).

REAGAN, Ronald. 27 videocassettes (3/4 in.). 25 videotapes (2 in.). 2 film reel (16 mm.). 2 sound reel tape (7 1/2 ips.). 21248166.

Collection contains 12 television commercials used during Reagan's campaign for the 1966 gubernatorial election in California. Includes 16 television commercials used in his campaign for the 1976 presidential election, 207 television commercials used in his 1980 campaign for president, and 128 television and 2 radio commercials used in his 1984 re-election campaign. Collection also includes miscellaneous television debates and speeches. (Republican Party).

REARDON, Jack. 1 videocassette (3/4 in.).

Collection contains 6 television commercials used during Reardon's 1984 campaign for U.S. Congress in Kansas. (Democratic Party).

REDFORD, James. 1 videotape (2 in.). 21741085.

Collection contains 1 television commercial used during Redford's campaign for the 1974 County Commissioner's election in Florida.

REDMOND, David. 1 videocassette (3/4 in.).

Collection contains 8 television commercials used during Redmond's 1986 primary campaign for Governor of Maine. (Democratic Party).

REED, Steve. 1 sound tape reel (7 1/2 ips.).

Collection contains 10 radio commercials used during Reed's 1980 campaign for Mayor in Harrisburg, Pennsylvania.

REGAN, Edward V. "Ned." 1 videotape (2 in.). 1 videocassette (3/4 in.). 21492284.

Collection contains 13 television commercials used during Regan's campaigns for State Comptroller in New York.

REHBERG, Jack Dennis. 1929-. 1 sound tape reel (7 1/2 ips.). 1 film reel (16 mm.). 22155905.

Collection contains 6 television spots from Rehberg's 1970 campaign for U.S. Congress and 4 radio commercials from his 1972 campaign for the same office in District 2 of Montana. (Republican Party).

REIBMAN, Jeanette. 1 videotape (2 in.). 24282714.

Collection contains 2 television commercials used during Reibman's campaign for the 1976 U.S. Senate election in Pennsylvania. (Democratic Party).

REID, Harry M. 1939-. 1 videotape (2 in.). 2 videocassettes (3/ 4 in.). 21358283.

Collection contains 1 television commercials used during Reid's campaign for the 1974 U.S. senatorial election in Nevada. Also contains 4 television spots for his 1984 re-election campaign to U.S. Congress in District 1 of Nevada and 15 television spots from his 1986 campaign for U.S. Senate in Nevada. (Democratic Party).

REID, Ogden. 1 videocassette (3/4 in.).

Collection contains 1 television commercial used during Reid's campaign for Congress in District 24 of New York. (Democratic Party).

REIGLE, Donald. 1 videocassette (3/4 in.). 24282731.

Collection contains 9 television commercials used during Reigle's campaign for the 1982 U.S. Senate election in Michigan. (Democratic Party).

REINECKE, Ed. 1 videocassette (3/4 in.).

Collection contains 1 television commercial used in Reinecke's 1974 primary campaign for Governor of California. (Republican Party).

RENDELL, Ed. 1 videocassette (3/4 in.).

Collection contains 14 television commercials used during Rendell's 1986 primary campaign for Governor of Pennsylvania. (Democratic Party).

RENK, Wilbur N. 1 film reel (16 mm.). 21388307.

Collection contains 1 television commercials used during Renk's campaign for the 1964 U.S. senatorial election in Wisconsin. (Republican Party).

RENNE, Roland Roger. 1905-. 1 sound tape reel (7 1/2 ips.). 1 film reel (16 mm.). 21382868.

Collection contains 28 radio and eight television commercials used during Renne's campaign for the 1964 gubernatorial election in Montana. (Democratic Party).

RESS, Bill. 2 videocassettes (3/4 in.). 24282720.

Collection contains 4 television commercials used during Ress' campaign for the 1982 U.S. Senate election in Ohio. (Republican Party).

REYNOSO, Cruz. 1 videotape (1 in.). 24282726.

Collection contains 3 television commercials used during Reynoso's campaign for the 1986 judgeship election in California.

RHODES, James A. 1909-. 6 sound tape reels (7 1/2 ips.). 1 film reel (16 mm.). 3 videotapes (1 in. & 2 in.). 5 videocassettes (3/4 in.). 21431666.

Collection contains 18 television commercials used during Rhodes' campaign for the 1974 gubernatorial election in Ohio, 13 radio commercials and 9 television commercials used during his 1978 re-election campaign, and 25 television commercials used during his campaign for the 1986 gubernatorial election; all in Ohio. (Republican Party).

RHODES, John J. 1 videotape (2 in.). 21358327.

Collection contains 5 television commercials used during Rhodes'
campaign for the 1974 U.S. congressional election in Arizona.
(Republican Party).

RHODES, Joseph. 1 sound tape reel (7 1/2 ips.).

Collection contains 1 radio commercial used during Rhodes'
campaign for the 1980 U.S. Senate election in Pennsylvania.
(Democratic Party).

RIBICOFF, Abraham. 1910-. 7 videotapes (2 in.). 21340951.

Collection contains 7 television commercials used during
Ribicoff's campaign for the 1974 U.S. senatorial election in
Connecticut. (Democratic Party).

RICHARDS, Ann. 1 videocassette (3/4 in.).

Collection contains 1 television commercial from Richards' 1982
campaign for State Treasurer in Texas, and television spots from
her 1990 gubernatorial campaign in Texas. (Democratic Party).

RICHARDS, Mike. 1 sound tape reel (7 1/2 ips.).

Collection contains 1 radio commercial used during Richard's 1982
campaign for State Comptroller in Texas.

**RICHARDSON, Bill. 1947-. 1 sound tape reel (7 1/2 ips.).
2 videocassettes (3/4 in.). 22164873.**

Collection contains 10 television spots from Richardson's 1982
campaign for U.S. Congress and 6 radio commercials and 1 television spot from his 1986 re-election campaign for the same office
in New Mexico. (Democratic Party).

RICHARDSON, Bill. 2 videocassettes (3/4 in.).

Collection contains 4 television commercials used during
Richardson's 1984 campaign for U.S. Congress in District 5 of
Ohio. (Democratic Party).

**RICHARDSON, Elliot L. 1920-. 1 videocassette (3/4 in.). 2 sound
tape reels (7 1/2 ips.). 21983889.**

Collection contains 1 radio commercial used during Richardson's
1964 campaign for Lt. Governor and 5 radio spots from his 1966
campaign for Attorney General in Massachusetts. Includes 5
television commercials from his 1984 campaign for U.S. Senate in
Massachusetts. (Republican Party).

RICHARDSON, H.L. 1 videotape (2 in.). 1 videocassette (3/4 in.). 21727192.

Collection contains 2 television commercials used during Richardson's campaign for the 1974 U.S. senatorial election in California and 3 television commercials from his 1986 campaign for Lt. Governor. (Republican Party).

RICHARDSON, Harrison L. 2 film reels (16 mm.). 21352763.

Collection contains 6 television spots from Richardson's 1974 campaign for State Senate in Maine. (Republican Party).

RICHARDSON, Mel. 4 videocassettes (3/4 in. & 1/2 in.).

Collection contains 5 television commercials used during Richardson's 1986 campaign for U.S. Congress in District 2 of Idaho. (Republican Party).

RICKS, Everett E. Jr. 1 sound tape reel (7 1/2 ips.). 22044494.

Collection contains 3 radio commercials used during Rick's 1978 campaign for Superior Court Judge in California.

RIDGE, Thomas J. 5 videocassettes (3/4 in.). 22245585.

Collection contains 6 television commercials used during Ridge's campaign for the 1982 U.S. congressional election in Pennsylvania, 21st District. Includes 16 television spots from his 1984 re-election campaign. (Republican Party).

RIEDEL, Duane. 1 videocassette (3/4 in.).

Collection contains 1 television commercial used during Riedel's 1984 campaign for State Senate in South Dakota.

RIEGLE, Phil. 1 sound tape reel. (7 1/2 ips.). 4 videocassettes (3/4 in.).

Collection contains 12 television commercials and 1 radio commercial used during Riegle's 1982 campaign for U.S. Senate in Michigan. (Republican Party).

RILES, Wilson. 1 videotape (2 in.). 24367871.

Collection contains 1 television commercial used during Riles' 1982 campaign for Superintendent of Public Instruction in California.

RILEY, Bob Cowley. 1 videotape (2 in.). 22442355.

Collection contains 1 television commercials used during Riley's 1972 campaign for Lt. Governor in Arkansas. (Democratic Party).

RILEY, Dorothy Comstock. 1 videocassette (3/4 in.). 24244979.

Collection contains 1 television commercial used during Comstock Riley's campaign for a judgeship in Michigan.

RILEY, Kathy.   1 sound tape reel (7 1/2 ips.).

Collection contains 5 radio commercials used during Riley's campaign for the 1982 State Senate election in Maryland.

RINEHART, Dana. 1 videocassette (3/4 in.).   24282740.

Collection contains 1 television commercial used during Rinehart's campaign for the 1982 State Treasurer election in Ohio. (Republican Party).

RIORDAN, Jim.   1 sound tape reel (7 1/2 ips.).

Collection contains 6 radio commercials used during Riordan's campaign for the 1982 Secretary of Agriculture election in Iowa. (Democratic Party).

RIORDAN, Ray. 4 videotapes (2 in.). 22446455.

Collection contains 4 television commercials used during Riordan's campaign for the 1972 state senatorial election in Wisconsin. (Republican Party).

RIPLEY, Bob.   1 videocassette (3/4 in.).

Collection contains 2 television commercials used during Ripley's 1984 campaign for U.S. Senate in Montana. (Democratic Party).

RITCHIE, John.   1 videocassette (3/4 in.).

Collection contains 1 television commercial used during Ritchie's 1984 campaign for U.S. Congress in Maryland. (Republican Party).

RIZZO, Frank. 1 film reel (16 mm.). 2 videocassettes (3/4 in.). 21479049.

Collection contains 4 television commercials used during Rizzo's campaign for the 1975 Mayoral election in Philadelphia, Pennsylvania. Also contains 8 television commercials used in a 1978 campaign to permit Mayor to serve another term. (Democratic Party).

ROBERTS, Barbara.   1 videocassette (3/4 in.).

Collection contains 2 television commercials used in Roberts' 1984 campaign for Secretary of State in Oregon. (Democratic Party).

ROBERTS, Betty R. 1923-. 1 videotape (2 in.). 1 videocassette (3/4 in.). 1 sound tape reel (7 1/2 ips.). 22245571.

Collection contains 30 radio spots from Roberts' 1968 campaign for State Senate in Oregon and 3 television commercials used during Roberts' 1974 campaign in Oregon. (Democratic Party).

ROBERTS, Bill. 6 videocassettes (3/4 in.).

Collection contains 10 television commercials from Roberts' 1978 campaign for Lt. Governor of Alabama. (Democratic Party).

ROBERTS, Clint. 1 videotape (2 in.). 1 videocassette (3/4 in.). 24282747.

Collection contains 7 television commercials used during Robert's campaign for the 1982 U.S. Senate election in South Dakota. (Republican Party).

ROBERTS, JOE. 1 videotape (2 in.).

Collection contains 1 television commercial used during Robert's 1980 campaign for Lt. Governor in Montana. (Democratic Party).

ROBERTSON, Pat. 7 videocassettes (3/4 in.). 21382666.

Collection contains 28 television commercials used during Robertson's campaign for the 1988 presidential election. (Republican Party).

ROBINSON, Bob. 1 sound tape reel. (7 1/2 ips.).

Collection contains 1 radio commercial used during Robinson's 1982 campaign for State Senate in District 6 in Nevada. (Democratic Party).

ROBINSON, Tommy. 2 videocassettes (3/4 in.).

Collection contains 21 television commercials used during Robinson's 1984 campaign for U.S. Congress in Arkansas and 2 television spots from his 1986 re-election campaign. (Democratic Party).

ROBRAHN, Reese. 1 videotape (2 in.). 21486415.

Collection contains 1 television commercial used during Robrahn's campaign for a 1972 judgeship in Kansas. (Republican Party).

ROCHE, John. 1 sound tape reel (7 1/2 ips.).

Collection contains 4 radio commercials used during Roche's campaign for the 1982 gubernatorial election in Illinois. (Tax Payers Party).

ROCHFORD, Dennis. 1 sound tape reel (7 1/2 ips.).

Collection contains 11 radio commercials used during Rochford's
campaign for the 1980 congressional election in District 7 in
Pennsylvania. (Republican Party).

ROCK, Phil. 5 videocassettes (3/4 in.).

Collection contains 6 television commercials used during Rock's
1984 primary campaign for U.S. Senate in Illinois. (Democratic
Party).

**ROCKEFELLER, John D. "Jay." 1937-. 4 film reels (16 mm.).
9 videocassettes (3/4 in.). 21358298.**

Collection contains 28 television commercials used during
Rockefeller's 1972 campaign and 19 television spots from his 1976
campaign, both for Governor in West Virginia. Also includes 2
television spots from his 1984 campaign for U.S. Senate. (Democratic Party).

**ROCKEFELLER, Nelson A. (Nelson Adrich). 1908-1979. 4 film reels
(16 mm.). 3 videocassettes (3/4 in.). 21382818.**

Collection contains 1 television commercial used during
Rockefeller's campaign for the 1958 gubernatorial election in New
York, 3 television commercials used in his campaign for the 1964
presidential election, 30 television commercials used in his
campaign for the 1966 gubernatorial election in New York, 1
television commercials used in his campaign for the 1968
presidential election, and 12 television commercials used in his
1970 re-election campaign for the gubernatorial election in New
York. (Republican Party).

ROCKEFELLER, Winthrop. 1 film reel (16 mm.). 24290649.

Collection contains 3 television commercials used during Rockefeller's campaign for the 1966 gubernatorial election in
Arkansas. (Republican Party).

RODEY, Patrick. 6 videocassettes (3/4 in.).

Collection contains 10 television commercials used in Rodey's
1978 campaign for Congressman At Large in Alaska. (Democratic
Party).

ROE, Dick. 1 sound tape reel. (7 1/2 ips.).

Collection contains 3 radio commercials used during Roe's 1982
campaign for State House in District 75 of California.
(Democratic Party).

ROEMER, Buddy.   1 videocassette (3/4 in.).

Collections consists of 1 television commercial from Roemer's 1976 campaign for Governor of Louisiana.

ROGERS, Cleeta John.   1 videocassette (3/4 in.).   1 videotape (2 in.).

Collections contains 8 television commercials used during Rogers' 1966 primary campaign for Governor of Oklahoma.   (Democratic Party).

ROMAN, Alexander R.   1 sound tape reel (7 1/2 ips.).

Collection contains 2 radio commercials used during Roman's 1980 campaign for Judge of Common Pleas in Cuyahoga County, Ohio.

ROME, Lew. 3 sound tape reels (7 1/2 ips.). 9 videocassettes (3/4 in.).

Collection contains 15 television commercials and 5 radio commercials used during Rome's 1982 campaign for Governor of Connecticut.   (Republican Party).

ROMER, Roy. 12 videotapes (1 in.).   24290658.

Collection contains 15 television commercials used during Romer's campaign for the 1986 gubernatorial election in Colorado. (Democratic Party).

This shot of Lenore Romney was used in a spot during the 1970 Michigan gubernatorial election.

ROMNEY, Lenore. 1 film reel (16 mm.). 21388393.

Collection contains 1 television commercial used during Romney's 1970 campaign for U.S. Senate in Michigan. (Republican Party).

RONCALIO, Teno. 1916-. 4 film reels (16 mm.). 21369698.

Collection contains 9 television spots from Roncalio's 1966 campaign for U.S. Senate and 1972 U.S. Congress in Wyoming. (Democratic Party).

ROOSEVELT, Franklin D.(Franklin Delano). 1882-1945. 1 film reel (16 mm.). 22137700.

This scene is part of a longer animated film produced by unions in support of Franklin Roosevelt's 1944 presidential campaign.

Collection contains commercials used during Roosevelt's campaign for the 1944 presidential election. Also includes animated film program sponsored by labor unions on behalf of Roosevelt's candidacy. (Democratic Party).

ROSE, BERNICE K. 1 videotape (2 in.).

Collection contains 1 television commercial used during Rose's campaign for the 1980 local supervisor election in Milwaukee, Wisconsin.

ROOSEVELT, James. 1 videocassette (3/4 in.).

Collection consists of 2 television spots used in Roosevelt's campaigns for Congress. (Democratic Party).

ROSE, Robert. 4 videocassettes (3/4 in.).

Collection contains 14 television commercials used during Rose's 1978 campaign for Governor of Nevada. (Democratic Party).

ROSELLINI, Albert. 1 sound tape reel (7 1/2 ips.).

Collection contains 14 radio commercials used during Rosellini's 1972 campaign for Lt. Governor in Washington. (Democratic Party).

ROSEN, Gerald E. 1 sound tape reel. (7 1/2 ips.).

Collection contains 3 radio commercials used during Rosen's 1982 campaign for Congress in District 17 of Michigan. (Republican Party).

ROSS, Barbara. 1 videocassette (3/4 in.).

Collection contains 4 television commercials used during Ross' 1986 campaign for U.S. Congress in District 5 of Oregon. (Democratic Party).

ROSS, Don.   1 videocassette (3/4 in.).

Collection contains 1 television commercial used during Ross'
1984 campaign for U.S. Congress in Florida.   (Republican Party).

ROSS, George H. 1 film reel (16 mm.). 21727319.

Collection contains 1 television commercial used during Ross'
campaign for a 1972 local election in Pennsylvania. (Democratic
Party).

ROST, Tom. 1 videotape (2 in.). 21983879.

Collection contains 1 television commercial used during Rost's
1972 campaign for a judgeship in Kansas. (Republican Party).

ROTENBURG, Jon Fred. 1947-. 1 videotape (2 in.). 21416174.

Collection contains 1 television commercial used during Rotenburg's campaign for the 1974 U.S. congressional election in
Massachusetts. (Independent Party).

ROTH, Mike. 1 videotape (2 in.).

Collection contains 3 television commercials used during Ruth's
1978 campaign for Attorney General in New York.

ROTH, Toby.   2 videocassettes (3/4 in.).

Collection contains 4 television commercials used during Roth's
1984 campaign for U.S. Congress in District 8 of Wisconsin.
(Republican Party).

**ROTH, William M. (William Matson). 1916-. 6 videotapes (2 in.).
21340867.**

Collection contains 16 television commercials used during Roth's
campaign for the 1974 gubernatorial election in California.
(Democratic Party).

ROTHENHOEFER, John.   2 sound tape reels (7 1/2 ips.).

Collection contains 3 radio commercials used during
Rothenhoefer's 1982 campaign for Governor in Maryland.
(Independent Party).

ROTHMAN, Kenneth J. 1 videocassette (3/4 in.).

Collection contains 2 television commercials used during
Rothman's 1984 campaign for Governor of Missouri.   (Democratic
Party).

ROTUNDI, Sam. 1 videocassette (3/4 in.). 24290667.

Collection contains 2 television commercials used during Rotundi's 1982 campaign for Lt. Governor in Massachusetts.

ROUDEBUSH, Richard L. 15 videotape (2 in.). 1 film reel (16 mm.). 21186352.

Collection contains 16 television commercials used during Roudebush's campaign for the 1970 U.S. Senatorial election in Indiana. (Republican Party).

ROUKEMA, Marge. 1 sound tape reel (7 1/2 ips).

Collection contains 4 radio spots from Roukema's 1984 campaign for U.S. Congress from District 5 in New Jersey. (Republican Party).

ROUSSELOT, John. 1 sound tape reel (7 1/2 ips.).

Collection contains 1 radio commercial used during Rousselot's campaign for the 1980 congressional election in District 26 in California. (Republican Party).

ROY, William R. 1 film reel (16 mm.). 16 videotapes (2 in.). 1 videocassette (3/4 in.). 21358305.

Collection contains 36 television commercials used during Roy's 1974 campaign and 10 television commercials from his 1978 campaign, both for U.S. Senate in Kansas. (Democratic Party).

ROYER, Charlie. 1 videocassette (3/4 in.).

Collection contains 3 television commercials used during Royer's campaign for the 1983 U.S. Senate election in Washington. (Democratic Party).

RUBIN, Betty Willis. 1 sound tape reel (7 1/2 ips.).

Collection contains 5 radio spots from Rubin's 1980 campaign for a judgeship in Cuyahoga County, Ohio. (Democratic Party).

RUDMAN, Warren. 8 videocassettes (3/4 in.).

Collection contains 5 television spots from Rudman's 1980 campaign and 7 television spots from his 1986 campaign for U.S. Senate in New Hampshire. (Republican Party).

RUPPE, Phil. 4 videocassettes (3/4 in.). 24290674.

Collection contains 14 television commercials used during Ruppe's campaign for the 1982 U.S. Senate election in Michigan. (Republican Party).

RUSSELL, Darrell.   1 sound tape reel (7 1/2 ips.).

Collection contains 1 radio spot from Russell's campaign for the 1982 State Attorney election in Maryland.   (Democratic Party).

RUSSO, Basil. 1 videotapes (2 in.). 24290685.

Collection contains 1 television commercial used during Russo's campaign for the 1976 congressional election in Ohio.

RUSSO, Marty. 1 videocassette (3/4 in.).

Collection contains 6 television commercials from Russo's 1980 campaign for U.S. Congress in District 3 of Illinois. (Democratic Party).

RYAN, Bob. 1 videocassette (3/4 in.).

Collection contains 9 television commercials used during Ryan's 1986 campaign for U.S. Congressman At Large in Nevada. (Republican Party).

RYAN, George T. 1 film reel (16 mm.). 24290696.

Collection contains 1 television commercial used during Ryan's 1972 campaign a judgeship in Minnesota.

RYLANDER, Carole Keeton. 1 videocassette (3/4 in.).

Collection contains 4 television spots from Rylander's 1986 campaign for U.S. Congress in Texas. (Republican Party).

SABA, Mike. 1 videocassette (3/4 in.). 1 sound tape reel (7 1/2 ips.).

Collection contains 1 television spot and 1 radio commercial from Saba's 1980 primary campaign for U.S. Senate in North Dakota. (Democratic Party).

SACHS, Steve. 2 videocassettes (3/4 in.). 1 sound tape reel (7 1/2 ips.).

Collection contains 6 television commercials from Sachs' 1978 campaign for Attorney General and 1 radio spot from his 1982 campaign for the same office in Maryland. Also includes 3 television spots from his 1986 campaign for Governor of Maryland. (Democratic Party).

SAIKI, Pat. 2 videocassettes (3/4 in.).

Collection contains 17 television commercials used during Saiki's 1986 campaign for U.S. Congress in District 1 of Hawaii. (Republican Party).

SALMON, Thomas P. 1932-. 3 sound tape reels (7 1/2 ips.). 21920849.

Collection contains 45 radio commercials used during Salmon's campaigns for the 1972 and 1974 gubernatorial elections in Vermont. (Democratic Party).

SALOMON, Gene. 1 sound tape reel (7 1/2 ips.).

Collection contains 3 radio commercials used during Salomon's campaign for the 1980 County Recorder of Deeds election in Cook County, Illinois. (Republican Party).

SALVI, Al. 1 videocassette (3/4 in.).

Collection contains 1 television commercial used during Salvi's 1986 campaign for U.S. Congress in District 19 of Illinois. (Republican Party).

SAMUELS, Howard Joseph. 8 videotapes (2 in.). 21388383.

Collection contains 8 television commercials used during Samuels' campaign for the 1974 gubernatorial election in New York. (Democratic Party).

SAMUELSON, Bob. 3 videocassettes (3/4 in.).

Collection contains 4 television commercials from Samuelson's 1978 campaign for Congress from District 2 in South Dakota. (Democratic Party).

SAMUELSON, Don, 1932-. 1 videotape (2 in.). 21191435.

Collection contains 7 television commercials used during Samuelson' campaign for the 1970 gubernatorial election in Idaho. (Republican Party).

SANASARIAN, H. 1 videotape (2 in.). 1 sound tape reel (7 1/2 ips.).

Collection contains 1 television commercial from Sanasarian's 1978 campaign for Lt. Governor of Wisconsin. Also includes 2 radio spots from his campaign for the 1982 congressional election in Wisconsin. (Democratic Party).

SANBORN, Bill. 1 sound tape reel (7 1/2 ips.).

Collection contains 1 radio commercial used during Sanborn's campaign for the 1982 State Senate election in District 17 in New Hampshire. (Republican Party).

SANDERS, Alexander M. 1 film reel (16 mm.). 21474907.

Collection contains 3 television commercials used during Sanders' 1974 campaign for Lt. Governor in South Carolina. (Democratic Party).

SANDERS, Harold Barefoot. 2 videotapes (2 in.). 1 sound tape reel (7 1/2ips.). 21314927.

Collection contains 2 television commercials and 12 radio spots used during Sanders' campaign for the 1972 U.S. senatorial election in Texas. (Democratic Party).

SANDLER, Rich. 1 sound tape reel (7 1/2 ips.).

Collection contains 1 radio commercial used during Sandler's campaign for the 1980 State Representative election in Pennsylvania.

SANFORD, Terry. 1 videotape (2 in.). 1 film reel (16 mm.). 4 videocassettes (3/4 in.).

Collection contains 7 television commercial used during Sanford's campaign for the 1972 presidential election. Also includes 8 television commercials from his 1986 campaign for U.S. Senate from North Carolina. (Democratic Party).

SANSLAW, Dick. 1 sound tape reel (7 1/2 ips.).

Collection contains 5 radio spots from Sanslaw's 1984 campaign for U.S. Congress in District 8 of Virginia. (Democratic Party).

SANSTEAD, Wayne G. 2 film reels (16 mm.). 1 videotape (2 in.). 21287241.

Collection contains 3 television commercials used during Sanstead's 1972 campaign for Lt. Governor and his 1976 campaign for Governor of North Dakota. (Democratic Party).

SANTINI, James David. 2 sound tape reels (7 1/2 ips.). 6 videocassettes (3/4 in. & 1/2 in.).

Collection contains 1 television and 1 radio commercial for Santini's 1980 campaign for Congress and 2 radio commercials used during Santini's 1982 campaign for U.S. Senate in Nevada. Also includes 42 television spots from his 1986 campaign for U.S. Senate in Nevada.

SANTORO, Nick. 1 film reel (16 mm.).

Collection contains 1 television commercial used during Santoro's 1970 campaign for State House in New York. (Republican Party).

SANTUCCI, John. 2 videocassettes (3/4 in.). 24290722.

Collection contains 2 television commercials used during
Santucci's campaign for the 1980 Queens District Attorney
election in New York.

SARASIN, Ronald. 6 videotapes (2 in.). 24290701.

Collection contains 21 television spots from Sarasin's 1978
campaign for Governor in California. (Republican Party).

**SARBANES, Paul. 1 videotape (2 in.). 1 sound tape reel
(7 1/2 ips.). 3 videocassettes (3/4 in.). 24290708.**

Collection contains 7 television commercials used during
Sarbanes' 1976 campaign for the U.S. Senate in Maryland and 3
radio commercials used in his 1982 campaign for the same office.

**SARGENT, Francis W. 2 videotapes (2 in.). 1 videocassette
(3/4 in.). 21388330.**

Collection contains 7 television commercials used during
Sargent's campaign for the 1974 gubernatorial election in
Massachusetts. (Republican Party).

SASSER, James. 5 videocassettes (3/4 in.).

Collection contains 23 television spots from Sasser's 1982
campaign for U.S. Senate in Tennessee. (Democratic Party).

SAWYER, Calvin. 1 videotape (2 in.).

Collection contains 1 television commercial used during Sawyer's
campaign for an appellate court judicial election in Illinois.
(Republican Party).

SAWYER, David. 1 sound tape reel (7 1/2 ips.).

Collection contains 1 radio commercial used during Sawyer's re-
election campaign for the 1980 County Prosecuting Attorney
election in Kent County, Michigan.

SAWYER, Harold. 1 sound tape reel (7 1/2 ips.).

Collection contains 1 radio commercial used during Sawyer's
campaign for the 1980 congressional election in District 5 in
Michigan. (Republican Party).

SAWYER, Keary. 1 videocassette (3/4 in.).

Collection contains 4 television commercials used during Sawyer's
1984 primary campaign for U.S. Congress in District 5 of
Michigan. (Republican Party).

SAWYER, Tom.   2 videocassettes (3/4 in.).

Collection contains 9 television commercials used during Sawyer's 1986 campaign for U.S. Congress in District 14 of Ohio.   (Democratic Party).

SCHABEN, James F. 3 videotapes (2 in.). 22226336.

Collection contains 12 commercials used during Schaben's campaign for the 1974 gubernatorial election in Iowa. (Democratic Party).

SCHAEFER, Mike.   1 videocassette (3/4 in.).

Collection contains 2 television commercials used during Schaefer's 1986 primary campaign for U.S. Senate in Maryland. (Republican Party).

SCHAEFFER, William Donald. 1 film reel (16 mm.).

Collection contains 5 television commercials used during Schaeffer's campaign for the 1971 Mayoral election in Maryland. (Democratic Party).

SCHAFER, Erle H.   1 sound tape reel (7 1/2 ips.).

Collection contains 3 radio commercials used during Schafer's campaign for the County Executive election in Maryland. (Democratic Party).

SCHAFFER, Gloria. 1 videotape (2 in.).   24290737.

Collection contains 1 television commercial used during Schaffer's campaign for the 1976 U.S. Senate election in Connecticut. (Democratic Party).

SCHAUSS, Nick. 1 sound tape reel (7 1/2 ips.).

Collection contains 5 radio commercials used during Schauss' 1982 campaign for Congress in District 6 of Connecticut. (Republican Party).

SCHEERING, Miriam. 1 sound tape reel. (7 1/2 ips.).

Collection contains 1 radio commercial used during Scheering's 1982 campaign for a judgeship in Nevada.

SCHERCK, Jim.   1 videocassette (3/4 in.).

Collection contains 2 television commercials used during Scherck's 1984 campaign for U. S. Congress in District 5 of Ohio. (Democratic Party).

SCHERR, Robert.   1 sound tape reel (7 1/2 ips.).

Collection contains 1 radio commercial used during Scherr's 1982 campaign for Congress in Maryland.   (Republican Party).

SCHICK, Les. 1 sound tape reel (7 1/2 ips.). 22226382.

Collection contains 1 radio commercial used during Schick's 1972 campaign for County Supervisor in Iowa. (Republican Party).

SCHLIE, Norbert. 1 film reel (16 mm.).   24290839.

Collection contains 6 television commercials used during Schlie's 1966 campaign for Secretary of State in California. (Democratic Party).

SCHLOSSTEIN, Frederic W.   1 videotape (2 in.). 21269076.

Collection contains 1 commercial used during Schlosstein's campaign for the 1972 state senatorial election in Massachusetts. (Democratic Party).

SCHMIDT, Helmut.   1 videocassette (3/4 in.).

Collection contains 7 television commercials used in the 1980 German Parliamentary Elections.

SCHMITT, Harrison H. "Jack."   1 film reel (16 mm.). 1 videotape (2 in.).   21416094.

Collection contains 8 television commercials used during Schmitt's campaign for the 1976 U.S. senatorial election in New Mexico. Also includes 1 television commercial from his 1982 campaign for the same office. (Republican Party).

SCHMITZ, John G., 1930-. 1 sound tape reel (7 1/2 ips.). 1 film reel (16 mm.). 22044467.

Collection contains 4 radio and 1 television commercial used during Schmitz' campaign for the 1972 presidential election. (American Independent Party).

SCHMOKE, Kurt.   1 sound tape reel (7 1/2 ips.).

Collection contains 4 radio commercials used during Schmoke's campaign for the 1982 State Attorney election in Maryland. (Democratic Party).

SCHNAUBELT, Fred. 1 sound tape reel (7 1/2 ips.). 22446466.

Collection contains 2 radio commercials used during Schnaubelt's campaign for the 1977 city council election in San Diego, California.

SCHNEIDER, Tom. 1 videotape (2 in.).

Collection contains 2 television commercials used during Schneider's 1980 campaign a judicial election in Wisconsin.

SCHREIBER, Martin. 1 videocassette (3/4 in.). 1 sound tape reel (7 1/2 ips.).

Collection contains 5 television commercials and 3 radio spots used during Schreiber's 1982 campaign for Governor of Wisconsin. (Democratic Party).

SCHROEDER, Patricia. 1 film reel (16 mm.). 24367913.

Collection contains 3 television commercials used during Schroeder's campaign for the 1972 congressional election in Colorado, District 1. (Democratic Party).

SCHUCK, Steve. 2 videocassettes (3/4 in.).

Collection contains 14 television commercials used during Schuck's 1986 primary campaign for Governor of Colorado. (Republican Party).

SCHUETTE, Bill. 12 videocassettes (3/4 in.).

Collection contains 9 television spots from Schuette's 1984 campaign and 15 television spots from his 1986 re-election campaign for U. S. Congress in Michigan. (Republican Party).

SCHULTZ, Frederick Henry. 1 film reel (16 mm.). 21388361.

Collection contains 21 television commercials used during Schultz' campaign for the 1970 U.S. senatorial election in Florida. (Democratic Party).

SCHULTZ, Jerry. 1 sound tape reel (7 1/2 ips.).

Collection contains 1 radio commercial used during Schultz's 1982 campaign for State House in District 35A of Maryland.

SCHULZ, William "Bill." 10 videotapes (2 in.). 8 videocassettes (3/4 in.). 24290950.

Collection contains 30 television commercials from Schulz's 1980 campaign for U. S. Senate in Arizona. (Democratic Party). Also contains 20 television spots from his 1986 campaign for Governor of Arizona. (Independent).

SCHUSTER, Virginia. 1 sound tape reel. (7 1/2 ips.).

Collection contains 2 radio commercials used during Schuster's 1982 campaign for State House in Maryland. (Democratic Party).

SCHWARTZ, John. 1 videocassette (3/4 in.).

Collection contains 5 television commercials used during Schwartz's 1986 campaign for State Senate in Michigan. (Republican Party).

SCHWEIKER, Richard S. (Richard Schultz), 1926-. 2 film reels (16 mm.). 21431693.

Collection contains 13 television commercials used during Schweiker's campaign for the 1974 U.S. senatorial election in Pennsylvania. (Republican Party).

SCHWENGEL, Fred. 1907-. 1 sound tape reel (7 1/2 ips.). 21979520.

Collection contains 7 radio commercials used during Schwengel's campaign for the 1972 U.S. congressional election in Iowa. (Republican Party).

SCHWERTFEGER, Carl "Skip." 1 videocassette (3/4 in.).

Collection contains 5 television commercials used during Schwertfeger's 1984 campaign for U. S. Congress in District 16 of Illinois. (Democratic Party).

SCHWINDEN, Ted. 1 videotape (2 in.). 2 videocassettes (3/4 in.). 24290849.

Collection contains 1 television commercial used during Schwinden's 1976 campaign for Lt. Governor in Montana and 10 television spots from his 1982 campaign for Governor. (Democratic Party).

SCOTT, Bob. 1 videocassette (3/4 in.).

Collection contains 3 television spots from Scott's 1980 primary campaign for Governor of North Carolina. (Democratic Party).

SCOTT, Bobby. 1 videocassette (3/4 in.).

Collection contains 1 television commercial used during Scott's 1986 campaign for U. S. Congress in District 1 of Virginia. (Democratic Party).

SCOTT, Edward Smith. 1928-. 1 sound tape reel (7 1/2 ips.). 5 film reels (16 mm.). 21492301.

Collection contains 6 radio commercials and 5 television commercials used during Scott's campaign for the 1978 U.S. congressional election in Colorado. (Republican Party).

SCOTT, Hugh. 1900-. 1 film reel (16 mm.). 21421429.

Collection contains 1 television spot from Scott's 1970 campaign for U.S. Senate in Pennsylvania. (Republican Party).

SCOTT, William J. 1926-. 1 film reel (16 mm.). 8 videotapes (2 in.). 21426528.

Collection contains 3 television commercials used during Scott's 1976 campaign for Attorney General in Illinois. Includes 8 television commercials used in his 1978 re-election campaign. (Republican Party).

SCOTT, William Lloyd. 1915-. 5 videotape (2 in.). 1 film reel (16 mm.). 1 sound tape reel (7 1/2 ips.). 21315035.

Collection contains 22 television commercials and 4 radio spots used during Scott's 1972 campaign for the U.S. senatorial election in Virginia. (Republican Party).

SCRANTON, Bill, Jr.. 1 videotape (2 in.). 4 videocassettes (3/4 in.). 24350958.

Collection contains 62 television spots from Scranton's campaigns for Governor in Pennsylvania. (Republican Party).

SCRANTON, William Warren. 1917-. 1 sound tape reel (3 3/4 ips.). 22044336.

Collection contains 1 interview used during Scranton's campaign for the 1964 presidential election. (Republican Party).

SEALANDER, Glean. 1 sound tape reel (7 1/2 ips.).

Collection contains 3 radio spots from Sealander's campaign for state office in Idaho. (Democratic Party).

SEALY, Albert Henry. 1917-. 1 videotape (2 in.). 1 sound tape reel (7 1/2 ips.). 21256358.

Collection contains commercials used during Sealy's campaign for the 1969 gubernatorial election in Ohio. (Republican Party).

SEATON, Dan. 1 sound tape reel. (7 1/2 ips.).

Collection contains 1 radio commercial used during Seaton's 1982 campaign for a judgeship in Nevada.

SECREST, Russell. 2 videotapes (2 in.). 21382689.

Collection contains 3 television commercials used during Secrest's 1972 campaign for State Insurance Commissioner in North Carolina.

SEESTRAND, Eric. 1 videocassette (3/4 in.).

Collection contains 2 television commercials from Seestrand's 1980 primary campaign for State Senate in District 17 of California. (Republican Party).

SEHON, Ed.   1 sound tape reel (7 1/2 ips.).

Collection contains 2 radio spots from Sehon's 1980 campaign for State Representative in Pennsylvania. (Republican Party).

SEITH, Alex. 9 videotapes (2 in.). 5 videocassettes (3/4 in.).

Collection contains 28 television commercials and 1 30-minute television program used during Seith's 1978 and 1980 campaigns for U.S. Senate in Illinois. (Democratic Party).

SEIVERLING, Don.   1 sound tape reel (7 1/2 ips.).

Collection contains 8 radio commercials used during Seiverling's campaign for the 1982 congressional election in District 17 in Pennsylvania. (Republican Party).

SELDEN, Armisted.   1 videocassette (3/4 in.).

Collection contains 5 television commercials from Selden's 1980 campaign for U. S. Senate in Alabama. (Republican Party).

SELLERS, David. 2 videocassettes (3/4 in.).

Collection contains 7 television spots from Sellers' 1982 campaign for Congress in District 7 of Georgia. (Republican Party).

SEMROW, Harry.   1 sound tape reel (7 1/2 ips.).

Collection contains 1 radio commercial used during Semrow's 1982 campaign for local office in Illinois. (Democratic Party).

SENSENBRENNER, F. James. 1 videotape (2 in.). 2 videocassettes (3/4 in.).

Collection contains 3 television commercials used during Sensenbrenner's campaign for the 1980 congressional election, District 9 in Wisconsin. Includes 2 television spots from his 1984 re-election campaign and 6 television spots from his 1986 re-election campaign. (Republican Party).

SERAPHIM. 1 videotape (2 in.).

Collection contains 1 television commercial used during Seraphim's campaign for the 1980 judicial election in Milwaukee, Wisconsin.

SERRANO, Emillio. 1 film reel (16 mm.).

Collection contains 1 television commercial used during Serrano's campaign for the 1970 school election in New York. (Republican Party).

SESLER, William. 1 film reel (16 mm.).

Collection contains 5 television commercials used during Sesler's campaign for the 1970 U.S. senatorial election in Pennsylvania. (Democratic Party).

SHADBURNE, Gordon. 1 videocassette (3/4 in.). 24290864.

Collection contains 1 television commercial used during Shadburne's 1982 campaign for Multnomah County Executive in Oregon.

SHAFRAN, George. 1 film reel (16 mm.). 24290877.

Collection contains 8 television commercials used during Shafran's 1971 campaign for Lt. Governor in Virginia. (Republican Party).

SHAMIE, Ray. 3 videocassettes (3/4 in.). 24290886.

Collection contains 2 television commercials used during Shamie's 1982 campaign and 8 television spots from his 1984 campaign; both for U. S. Senate in Massachusetts. (Republican Party).

SHAMO, John. 1 videocassette (3/4 in.). 24290896.

Collection contains 2 television commercials used during Shamo's campaign for a 1982 judgeship in Michigan.

SHANNON, Jim. 5 videocassettes (3/4 in.).

Collection contains 4 television spots from Shannon's 1984 primary campaign for U. S. Senate in Massachusetts. Also contains 3 television spots from his 1986 campaign for Attorney General in Massachusetts. (Democratic Party).

SHAPP, Milton. 1 videocassette (3/4 in.).

Collection contains 1 television documentary used in Shapp's 1974 campaign for Governor of Pennsylvania. (Democratic Party).

SHARP, Phil. 4 videocassettes (3/4 in.).

Collection contains 3 commercials from Sharp's 1976 campaign, 6 television spots from his 1982 campaign, 3 television spots from his 1984 campaign, and 4 television spots from his 1986 campaign; all for U. S. Congress in Indiana. (Democratic Party).

SHARP, Sharon. 1 videotape (2 in.).

Collection contains 1 television commercials used during Sharp's 1978 campaign for Secretary of State.

SHEARING, Mariam. 1 sound tape reel (7 1/2 ips.).

Collection contains 1 radio commercial used during Shearing's 1980 campaign for Judge of District Court in Nevada.

SHEEHY, John C. 1 film reel (16 mm.). 24290909.

Collection contains 1 television spot from Sheehy's 1972 campaign for Attorney General in Montana. (Republican Party).

SHELBY, Richard. 2 videocassettes (3/4 in.).

Collection contains 20 television spots from Shelby's 1986 campaign for U. S. Senate in Alabama. (Democratic Party).

SHELTON, Jim. 1 videotape (2 in.). 24290916.

Collection contains 1 television commercial used during Shelton's campaign for the 1978 State Treasurer election in Illinois. (Republican Party).

SHEVIN, Robert. 1 videocassette (3/4 in.).

Collection contains 10 television commercials from Shevin's 1978 campaign for Governor of Florida. (Democratic Party).

SHIMIZU, Tom. 1 videocassettes (3/4 in.).

Collection contains 1 television commercial used during Shimizu's campaign for the 1982 commissioner's election in Vermont.

SHIPLEY, George. 1 film reel (16 mm.). 24290925.

Collection contains 3 television commercials used during Shipley's campaign for the 1972 congressional election in District 22 of Illinois. (Democratic Party).

SHIPPERS, David. 1 sound tape reel (7 1/2 ips.).

Collection contains 4 radio commercials used during Shippers' campaign for the 1980 State Supreme Court Justice election in Illinois. (Democratic Party).

SHORT, Alan. 1 videotape (2 in.). 21319782.

Collection contains 1 television commercial used during Short's campaign for the 1974 State Treasurer election in California. (Democratic Party).

SHORT, Bob. 1 videocassette (3/4 in.).

Collection contains 3 television spots from Short's 1978 campaign for U. S. Senate in Minnesota. (Democratic Farmer Labor Party).

SHOUP, Richard G. 1 film reel (16 mm.). 24290938.

Collection contains 9 television commercials used during Shoup's campaign for the 1972 congressional election in District 1 of Montana. (Republican Party).

SHOWENGERDT, Mary. 2 videotapes (2 in.). 21426453.

Collection contains 2 television commercials used during Showengerdt's campaign for a 1974 judgeship in Kansas.

SHRIVER, Terry. 1 sound tape reel (7 1/2 ips.).

Collection contains 1 radio commercial used during Shriver's campaign for the 1980 State Representative election in Pennsylvania. (Republican Party).

SHRIVER, Tom. 1 videocassette (3/4 in.).

Collection contains 1 television commercial used during Shriver's campaign for the 1982 District Attorney election in Tennessee.

SHULTZ, Reynolds. 1 videotape (2 in.). 21244024.

Collection contains 1 television commercial used during Shultz's 1972 campaign for Governor in Kansas. (Republican Party).

SHUMAKER. 3 videotapes (2 in.). 24291035.

Collection contains 4 television commercials used during Shumaker's campaign for a 1984 Pennsylvania election.

SHUMSKI, Rosemary. 1 sound tape reel (7 1/2 ips.).

Collection contains 1 radio spot from Shumski's campaign for the 1980 Municipal Court election in Los Angeles in California.

SIEGELMAN, Don. 2 videotapes (2 in.). 24291041.

Collection contains 3 television commercials used during Siegelman's campaign for a 1986 Alabama election.

SIKORSKI, Gerry. 3 videocassettes (3/4 in.).

Collection contains 2 television commercials used during Sikorski's 1984 campaign and 3 television spots from the 1986 campaign for U. S. Congress in District 6 of Minnesota. (Democratic Party).

SILJANDER, Mark.   4 videocassettes (3/4 in.).

Collection contains 7 television commercials used during Siljander's 1986 campaign for U. S. Congress in District 4 of Michigan.

SILVERLING, Daniel.   1 sound tape reel (7 1/2 ips.).

Collection contains 1 radio commercial used during Silverling's campaign for the 1980 congressional election in Pennsylvania. (Republican Party).

SILVESTRI.   1 sound tape reel (7 1/2 ips.).

Collection contains 1 radio commercial used during Silvestri's 1982 campaign for State Supreme Judge in Pennsylvania.

SIMKINS, Joe.   1 videocassette (3/4 in.).

Collection contains 8 television commercials used during Simkins' 1984 primary campaign for U. S. Congress in District 5 of Michigan.   (Republican Party).

SIMON, Paul. 1928-. 11 videocassettes (3/4 in.). 2 film reels (16 mm.). 21145078.

Collection contains 11 television commercials used during Simon's campaign for the 1972 gubernatorial election, 6 television commercials used in his campaign for the 1974 congressional election, and 71 television commercials used in his 1984 campaign for the U.S. Senate election; all in Illinois. Includes 17 television commercials used in his campaign for the 1988 presidential election. (Democratic Party).

SIMON, Seymore. 1915-. 2 sound tape reels (7 1/2 ips.). 22044450.

Collection contains 1 radio commercial used during Simon's campaign for the 1962 President of Cook County Board election in Illinois. Also contains 4 radio commercials from his 1980 campaign for Supreme Court Judge in Illinois. (Democratic Party).

SIMON, Stanley, 1930-. 1 sound tape reel (7 1/2 ips.). 1 videotape (2 in.). 1 videocassette (3/4 in.). 22137728.

Collection contains 1 radio commercial and 2 television spots used during Simon's campaign for the 1979 Bronx Borough presidential election in New York. (Democratic Party).

SIMPSON, Alan K. 4 videotapes (2 in.).

Collection contains 19 television commercials used during Simpson's 1978 campaign for the U.S. Senate election in Wyoming. (Republican Party).

SIMPSON, John.   1 videocassette (3/4 in.).

Collection contains 1 television commercial for Simpson's 1980 campaign for U. S. Senate in Kansas.   (Democratic Party).

SIMPSON, Samuel. 1 film reel (16 mm.). 22441627.

Collection contains 1 television commercial used during Simpson's 1976 campaign for a judgeship in Michigan.

SINNER, George.   1 videocassette (3/4 in.).

Collection contains 2 television commercials used during Sinner's 1984 campaign for Governor of North Dakota.   (Democratic Party).

SISITSKY, Alan David. 1942-. 3 videotapes (2 in.). 21254540.

Collection contains 8 television commercials used during Sisitsky's 1972 campaign for State Senate in Massachusetts. (Democratic Party).

SKAGGS, David.   3 videocassettes (3/4 in.).

Collection contains 6 television commercials used during Skaggs' 1986 campaign for U. S. Congress in District 2 of Colorado. (Democratic Party).

SKALL, Ben. 1 videocassette (3/4 in.).   24291053.

Collection contains 7 television commercials used during Skall's campaign for the 1982 State Senate election in District 25 of Ohio. (Republican Party).

SKELTON, Ike. 1 videotape (2 in.).   24291215.

Collection contains 1 television commercial used during Skelton's campaign for the 1976 congressional election in Missouri. (Democratic Party).

SKINNER, Cal.   1 sound tape reel (7 1/2 ips.).

Collection contains 3 radio commercials used during Skinner's campaign for the 1982 State Comptroller election in Illinois. (Republican Party).

SKLODWSKI, Robert C.   1 sound tape reel (7 1/2 ips.).

Collection contains 1 radio commercial used during Sklodwski's campaign for the 1980 State Supreme Court Justice election in Illinois.   (Republican Party).

SLABY, Lynn. 3 videocassettes (3/4 in.).

Collection contains 5 television commercials used during Slaby's 1986 campaign for U. S. Congress in District 14 of Ohio. (Republican Party).

SLADE, Tom. 1 videotape (2 in.). 21980086.

Collection contains 1 television commercial used during Slade's 1970 campaign for State Treasurer in Florida. (Republican Party).

SLATE, Kelly. 1 sound tape reel. (7 1/2 ips.).

Collection contains 1 radio commercial used during Slate's 1982 campaign for a judgeship in Nevada. (Democratic Party).

SLAUGHTER, Louise. 1 videocassette (3/4 in.).

Collection contains 17 television commercials used during Slaughter's 1986 campaign for U. S. Congress in District 30 of New York. (Democratic Party).

SLOANE, Harvey. 2 videocassettes (3/4 in.). 1 sound tape reel (7 1/2 ips.).

Collection contains 5 television spots from Sloane's 1979 primary campaign and 15 television spots from his 1983 primary campaign for Governor of Kentucky. Includes 5 television spots and 1 radio spot from his campaign for Mayor of Louisville, Kentucky. (Democratic Party).

SMATHERS, Bruce A. 1 film reel (16 mm.). 21498957.

Collection contains 2 television spots from Smathers' campaign for the 1974 Secretary of State in Florida. (Democratic Party).

SMICK, Dave. 1 sound tape reel (7 1/2 ips.).

Collection contains 1 radio spot from Smick's 1984 campaign for U. S. Congress in District 3 of Maryland. (Republican Party).

SMITH, Art. 2 videocassettes (3/4 in.).

Collection contains 2 television spots from Smith's 1984 campaign for U. S. Congress in District 7 of Indiana. (Democratic Party).

SMITH, Bob. 2 sound tape reels (7 1/2 ips.). 1 videocassette (3/4 in.).

Collection contains 8 radio commercials used during Smith's 1982 campaign for Congress in District 1 of New Hampshire. Includes 5 television spots from his 1984 campaign for the same office. (Republican Party).

SMITH, Bruce.   1 sound tape reel (7 1/2 ips.).

Collection contains 3 radio commercials used during Smith's campaign for the 1980 State Representative election in District 92 in Pennsylvania. (Republican Party).

SMITH, Charles.   1 sound tape reel (7 1/2 ips.).

Collection contains 2 radio commercials used during Smith's campaign for the 1982 State Treasurer election in Wisconsin.

SMITH, Chris.   1 sound tape reel (7 1/2 ips.).

Collection contains 2 radio commercials used during Smith's campaign for the 1982 congressional election in District 4 in New Jersey. (Republican Party).

SMITH, Denny. 7 videocassettes (3/4 in.).   24291229.

Collection contains 14 television commercials used during Smith's 1980, 1984 and 1986 campaigns for U. S. Congress in District 5 of Oregon. (Republican Party).

SMITH, Ed. 1 film reel (16 mm.).   24291075.

Collection contains 3 television commercials used during Smith's campaign for the 1972 gubernatorial election in Montana. (Republican Party).

SMITH, Jeff.   1 videocassette (3/4 in.).

Collection contains 6 television commercials used during Smith's 1984 campaign for U. S. Congress in District 4 of South Carolina. (Democratic Party).

SMITH, Jerry.   1 videocassette (3/4 in.).

Collection contains 1 television commercial used during Smith's 1984 campaign for U. S. Congress in District 4 of Oklahoma. (Republican Party).

SMITH, Jim.   2 videocassettes (3/4 in.).

Collection contains 49 television commercials used during Smith's 1986 primary campaign for Governor of Florida. (Democratic Party).

SMITH, Larry.   1 videocassette (3/4 in.).

Collection contains 3 television commercials used during Smith's 1984 campaign for U. S. Congress in District 16 of Florida. (Democratic Party).

SMITH, Neal. 1 videocassette (3/4 in.). 1 sound tape reel (7 1/2 ips.).

Collection contains 2 radio commercials from Smith's 1972 campaign for U. S. Congress in District 4 of Iowa and 2 television commercials used during his 1986 campaign for the same office. (Democratic Party).

SMITH, Norm. 1 videocassette (3/4 in.). 24291239.

Collection contains 1 television commercial used during Smith's 1982 campaign for State House in District 9 of Oregon.

SMITH, Peter. 3 videocassettes (3/4 in.).

Collection contains 2 television commercials used during Smith's 1982 campaign for Lt. Governor in Vermont and 1 television spot from his 1984 re-election campaign. Also includes 13 television spots from his 1986 campaign for Governor in Vermont. (Republican Party).

SMITH, Preston. 1912-. 2 film reels (16 mm.) and 1 videotape (2 in.). 21287273.

Collection contains 4 television commercials used during Smith's campaigns for the 1970 and 1972 gubernatorial election in Texas. (Democratic Party).

SMITH, Thomas. 1 videocassette (3/4 in.).

Collection contains 1 television commercial used during Smith's campaign for a 1982 judgeship in Tennessee.

SMITH, Thomas F. X. 3 videocassettes (3/4 in.).

Collection contains 7 television commercials used in Smith's 1981 primary campaign for Mayor of Jersey City, New Jersey. (Democratic Party).

SMITH, Virginia. 8 videocassettes (3/4 in. & 1/2 in.).

Collection contains 10 television commercials used during Smith's 1984 campaign and 4 television spots from her 1986 campaign for U. S. Congress in Nebraska, District 3. (Republican Party).

SMOLEY, Sandy. 1 videotape (2 in.). 24291093.

Collection contains 1 television commercial used during Smoley's campaign for a 1976 local supervisor election in California.

SMYKOWSKI, Jim.   1 videocassette (3/4 in.).

Collection contains 1 television spot from Smykowski's 1980 campaign for Congress in North Dakota.   (Republican Candidate).

SNELLING, Richard. 9 videocassettes (3/4 in. & 1/2 in.).

Collection contains 15 television commercials used during Snelling's 1980 and 1982 campaigns for Governor in Vermont. Also includes 29 television spots from his 1986 campaign for U. S. Senate in Vermont. (Republican Party).

SNELSON, Pete.   1 videocassette (3/4 in.).

Collection contains 3 television commercials used during Snelson's 1986 campaign for U. S. Congress in Texas. (Democratic Party).

This commercial was used by Olympia Snowe in her 1986 congressional campaign in Maine.

SNOWE, Olympia. 6 videocassettes (3/4 in.).

Collection contains 8 television commercials used during Snowe's 1986 campaign for U. S. Congress in District 2 of Maine. (Republican Party).

SOLOMON, Anthony. 3 videocassettes (3/4 in.).

Collection contains 5 television commercials used during Solomon's 1984 campaign for Governor of Rhode Island.   (Democratic Party).

SOLOMON, Gerald.   1 videocassette (3/4 in.).

Collection contains 3 television commercials used during Solomon's 1986 campaign for U. S. Congress in District 24 of New York.   (Republican Party).

SOWERS, Roy Gerodd. 1927-. 1 videotape (2 in.). 21314936.

Collection contains 4 television commercials used during Sowers 1972 campaign for Lt. Governor in North Carolina. (Democratic Party).

SPAINHOWER, James I. 1 film reel (16 mm.).

Collection contains 14 television spots from Spainhower's 1972 campaign for State Treasurer in Maryland. (Democratic Party).

SPARKMAN, John. 1 film reel (16 mm.). 24291104.

Collection contains 2 television spots from Sparkman's 1972 campaign for U.S. Senate in Alabama. (Democratic Party).

SPARLING, James M. 1928-. 1 videotape (2 in.). 21352782.

Collection contains 2 television commercials used during Sparling's campaign for the 1974 U.S. congressional election in Michigan, 8th District. (Democratic Party).

SPAULDINE, Sy. 1 sound tape reel (7 1/2 ips.).

Collection contains 2 radio spots from Spauldine's campaign for U. S. Senate in Massachusetts.

SPAULDING, Josiah. 1923-. 1 film reel (16 mm.). 21538853.

Collection contains 3 television commercials used during Spaulding's 1974 campaign for Attorney General in Massachusetts. (Republican Party).

SPAULDING, Peter. 1 sound tape reel (7 1/2 ips.).

Collection contains 1 radio commercial used during Spaulding's 1982 campaign for Governor's Executive Council in New Hampshire. (Republican Party).

SPEAKUS, James. 1 sound tape reel (7 1/2 ips.).

Collection contains 3 radio commercials used during Speakus' campaign for a 1982 judgeship election in Maryland.

SPECTER, Arlen. 4 videotapes (2 in.). 2 videocassettes (3/4 in.). 24291251.

Collection contains 4 television commercials used during Specter's 1976 campaign for U.S. Senate in Pennsylvania. Also includes 29 television spots from his 1986 campaign for the same office. (Republican Party).

SPELLMAN, John. 2 videocassettes (3/4 in.).

Collection contains 6 television spots used during Spellman's 1980 campaign for Governor of Washington and 11 television commercials from his 1984 re-election campaign. (Republican Party).

SPENCER, Vaino Hassan. 1920-. 1 sound tape (3 3/4 ips.). 21979524.

Collection contains 2 radio commercials used during Spencer's 1978 campaign for a judgeship in California.

SPICER, Keith.   1 videocassette (3/4 in.).

Collection contains 2 television commercials used during Spicer's 1984 campaign for U. S. Congress in District 1 of Minnesota. (Republican Party).

SPONG, William B. (William Belser), 1920-. 2 film reels (16 mm.). 21887791.

Collection contains 9 television commercials used during Spong's campaign for the 1972 U.S. senatorial election in Virginia. (Democratic Party).

SPOTTSWOOD, John, Jr. 2 videotapes (2 in.).   24291124.

Collection contains 2 television commercials used during Spottswood's campaign for the 1978 State Senate election in Florida. (Democratic Party).

SPRIK, Dale.   1 sound tape reel (7 1/2 ips.).

Collection contains 1 radio commercial used during Sprik's campaign for the 1980 congressional election in District 5 in Michigan.   (Democratic Party).

SPRINGER, Jerry. 3 videocassettes (3/4 in.).   24291361.

Collection contains 25 television commercials used during Springer's campaign for the 1982 gubernatorial election in Ohio. (Democratic Party).

ST. GERMAIN, Ferdinand.   1 videocassette (3/4 in.).

Collection contains 3 television commercials used during St. Germain's 1986 campaign for U. S. Congress in Rhode Island. (Democratic Party).

STACHEWICZ, Raymond A. 1 videotape (2 in.).   24291372.

Collection contains 1 television commercial used during Stachewicz's campaign for the 1976 congressional election in Ohio.

STACKHOUSE, Ronald.   1 sound tape reel (7 1/2 ips.).

Collection contains 1 radio commercial used during Stackhouse's campaign for the 1980 Cuyahoga County Engineer election in Ohio.

STACKLER, Ron. 1 videotape (2 in.). 24291384.

Collection contains 1 television spot from Stackler's 1976 campaign for Attorney General in Illinois. (Democratic Party).

STADLMAN, Neil H. 1 sound tape (7 1/2 ips.). 22155933.

Collection contains 2 radio spots from Stadlman's 1972 campaign for Secretary of Agriculture in Iowa. (Republican Party).

STAFFORD, Jeff. 4 videocassette (3/4 in.).

Collection contains 8 television commercials used during Stafford's 1984 campaign for U. S. Congress in District 9 of Virginia. (Republican Party).

STAFFORD, Robert. 4 videocassettes (3/4 in.).

Collection contains 9 television commercials used during Stafford's campaign for the 1982 U.S. Senate election in Vermont. (Republican Party).

STAGGERS, Harley, Jr. 1 videocassette (3/4 in.).

Collection contains 1 television commercial used during Staggers' 1986 campaign for U. S. Congress in District 2 of West Virginia. (Democratic Party).

STAISEY, Leonard. 1 sound tape reel (7 1/2 ips.).

Collection contains 15 radio commercials used during Staisey's campaign for the 1972 County Commissioner election in Pennsylvania.

STALLINGS, Richard. 3 videocassettes (3/4 in.).

Collection contains 8 television commercials used during Stallings' 1984 campaign and 1 television spot from his 1986 re-election campaign for U. S. Congress in District 2 of Idaho. (Democratic Party).

STAMOS, John. 1 sound tape reel (7 1/2 ips.).

Collection contains 1 radio commercial used during Stamos' campaign for the 1980 State Supreme Court Justice election in Illinois. (Democratic Party).

STANLEY, David. 1 film reel (16 mm.). 24291661.

Collection contains 6 television commercials used during Stanley's campaign for the 1970 congressional election in Iowa. (Republican Party).

STANTON, Jim. 4 videotapes (2 in.). 24291406.

Collection contains 10 television commercials used during Stanton's campaign for the 1976 U.S. Senate election in Ohio. (Democratic Party).

STEELE, Robert H. 1938-. 3 videotapes (2 in.). 21270323.

Collection of 3 television commercials used during Steele's campaigns for the 1972 congressional election and 1974 gubernatorial election in Connecticut. (Republican Party).

STEEN, John. 1 sound tape reel (7 1/2 ips.).

Collection contains 9 radio commercials used during Steen's campaign for the 1981 Mayoral election in San Antonio, Texas.

STEIGER, William. 1 film reel (16 mm.)

Collection contains 3 television commercials used during Steiger's campaign for the 1968 congressional election, 6th District in Wisconsin. (Republican Party).

STEIN, Andrew. 3 videocassettes (3/4 in.).

Collection contains 6 television commercials from Stein's 1981 campaign for Manhattan Borough President in New York.

STEINMETZ, Don. 2 videotapes (2 in.).

Collection contains 6 television spots from Steinmetz's 1980 campaign for State Supreme Court Judge in Wisconsin.

STENNIS, John. 1 videocassette (3/4 in.). 24291400.

Collection contains 8 television commercials used during Stennis' campaign for the 1982 U.S. Senate election in Mississippi. (Democratic Party).

STEPHANIS, James T. 1 videotape (2 in.). 21268970.

Collection contains 2 television commercials used during Stephanis' campaign for the 1972 U.S. congressional election in Florida. (Democratic Party).

STEPHEN, Bobby. 1 sound tape reel (7 1/2 ips.).

Collection contains 2 radio commercials used during Stephen's campaign for the 1982 State Senate election in District 18 in New Hampshire. (Democratic Party).

STEPHENS, Bob. 1 videocassette (3/4 in.).

Collection contains 6 television commercials used during Stephens' 1986 campaign for Attorney General of Kansas. (Republican Party).

STERN, Grace Mary. 1 sound tape reel (7 1/2 ips.).

Collection contains 8 radio commercials used during Stern's 1982 campaign for Lt. Governor in Illinois. (Democratic Party).

STEVENSON, Adlai E. (Adlai Ewing), 1900-1965. 30 sound tape reels (7 1/2 ips.). 9 film reels (16 mm.). 18 sound tape reels (3 3/4 ips.). 1 videocassette (3/4 in.). 2 sound tape reels (1 7/8 ips.). 21140067.

Collection contains 13 television and 10 radio commercials used during Stevenson's campaign for the 1952 presidential election, and 51 television and 67 radio commercials used during Stevenson's 1956 campaign for president. Includes 1 1953 radio item, 8 1955 radio items, and 1 1957 radio item (speeches, interviews, etc.). (Democratic Party).

This 1952 commercial for Adlai Stevenson was not an official spot sponsored by his campaign.

STEVENSON, Adlai Ewing, III. 1930-. 3 film reels (16 mm.). 1 videotape (2 in.). 1 sound tape reel (7 1/2 ips.). 4 video-cassettes (3/4 in.). 21145104.

Collection contains 2 television commercials used during Stevenson's 1966 campaign for State Treasurer, 7 television commercials used during his 1974 campaign for Governor, 4 television spots and 4 radio commercials from his 1982 campaign for Governor, and 9 television commercials used in his 1986 campaign for Governor; all in Illinois. (Democratic Party).

STEVENSON, Bill. 1 sound tape reel (7 1/2 ips.).

Collection contains 2 radio commercials used during Stevenson's campaign for the 1972 State Labor Commissioner election in Oregon.

STEWART, David A. 1941-. 1 videotape (2 in.). 1 sound tape reel (7 1/2 ips.). 21631259.

Collection contains 4 television and 4 radio commercials used during Stewart's 1974 campaign for U.S. Congress in District 3 of Arkansas. (Democratic Party).

STEWART, Donald. 2 videocassettes (3/4 in.).

Collection contains 6 television spots from Stewart's 1980 campaign for U. S. Senate in Alabama. (Democratic Party).

STEWART, Ken. 1 sound tape reel (7 1/2 ips.).

Collection contains 1 radio commercial used during Stewart's campaign for local office in Nevada.

STEWART, Monica Faith. 1 sound tape reel (7 1/2 ips.).

Collection contains 1 radio commercial used during Stewart's campaign for the 1982 congressional election in District 2 in Illinois. (Democratic Party).

STEWART, Shelton. 1 sound tape reel (7 1/2 ips.).

Collection contains 1 radio commercial used during Stewart's campaign for the 1982 City Sheriff election in Baltimore, Maryland. (Democratic Party).

STOCKETT, Ann. 1 videocassette (3/4 in.).

Collection contains 5 television commercials used in the 1978 campaign for Governor/Lt. Governor in Maryland. Stockett was the Lt. Governor candidate with Ted Venetoulis the gubernatorial candidate. (Democratic Party).

STOFFERAHN, Kenneth. 1 videocassette (3/4 in.).

Collection contains 1 television spot from Stofferahn's 1980 campaign for U. S. Congress in District 2 of South Dakota. (Democratic Party).

STOKES, Carl. 1 film reel (16 mm.). 24291418.

Collection contains 6 television commercials used during Stokes' 1968 campaign for Mayor in Cleveland, Ohio. (Democratic Party).

STONE, Joe. 1 videocassette (3/4 in.).

Collection contains 1 television commercial used during Stone's 1986 campaign for State Senate in Mississippi.

STONE, Richard. 1928-. 3 videotapes (2 in.). 21348074.

Collection contains 15 television commercials used during Stone's campaign for the 1974 U.S. senatorial election in Florida. (Democratic Party).

STONER, J.B. 1 videotape (2 in.). 1 videocassette (3/4 in.). 21256368.

Collection contains 1 television commercial used during Stoner's 1972 campaign for the U.S. Senate and 1 television commercial from his 1978 gubernatorial campaign in Georgia. (Democratic Party).

STONER, Tom. 1 videocassette (3/4 in.).

Collection contains 4 television commercials from Stoner's 1980 campaign for U. S. Senate in Iowa. (Republican Party).

STORY, Bill. 1 videocassette (3/4 in.).

Collection contains 3 television commercials used during Story's 1986 campaign for U. S. Congress in Colorado. (Democratic Party).

STOUT, Jerry. 1 videocassette (3/4 in.).

Collection contains 1 television commercials used during Stout's 1986 campaign for State Legislative District 104 in Illinois.

STRACHEN, Margaret. 1 videocassette (3/4 in.).

Collection contains 3 television commercials used during Strachen's 1986 campaign for City Council in Portland, Oregon.

STRAIGHT, George. 1 sound tape reel (7 1/2 ips.).

Collection contains 1 radio commercial used during Straight's 1982 campaign for Lt. Governor of Texas. (Republican Party).

STRANGE, Mike. 5 videocassettes (3/4 in.).

Collection contains 3 television spots from Strange's 1984 campaign and 6 television spots from his 1986 campaign for U. S. Congress in District 3 of Colorado. (Republican Party).

STRANGELAND, Arlan. 9 videocassettes (3/4 in. & 1/2 in.).

Collection contains 5 television commercials from Strangeland's 1982 campaign and 3 television commercials used during his 1984 campaign for U. S. Congress in District 7 of Minnesota. Also includes 10 television spots from his 1986 campaign for the same office. (Republican Party).

STRAUB, Robert. 1 film reel (16 mm.). 1 videocassette (3/4 in.). 1 sound tape reel (7 1/2 ips.).

Collection contains 14 television commercials and 1 radio spot used during Straub's 1970 campaign and 3 television commercials from his 1974 campaign; both for Governor of Oregon. (Democratic Party).

STRAUSS, Kathleen. 1 videotape (2 in.). 21887868.

Collection contains 1 television commercial used during Strauss' campaign for the 1974 U.S. congressional election in Michigan. (Democratic Party).

STRETTIN, Sam. 1 sound tape reel (7 1/2 ips.).

Collection contains 1 radio commercial used during Strettin's campaign for the 1982 State Senate election in Pennsylvania.

STRICKLAND, Ted. 1 videocassette (3/4 in.).

Collection contains 1 television commercial used during Strickland's 1986 campaign for Governor of Colorado. (Democratic Party).

In this 1986 Colorado gubernatorial campaign spot, Ted Strickland accused his opponent of wearing many hats.

STROOCK, Thomas F. 1925-. 1 film reel (16 mm.). 21474983.

Collection contains 5 television commercials used during Stroock's campaign for the 1974 U.S. congressional election in Wyoming. (Republican Party).

STROUP, Robert L. 2 film reels (16 mm.). 21474871.

Collection contains 6 television commercials used during Stroup's campaign for the 1976 U.S. senatorial election in North Dakota. (Republican Party).

STUBBEREHN, Ken. 1 sound tape reel (7 1/2 ips.).

Collection contains 6 radio commercials used during Stubberehn's campaign for the 1972 U.S. Senate election in South Dakota.

STUCKEY, Jim.   2 videocassettes (3/4 in.).

Collection contains 10 television commercials used during Stuckey's 1986 campaign for U. S. Congress in District 1 of South Carolina.   (Democratic Party).

SUHADOLNIK, Gary.   2 videocassettes (3/4 in.).

Collection contains 2 television commercials used during Suhadolnik's 1984 campaign for State Senate in Ohio.   Also includes 6 television spots from his 1986 campaign for U. S. Congress in District 19 of Ohio.   (Republican Party).

SULLIVAN, Charles. 1 film reel (16 mm.).

Collection contains 5 television commercials used during Sullivan's campaign for the 1971 gubernatorial election in Mississippi.   (Democratic Party).

SULLIVAN, Florence. 1 videocassette (3/4 in.).

Collection contains 1 television commercial used during Sullivan's campaign for the 1982 U.S. Senate election in New York. (Republican Party).

SULLIVAN, John T.   1 sound tape reel (7 1/2 ips.).

Collection contains 1 radio commercial used during Sullivan's 1980 campaign for Supreme Court Judge in Illinois.   (Independent Party).

SULLIVAN, Michael T.   1 sound tape reel (7 1/2 ips.).

Collection contains 3 radio commercials used during Sullivan's campaign for the 1982 State Senate election in Wisconsin. (Democratic Party).

SUNDLUN, Bruce.   1 videocassette (3/4 in.).

Collection contains 5 television commercials used during Sundlun's 1986 campaign for Governor of Rhode Island. (Democratic Party).

SUNDQUIST, Don. 6 videocassettes (3/4 in.).

Collection contains 11 television commercials used during Sundquist's campaign for the 1982 congressional election in District 7 of Indiana. (Republican Party).

SUNUNU, John. 18 videocassettes (3/4 in. & 1/2 in.). 24291428.

John Sununu used this play on the Pinocchio story to accuse his opponent of lying in a New Hampshire gubernatorial campaign.

Collection contains 9 television commercials used during Sununu's 1982 campaign, 10 television spots from his 1984 campaign, and 19 television spots from his 1986 campaign for Governor of New Hampshire. (Republican Party).

SUTTON, Percy. 1 videocassette (3/4 in.).

Collection consists of 5 television spots from Sutton's 1977 campaign for Mayor in New York. (Democratic Party).

SUTTON, R.E. 1 videocassette (3/4 in.).

Collection contains 1 television commercial used during Sutton's 1982 campaign for a judgeship in Tennessee.

SWANSTROM, Nord Lee. 1949-. 2 videotapes (2 in.). 22441656.

Collection contains 1 television spot from Swanstrom's 1978 campaign for State Representative in Illinois and 2 television spots from his 1980 campaign for the same office. (Republican Party).

SWEENEY, John T. 1 videotape (2 in.). 2 videocassettes (3/4 in.). 24291436.

Collection contains 5 television spots from Sweeney's 1982 campaign for State Senate in Ohio. (Republican Party).

SWEENEY, Mac. 4 videocassettes (3/4 in.).

Collection contains 5 television spots from Sweeney's 1984 campaign for Congress in Texas. (Republican Party).

SWIFT, Al. 2 videocassettes (3/4 in.).

Collection contains 4 television spots from Swift's 1982 and 1984 campaigns for U. S. Congress in District 2 of Washington. (Democratic Party).

SWIFT, Joan. 1 sound tape reel. (7 1/2 ips.).

Collection contains 2 radio commercials used during Swift's 1982 campaign for local office in Nevada.

SWINDALL, Pat. 1 videocassette (3/4 in.).

Collection contains 3 television commercials used during Swindall's 1984 campaign for U.S. Congress in District 4 of Georgia. (Republican Party).

SWISHER, William. 1 videocassette (3/4 in.). 2 sound tape reels (7 1/2 ips.).

Collection contains 2 television commercials used in Swisher's 1978 campaign for Baltimore County State's Attorney in Maryland. Also includes 2 radio commercials from a local Maryland campaign and 4 radio spots from his 1982 State's Attorney campaign. (Democratic Party).

SYMINGTON, Stuart. 2 film reels (16 mm.). 24291447.

Collection contains 7 television commercials used during Symington's campaign for the 1970 U.S. Senate election in Missouri. (Democratic Party).

SYMMS, Steven D. (Steven Douglas), 1938-. 1 sound tape (7 1/2 ips.). 7 videotapes (2 in.). 6 videocassettes (3/4 in.). 22164892.

Collection contains 5 radio commercials used during Symms' campaign for the 1972 U.S. congressional election in Idaho. Also contains 24 television commercials used during Symms' 1980 campaign, 2 television spots from his 1984 campaign, and 48 commercials from his 1986 campaign; all for U.S. Senate in Idaho. (Republican Party).

SYNAR, Mike. 1 videocassette (3/4 in.).

Collection contains 5 television commercials used during Synar's 1984 campaign for U.S. Congress in District 2 of Oklahoma. (Democratic Party).

TABOR, Eric. 2 videocassettes (3/4 in.).

Collection contains 3 television commercials used during Tabor's 1986 campaign for U.S. Congress in District 2 of Iowa. (Democratic Party).

TAFT, Robert. 1917-. 2 film reels (16 mm.). 9 videotapes (2 in.). 21426440.

Collection contains 2 television commercials used during Taft's campaign for the 1964 U.S. senatorial election, 26 television commercials used in his 1976 U.S. Senate election; both in Ohio. (Republican Party).

TAFT, Seth. 1 videocassette (3/4 in.). 24291456.

Collection contains 3 television commercials used during Taft's campaign for the 1982 gubernatorial election in Ohio. (Republican Party).

TALIAFERRO, Henry Beauford. 1 videotape (2 in.). 21244036.

Collection contains 1 television commercial used during Taliaferro's campaign for the 1966 U.S. congressional election in Oklahoma. (Democratic Party).

TALMADGE, Herman. 3 videocassettes (3/4 in.).

Collection contains 21 television commercials used during Talmadge's 1980 campaign for U.S. Senate in Georgia. (Democratic Party).

TALMADGE, Phil. 1 videocassette (3/4 in.).

Collection contains 3 television commercials used during Talmadge's 1984 campaign for Attorney General in Washington. (Democratic Party).

TARNOW, Arthur J. 1 film reel (16 mm.). 24351342.

Collection contains 1 television commercial used during Tarnow's campaign for the 1972 judgeship election in Minnesota.

TAUKE, Tom. 1 videocassette (1/2 in.).

Collection contains 1 television commercials used during Tauke's 1986 campaign for U.S. Congress in Iowa. (Republican Party).

TAUZIN, Billy. 1 videocassette (3/4 in.).

Collection contains 2 television spots used in Tauzin's 1980 campaign for U.S. Congress in District 3 of Louisiana. (Democratic Party).

TAWES, J. Millard. 1894-. 1 videotape (2 in.). 21186218.

Collection contains 1 television commercial used during Tawes' campaign for the 1962 gubernatorial election in Maryland. (Democratic Party).

TAYLOR, Clarence. 2 videocassettes (3/4 in.).

Collection contains 5 television commercials used during Taylor's 1984 campaign for U.S. Congress in North Carolina. (Republican Party).

TAYLOR, H. Patrick. 1924-. 1 videotape (2 in.). 21388318.

Collection contains 1 television commercial used during Taylor's campaign for the 1972 gubernatorial election in North Carolina. (Democratic Party).

TAYLOR, Roy. 1910-. 1 film reel (16 mm.). 21567349.

Collection contains 2 television commercials used during Taylor's campaign for the 1972 U.S. congressional election in North Carolina, District 11. (Democratic Party).

TEAGUE, John. 2 videotapes (2 in.). 24351349.

Collection contains 2 television commercials used during Teague's 1986 campaign for Lt. Governor in Alabama. (Democratic Party).

TEASDALE, Joseph P. 1 videotape (2 in.). 21269048.

Collection contains 1 television commercial used during Teasdale's campaign for the 1972 gubernatorial election in Missouri. (Democratic Party).

TERRILL, Al. 1937-. 1 videotape (2 in.). 21319763.

Collection contains 10 television commercials used during Terrill's 1972 campaign for U.S. Senate in Oklahoma. (Democratic Party).

TERRY, Lee. 1 videotape (2 in.). 24351355.

Collection contains 1 television commercial used during Terry's campaign for the 1976 congressional election in Nebraska. (Republican Party).

THEODORE, Nick. 1 videocassette (3/4 in.).

Collection contains 3 television commercials used during Theodore's 1986 campaign for Lt. Governor in South Carolina. (Democratic Party).

THEUNEN, George. 1 sound tape (7 1/2 ips.). 22226314.

Collection contains 1 radio commercial used during Theunen's 1972 campaign for Supervisor in Scott County, Iowa.

THEUSCH, Charles.   1 sound tape reel (7 1/2 ips.).

Collection contains 20 radio spots from Theusch's 1984 campaign for Congress in District 11 of Illinois.   (Republican Party).

THODE, Thomas. 1 videotape (2 in.). 24351364.

Collection contains 1 television commercial used during Thode's campaign for a 1986 election.

THOMAS, Priscilla. 1 videotape (2 in.). 24351369.

Collection contains 1 television commercial used during Thomas' campaign for a 1984 Pennsylvania election.

THOMAS, Richard. 3 videotapes (2 in.). 21741091.

Collection contains 3 television commercials used during Thomas' campaign for the 1972 Hampton County Commissioner election in Massachusetts. (Democratic Party).

THOMASSON, Jerry. 1 film reel (16 mm.).

Collection contains 4 television commercials used during Thomasson's 1968 campaign for Attorney General in Arkansas.

THOMPSON, Barbara. 2 videotapes (2 in.).

Collection contains 2 television commercials used during Thompson's campaign for the 1981 school election in Wisconsin.

THOMPSON, James R. 10 videocassettes (3/4 in.). 12 videotapes (2 in.).

Collection contains 22 television commercials used in Thompson's 1976 campaign and 24 commercials from his 1978 campaign; both for Governor of Illinois. Also included are 18 television commercials from his 1982 re-election campaign and 18 television commercials used during his 1986 re-election campaign for Governor. Includes his 1976 acceptance speech for Governor; all elections in Illinois. (Republican Party).

THOMPSON, Mike. 1 videotape (2 in.). 21741129.

Collection contains 1 television commercial used during Thompson's campaign for the 1972 U.S. congressional election in Florida. (Republican Party).

THOMPSON, Tommy.   3 videocassettes (3/4 in.).

Collection contains 17 television commercials used during Thompson's 1986 campaign for Governor of Wisconsin.   (Republican Party).

THONE, Charles. 2 videocassettes (3/4 in.). 24351375.

Collection contains 4 television commercials used during Thone's campaign for the 1982 gubernatorial election in Nebraska. (Republican Party).

THORNBERRY, Fred. 1 sound tape reel (7 1/2 ips.).

Collection contains 1 radio commercial used during Thornberry's 1982 campaign for Agriculture Commissioner in Texas. (Republican Party).

THORNBURGH, Richard L. "Dick." 1932 -. 2 sound tape reels (7 1/2 ips.). 6 videocassettes (3/4 in.). 1 videotape (2 in.). 21930014.

Collection contains 1 radio commercial and 4 television commercials used during Thornburgh's 1978 campaign for Governor of Pennsylvania and 15 television commercials and 3 radio spots used during his 1982 re-election campaign. (Republican Party).

THORNBURN, James S. 2 videotapes (2 in.). 21741170.

Collection contains 3 television commercials used during Thornburn's 1972 campaign for State Supreme Court in Michigan. (Republican Party).

THORSNESS, Leo K. 3 videotapes (2 in.). 22186032.

Collection contains 8 television commercials used during Thorsness' 1974 campaign for U.S. Senate n South Dakota. (Republican Party).

THURMAN, John. 1 videocassette (3/4 in.).

Collection contains 1 television spot used in Thurman's 1980 campaign for State Senate in California.

THURMOND, Strom. 2 videocassettes (3/4 in.).

Collection contains 1 television commercials used during Thurmond's 1984 campaign for U.S. Senate in South Carolina. Also includes 2 television spots of Thurmond endorsing Jeremiah Denton and Don Nickles in 1986, paid for by the Fund for a Conservative Majority. (Republican Party).

TIERNEY, Jim. 3 videocassettes (3/4 in.).

Collection contains 20 television commercials used during Tierney's 1986 campaign for Governor of Maine. (Democratic Party).

TIMILTY, Joe. 1 film reel (16 mm.).

Collection contains 2 television spots from Timilty's 1971 campaign for Mayor in Massachusetts.

TOOLE, Jack C. 1 sound tape reel (7 1/2 ips.). 22044505.

Collection contains 6 radio spots from Toole's 1964 campaign for U.S. Congress in Montana. (Democratic Party).

TORRANCE, Joe. 1 videocassette (3/4 in.).

Collection contains 1 television commercial used during Torrance's campaign for a 1982 local election in Tennessee.

TOTIN, Bob. 1 sound tape reel (7 1/2 ips.).

Collection contains 1 radio commercial used during Totin's 1982 campaign for a judgeship in Nevada.

TOWER, John. 1 videocassette (3/4 in.).

Collection consists of 12 television commercials used in Tower's 1972 campaign for U.S. Senate in Texas. (Republican Party).

TOWNSEND, Kathleen Kennedy. 1 videocassette (3/4 in.).

Collection contains 4 television spots from Townsend's 1986 campaign for U.S. Congress in District 2 of Maryland. (Democratic Party).

TOWNSEND, Jim. 1 videocassette (3/4 in.).

Collection contains 1 television spot from Townsend's 1982 campaign for Corporation Commissioner in Oklahoma.

TOWNSEND, Wayne. 1 videocassette (3/4 in.).

Collection contains 2 television spots from Townsend's 1984 campaign for Governor of Indiana. (Democratic Party).

TRIBBITT, Sherman. 1 sound tape reel (7 1/2 ips.).

Collection contains 6 radio spots from Tribbitt's 1972 campaign for Governor of Delaware. (Democratic Party).

TRIBLE, Paul. 5 videotapes (2 in.). 1 videocassette (3/4 in.). 1 sound tape reel (7 1/2 ips.). 24351382.

Collection contains 10 television commercials used during Trible's 1976 campaign for the U.S. Congress in Virginia and 16 radio spots from his 1982 U.S. Senate campaign. (Republican Party).

TRIMARCO, Tom.   1 videocassette (3/4 in.).

Collection contains 2 television spots from Trimarco's 1980 campaign for U.S. Congress in District 6 of Massachusetts.

TROXEL, Leona. 1 film reel (16 mm.).

Collection contains 4 television commercials used during Troxel's campaign for the 1968 State Treasurer election in Arkansas.

TROY, Richard J. 1 videotape (2 in.). 24351388.

Collection contains 1 television commercial used during Troy's 1978 campaign for Attorney General in Illinois. (Democratic Party).

TRUMAN, Harry.   1 videocassette (3/4 in.). 1 film reel (16 mm.).

Collection consists of 1 television commercial used in the 1948 presidential campaign as a "get-out-the-vote" spot. (Democratic Party).

TSONGAS, Paul E. 1 videotape (2 in.). 21348110.

Collection contains 1 television commercial used during Tsongas' campaign for the 1974 U.S. congressional election in Massachusetts, District 5. (Democratic Party).

TUCKER, James Guy. 1 videotape (2 in.). 1 sound tape reel (7 1/2 ips). 22441669.

Collection contains 1 television commercial and 5 radio spots used during Tucker's campaign for the 1972 Attorney General election in Arkansas. (Democratic Party).

TURPEN, Mike. 1 videocassette (3/4 in.).

Collection contains 4 television commercials used during Turpen's 1986 primary campaign for Governor of Oklahoma. (Democratic Party).

TYDINGS, Joseph D. (Joseph Davies). 1928-. 3 videotapes (2 in.). 1 film reel (16 mm.). 2 videocassettes (3/4 in.). 21186305.

Collection contains 7 television commercials used during Tydings' 1970 campaign and 5 television spots from his 1976 campaign for U. S. Senate in Maryland. (Democratic Party).

TYLER, WHITEY. 1 film reel (16 mm.).

Collection contains 4 television commercials used during Tyler's 1968 campaign for State Auditor in Arkansas.

TYREE, Randy. 3 videocassettes (3/4 in.).

Collection contains 28 television commercials used during Tyree's campaign for the 1982 gubernatorial election in Tennessee. (Democratic Party).

UDALL, Morris K. 1 sound tape reel (7 1/2 ips.). 3 videocassettes (3/4 in.). 3 videotapes (2 in.). 22186038.

Collection contains 13 radio and 6 television commercials used during Udall's campaign for the 1976 presidential election. Also contains 20 television spots from his 1980 campaign and 7 television spots from his 1982 campaign for U.S. Congress in Arizona. (Democratic Party).

ULLMAN, Al. 1 film reel (16 mm.). 1 videocassette (3/4 in.).

Collection contains 3 television commercials used during Ullman's 1970 campaign and 11 television commercials from his 1980 campaign for U.S. Congress in District 2 in Oregon. (Democratic Party).

UNDERWOOD, Norman. 2 videocassettes (3/4 in.).

Collection contains 3 television spots from Underwood's 1980 primary campaign for U.S. Senate and 13 television commercials from his 1982 primary campaign for Governor in Georgia. (Democratic Party).

UNRUH, Jesse. 1922-. 4 videotapes (2 in.). 21248218.

Collection contains 4 television commercials used during Unruh's campaign for the 1970 gubernatorial election in California. (Democratic Party).

UPDIKE, Lyle. 1 videotape (2 in.).

Collection contains 2 television commercials from Updike's 1976 campaign for State Assembly from Wisconsin. (Democratic Party).

UPHAM, William H. 1 videocassette (3/4 in.). 2255703.

Collection contains 1 television commercial used during Upham's campaign for the 1974 gubernatorial election in Wisconsin. (American Independent Party).

UPTON, Fred. 1 videocassette (3/4 in.).

Collection contains 1 television commercial used during Upton's 1986 campaign for U.S. Congress in District 4 of Michigan. (Republican Party).

URDAHL, Mark. 1 videotape (1 in.). 24351394.

Collection contains 4 television commercials used during Urdahl's campaign for a 1986 California election.

UTHLAUT, Ralph. 1933-. 1 sound tape reel (7 1/2 ips.). 22256881.

Collection contains 4 radio commercials used during Uthlaut's campaign for the 1972 state senatorial election in Missouri, 23rd District. (Republican Party).

VAALER, Martin. 1 videotape (2 in.). 24351402.

Collection contains 6 television commercials used during Vaaler's campaign for the 1976 gubernatorial election in North Dakota. (American Independent Party).

VALDES, Alfonso. 1 videocassette (3/4 in.).

Collection contains 1 television commercial from Valdes' 1976 campaign for Senate in Puerto Rico. (Popular Democratic Party).

VAN DE KAMP, John. 1 videotape (2 in.).

Collection contains 2 television commercials used during Van de Kamp's 1982 campaign for Attorney General in California. (Democratic Party).

VAN DEERLIN, Lionel. 1 sound tape reel (7 1/2 ips.).

Collection contains 5 radio commercials used during Van Deerlin's campaign for the 1980 congressional election in District 42 in California. (Democratic Party).

VAN METER, Thomas A. 1 videocassette (3/4 in.). 24351415.

Collection contains 20 television commercials used during Van Meter's 1982 campaign for Governor of Ohio. (Republican Party).

VAN NATTA, Ralph. 1 videocassette (3/4 in.).

Collection contains 3 television commercials used during Van Natta's 1982 campaign for U.S. Congress in Indiana. (Republican Party).

VAN SICKLE, Tom R. 1937-. 5 videotapes (2 in.). 21268956.

Collection contains 9 television commercials used during Van Sickle's campaigns for the 1972 State Treasurer and 1974 Attorney General in Kansas. (Republican Party).

VAN WAGGONER, Bob.   1 sound tape reel (7 1/2 ips.).

Collection contains 1 radio commercial used during Van Waggoner's 1982 campaign for a judgeship in Nevada.

VANCE, Jimmy. 1 videocassette (3/4 in.).

Collection contains 1 television commercials used during Vance's 1982 campaign for a judgeship in Tennessee.

VANDER JAGT, Guy. 1931-. 2 videotapes (2 in.). 5 videocassettes (3/4 in.).   21268939.

Collection contains 3 television commercials used during Vander Jagt's campaign for the 1972 U.S. congressional election in Michigan, 9th District. Also contains 4 television commercials from his 1984 campaign and 3 television spots from his 1986 campaign for the same office. (Republican Party).

VANDER LAAN, Robert. 1930-. 1 film reel (16 mm.). 21726391.

Collection contains 2 television commercials used during Vander Laan's campaign for the 1974 U.S. congressional election in Michigan, District 5. (Republican Party).

VANDER VEEN, Richard Franklin. 1922-. 1 film reel (16 mm.). 22044481.

Collection contains 3 television commercials used during Vander Veen's campaign for the 1974 U.S. congressional election in Michigan. (Democratic Party).

VARELLI, Mike. 1 sound tape reel. (7 1/2 ips.).

Collection contains 1 radio commercial used during Varelli's 1982 campaign for U.S. Senate in District 5 in Nevada. (Democratic Party).

VAUGHN, Tommy. 1 sound tape reel (7 1/2 ips.).

Collection contains 1 radio commercial used during Vaughn's campaign for the 1972 County Commissioner election in Georgia.

VENETOULIS, Ted. 1 videocassette (3/4 in.).

Collection consists of 9 television commercials from Venetoulis' 1978 campaign for Governor of Maryland. (Democratic Party).

VIOLETTE, Elmer. 2 film reels (16 mm.). 24350949.

Collection contains 8 television commercials used during Violette's campaign for the 1972 congressional election in Minnesota. (Democratic Party).

VOINOVICH, George. 6 videotapes (2 in.).

Collection contains 21 television commercials used during Voinovich's campaign for the 1979 Mayoral election in Ohio.

VOLKMER, Harold. 2 videocassettes (3/4 in.).

Collection contains 5 television commercials used during Volkmer's 1986 campaign for U.S. Congress in District 9 of Missouri. (Democratic Party).

VUCANOVICH, Barbara. 3 videocassettes (3/4 in. & 1/2 in.).

Collection contains 2 television commercials used during Vucanovich's 1984 campaign and 2 television spots from her 1986 campaign for U.S. Congress in District 2 of Nevada. (Republican Party).

WACHOB, Bill. 4 videocassettes (3/4 in.).

Collection contains 2 television commercials used during Wachob's 1984 campaign and 11 television spots from his 1986 campaign for U.S. Congress in District 23 of Pennsylvania. (Democratic Party).

WADE, George. 1 sound tape reel (7 1/2 ips.).

Collection contains 6 radio commercials used during Wade's campaign for the 1972 State Senate election in Pennsylvania. (Republican Party).

WADE, Harold. 1 videotape (2 in.). 24350964.

Collection contains 1 television commercial used during Wade's campaign for a 1986 election in Alabama.

WADE, Lewis M. 1 videotape (2 in.). 21479092.

Collection contains 1 television commercial used during Wade's 1972 campaign for Secretary of State in North Carolina.

WAGGONER, Jabbo. 3 videocassettes (3/4 in.).

Collection contains 5 television commercials used during Waggoner's 1984 campaign for U.S. Congress in District 1 of Alabama. (Republican Party).

WAGNER, Vern E. 1 sound tape reel (7 1/2 ips.).

Collection contains 1 radio commercial used during Wagner's re-election campaign for the 1980 Speaker of the House election in North Dakota. (Republican Party).

WAIHEE, John.   3 videocassettes (3/4 in.).

Collection contains 39 television commercials used during Waihee's 1986 campaign for Governor of Hawaii.   (Democratic Party).

WALGREN, Doug. 1940-. 1 videotape (2 in.).   5 videocassettes (3/4 in. & 1/2 in.).   21287248.

Collection contains 4 television commercials used during Walgren's campaign for the 1972 U.S. congressional election in Pennsylvania. Also contains 45 television spots from his 1986 re-election campaign.   (Democratic Party).

WALKER, Dan. 7 videotapes (2 in.). 24350973.

Collection contains 9 television commercials used during Walker's campaign for the 1972 gubernatorial election in Illinois. (Democratic Party).

WALKER, Franklin. 1 videotape (2 in.).

Collection contains 1 television commercial used during Walker's campaign for the 1978 State House of representatives election in Illinois.   (Democratic Party).

WALKER, John Alexander. 1922-. 1 film reel (16 mm.). 21726906.

Collection contains 4 television commercials used during Walker's 1972 campaign for Lt. Governor in North Carolina. (Republican Party).

WALKER, Robert S. 3 videocassettes (3/4 in.). 24350983.

Collection contains 2 television commercials used during Walker's campaign for the 1982 congressional election and 2 television spots from his 1986 campaign in District 16 of Pennsylvania. (Republican Party).

WALLACE, Bob.   1 sound tape reel (7 1/2 ips.).

Collection contains 1 radio commercial used during Wallace's campaign for the 1980 U.S. Senate election in Illinois.   (Democratic Party).

WALLACE, George C. 1 film reel (16 mm.). 7 videotape (2 in.). 21134006.

Collection contains 9 television commercials used during Wallace's campaigns for the 1968 presidential elections. (Independent Party). Includes 15 television commercials used during his campaign for the 1972 presidential election and 1 television commercial used during his 1976 campaign for president. (Democratic Party).

This commercial comes from George Wallace's 1968 presidential campaign.

WALLACE, George, Jr. 1 videotape (2 in.). 24350985.

Collection contains 1 television commercial used during Wallace's campaign for a 1986 Alabama election. (Democratic Party).

WALLACE, Sam. 1 videocassette (3/4 in.).

Collection contains 1 television commercial used during Wallace's 1982 campaign for a judicial election in Tennessee.

WALLING, Bob. 1 sound tape reel (7 1/2 ips.).

Collection contains 1 radio commercial used during Walling's campaign for a 1972 judgeship election.

WALLOP, Malcolm. 1 videotape (2 in.). 5 videocassettes (3/4 in.). 24350992.

Collection contains 3 television commercials used during Wallop's 1976 campaign and 4 television commercials from his 1982 campaign for U.S. Senate election in Wyoming. (Republican Party).

WALSH, Lawrence E. 1926-. 1 videotape (2 in.). 21486447.

Collection contains 5 television commercials used during Walsh's 1974 campaign for Lt. Governor in California. (Democratic Party).

274

WALTA, Jon. 1 videotape (2 in.).,

Collection contains 1 television commercial used during Walta's campaign for Appellate Court Judge in Illinois. (Republican Party).

WALTERS, David. 3 videocassettes(3/4 in.).

Collection contains 15 television commercials used during Walter's 1986 campaign for Governor of Oklahoma. (Democratic Party).

WAMBACH, Pete. 1 sound tape reel (7 1/2 ips.).

Collection contains 1 radio commercial used during Wambach's campaign for the 1980 State Representative election in District 103 in Pennsylvania.

WARCEK, Steve. 1 videocassette (3/4 in.).

Collection contains 2 television commercials used during Warcek's 1982 primary campaign for U.S. Congress in Connecticut. (Democratic Party).

WARD, Tom. 1 videocassette (3/4 in.).

Collection contains 6 television commercials used during Ward's 1986 campaign for U.S. Congress in District 3 of Indiana. (Democratic Party).

WARD, Peter. 1 sound tape reel (7 1/2 ips.).

Collection contains 3 radio commercials used during Ward's 1082 campaign for a judgeship in Baltimore, Maryland.

WARNER, Carolyn. 10 videotapes (2 in.). 5 videocassettes (3/4 in.). 24351003.

Collection contains 14 television commercials used during Warner's campaign for the 1986 gubernatorial election in Arizona.

WARNER, Glenn. 1 videocassette (3/4 in.).

Collection contains 2 television commercials used during Warner's 1982 campaign for U.S. Congress in Ohio. (Republican Party).

WARNER, John W. 1927-. 1 sound tape reel (7 1/2 ips.). 3 videocassette (3/4 in.). 22044694.

Collection contains 1 radio commercial and 4 television commercials used during Warner's 1984 campaign for U.S. Senate in Virginia. (Republican Party).

WHITTEN, Vernon. 1 videotape (2 in.). 21421240.

Collection contains 1 television commercial used during Whitten's 1972 campaign for Secretary of State in Arkansas.

WICKERSHAM, Richard. 1 sound tape reel (7 1/2 ips.).

Collection contains 1 radio commercial used during Wickersham's campaign for the 1979 State Supreme Court Justice election in Pennsylvania. (Republican Party).

WIEWAL, Brad. 1 videocassette (3/4 in.).

Collection contains 1 television commercials used during Wiewal's 1984 campaign for State Representative in District 51 of Texas.

WILKIE, Wendell Lewis. 1892-1944. 1 videocassette (3/4 in.). 22446443.

Collection contains 1 copy of a film commercial used during Wilkie's campaign for the 1940 presidential election. (Republican Party).

WILLIAMS, Edward Vernon. 1928-. 1 sound tape reel (7 1/2 ips.). 22245595.

Collection contains 4 radio commercials used during Williams' campaign for the 1972 U.S. congressional election in Idaho, 1st District. (Democratic Party).

WILLIAMS, Faye. 1 videocassette (3/4 in.).

Collection contains 3 television commercials used during Williams' 1986 campaign for U.S. Congress in Louisiana. (Democratic Party).

WILLIAMS, G. Mennen. 1911-. 1 sound tape reel (7 1/2 ips.). 1 videotape (2 in.). 21892528.

Collection contains 3 radio and 1 television commercial used during Williams' 1966 campaign for U.S. Senate and his 1970 campaign for Judge in Michigan. (Democratic Party).

WILLIAMS, Glene. 1 sound tape reel (7 1/2 ips.).

Collection contains 1 radio spot from Williams' 1972 campaign for State Treasurer in Pennsylvania. (Republican Party).

WILLIAMS, Harley. 1 sound tape reel (7 1/2 ips.).

Collection contains 2 radio commercials from Williams' 1984 campaign for U. S. Congress in District 1 of Maryland. (Republican Party).

WILLIAMS, Harrison.   1 film reel (16 mm.).

Collection contains 10 television commercials used during Williams' 1970 campaign for U.S. Senate.   (Democratic Party).

WILLIAMS, Larry.   2 videocassettes (3/4 in.).

Collection contains 22 television commercials used during Williams' 1982 campaign for U.S. Senate in Montana.   (Republican Party).

WILLIAMS, Liles. 1 videocassette (3/4 in.). 24350782.

Collection contains 13 television commercials used during Williams' campaign for the 1982 congressional election in District 4 of Mississippi. (Republican Party).

WILLIAMS, Pat.   1 videocassette (3/4 in.).

Collection contains 2 television commercials used during Williams' 1984 campaign for U.S. Congress in District 1 of Montana.   (Democratic Party).

WILLNER, Don S. 1926-. 2 videotapes (2 in.). 21479123.

Collection contains 2 television commercials used during Willner's campaign for the 1972 U.S. senatorial election in Oregon. (Democratic Party).

WILSON, Don.   1 videocassette (3/4 in.).

Collection consists of 10 television commercials from Wilson's 1966 campaign for County Assessor in Oklahoma. (Democratic Party).

WILSON, Frank G. 1919-. 1 sound tape reel (7 1/2 ips.). 21983899.

Collection contains 3 radio commercials used during Wilson's 1972 campaign for State Representative in Vermont, District 13-2. (Republican Party).

WILSON, John.   3 videocassettes (3/4 in.).

Collection contains 2 television commercial for Wilson's 1980 campaign for City Council in Ward 2 of Washington, D.C. and 4 television spots from his 1982 campaign for Mayor.

WILSON, Malcolm. 1914-. 1 film reel (16 mm.). 21431611.

Collection contains 3 television commercials used during Wilson's campaign for the 1974 gubernatorial election in New York. (Republican Party).

**WILSON, Pete. 12 videotapes (2 in.). 6 videocassettes (3/4 in.).
1 sound tape reel (7 1/2 ips).**

Collection contains 19 television and 5 radio commercials used
during Wilson's campaign for the 1982 U.S. senatorial election in
California.   (Republican Party).

WILSON, Ted. 3 videocassettes (3/4 in.). 24350794.

Collection contains 14 television commercials used during
Wilson's campaign for the 1982 U.S. Senate election in Utah.
(Democratic Party).

WINER, Jerry. 4 videotapes (2 in.). 21486468.

Collection contains 4 television commercials used during Winer's
campaign for the 1972 State Representative election in Massachusetts.

**WINTER, William F. 1 film reel (16 mm.).   4 videotapes (2 in.).
2 videocassettes (3/4 in.).   21538712.**

Collection contains 10 television commercials used during
Winter's campaign for the 1975 gubernatorial election in
Mississippi.   Also contains 23 television spots used in his 1984
campaign for U.S. Senate in Mississippi.   (Democratic Party).

**WINTERS, Leo. 6 videotapes (2 in.). 1 videocassette (3/4 in.).
21341024.**

Collection contains 8 television commercials used during Winters'
1966 campaign for State Treasurer in Oklahoma. Includes 2 television commercials used in his 1970 re-election campaign, 3 television commercials used in his 1974 re-election campaign, and 3
television commercials from his 1978 re-election campaign.
(Democratic Party).

**WIRTH, Tim. 2 videotapes (2 in.). 5 videocassettes (3/4 in.).
24367857.**

Collection contains 5 television commercials used during Wirth's
1978 campaign, 10 television commercials from his 1982 campaign,
14 television spots from his 1984 campaign, and 3 television
spots from his 1986 campaign; all for U.S. Congress in District 2
in Colorado.   (Democratic Party).

WISE, Bob.   1 videocassette (3/4 in.).

Collection contains 3 television commercials used during Wise's
1986 campaign for U.S. Congress in West Virginia.   (Democratic
Party).

282

WISE, Martha. 1 videocassette (3/4 in.). 24350808.

Collection contains 1 television commercial used during Wise's campaign for the 1982 State Senate election in District 13 of Ohio.

WITHROW, Mary Ellen. 1 videotape (2 in.). 2 videocassettes (3/4 in.). 24350820.

Collection contains 3 television commercials used during Withrow's campaign for the 1982 state insurance director election in Ohio. Also includes 8 television spots from her 1986 campaign for State Treasurer in Ohio. (Democratic Party).

WITTENBERG, Richard L. 1 videocassette (3/4 in.). 24350832.

Collection contains 1 television commercial used during Wittenberg's 1982 campaign for State Treasurer election in Ohio.

WOLD, John S. (John Schiller), 1916-. 1 film reel (16 mm.). 21887799.

Collection contains 8 television commercials used during Wold's 1970 campaign for U.S. Senate in Wyoming. (Republican Party).

WOLF, Frank. 1 sound tape reel (7 1/2 ips.).

Collection contains 13 radio commercials used during Wolf's campaign for the 1982 congressional election in District 10 in Virginia. (Republican Party).

WOLPE, Howard. 8 videocassettes (3/4 in.).

Collection contains 13 television commercials used during Wolpe's 1978 campaign, 12 television spots from his 1980 campaign, and 7 television spots from his 1986 campaign for Congress in District 3 of Michigan. (Democratic Party).

WOLPE, Howard. 1 sound tape reel (7 1/2 ips.).

Collection contains 1 radio spot from Wolpe's 1980 campaign for U.S. Congress in Michigan. (Democratic Party).

WOLPER, Walt. 1 sound tape reel (7 1/2 ips.).

Collection contains 1 radio commercial used during Wolper's campaign for State House in District 72 of Texas.

WOODAHL, Robert Lee. 1 film reel (16 mm.). 24350841.

Collection contains 3 television commercials used during Woodahl's 1972 campaign Attorney General in Montana. (Republican Party).

WOODARD, Jack. 1 sound tape reel (7 1/2 ips.). 2 videotapes (2 in.). 22226372.

Collection contains 1 radio and 4 television commercials used during Woodard's campaign for the 1972 sheriff election in Polk County, Iowa.

WOODBURY, Bruce. 1 sound tape reel. (7 1/2 ips.).

Collection contains 1 radio commercial used during Woodbury's 1982 campaign for local office in Nevada.

WOODS, Harriet. 1 videotape (1 in.). 4 videocassettes (3/4 in.). 24350857.

Collection contains 7 television commercials from Woods' 1982 campaign and 23 television commercials from her 1986 campaign; both for U.S. Senate in Missouri. (Democratic Party).

Harriett Woods used this scene in one of her statewide campaign in Missouri.

WOODWARD, Bill. 1 videocassette (3/4 in.).

Collection contains 5 television commercials used during Woodward's 1978 campaign for State Senate in District 26 of New York. (Democratic Party).

WORKMAN, Bill. 1 videocassette (3/4 in.).

Collection contains 3 television commercials used during Workman's 1986 campaign for U.S. Congress in South Carolina. (Republican Party).

WORRALL, R.E., Jr. 1 videocassette (3/4 in.).

Collection contains 1 television commercial used during Worrall's 1982 campaign for County Court Clerk in Tennessee.

WORTLEY, George. 4 videocassette (3/4 in. & 1/2 in.).

Collection contains 3 television commercials used during Wortley's 1982 campaign and 3 television spots from his 1986 campaign for U.S. Congress in District 27 of New York. (Republican Party).

WRIGHT, Jim. 1 videotape (2 in.). 24350869.

Collection contains 1 television commercial used during Wright's 1978 campaign for County Clerk in Illinois.

WUWERNEK, JOHN. 1 sound tape reel (7 1/2 ips.).

Collection contains 1 radio commercial used during Wuwernek's 1982 campaign for a judgeship in Nevada.

WYDEN, Ron. 4 videocassettes (3/4 in.).

Collection contains 7 television spots from Wyden's 1980 campaign for U.S. Congress in District 3 of Oregon. Also contains 6 television spots from his 1984 campaign and 2 television commercials from his 1986 campaign for the same office. (Democratic Party).

WYLIE, Chalmers P. 1 videocassette (3/4 in.).

Collection contains 2 television commercials used during Wylie's 1986 campaign for U.S. Congress in Ohio. (Republican Party).

YARBOROUGH, Ralph Webster. 1903-. 3 film reels (16 mm.). 1 videotape (2 in.). 1 sound tape reel (7 1/2 ips.). 21567342.

Collection contains 5 television commercials used during Yarborough's re-election campaign for the 1970 U.S. senatorial election in Texas. Includes 9 television commercials and 18 radio spots used during Yarborough's campaign for the 1972 U.S. Senate election in Texas. (Democratic Party).

YATES, Sidney R. 3 sound tape reels (7 1/2 ips.). 21979439.

Collection contains 2 radio commercials used during Yates' campaign for the 1962 U.S. senatorial election in Illinois. Also includes 4 radio spots from his 1982 congressional race and 1 radio spot from his 1984 congressional campaign in District 9. (Democratic Party).

YATRON, Gus. 2 videocassettes (3/4 in.). 24350587.

Collection contains 2 television commercials used during Yatron's campaign for the 1982 congressional election and 3 television spots from his 1986 re-election campaign in District 6 of Pennsylvania. (Democratic Party).

YEAGER, Weldon. 3 videocassettes (3/4 in.).

Collection contains 5 television commercials used during Yeager's 1986 campaign for Secretary of State in Michigan. (Republican Party).

YEE, Wadsworth. 1 videocassette (3/4 in.).

Collection contains 1 television commercial used during Yee's 1982 campaign in Hawaii.

YELDELL, Joe. 1 sound tape reel (7 1/2 ips.).

Collection contains 7 radio spots used in Yeldell's campaign for U.S. Congress.

YOUNG, Andrew. 1 videocassette (3/4 in.).

Collection contains 3 television spots from Young's 1981 campaign for Mayor of Atlanta, Georgia.

YOUNG, Coleman A. 4 videotapes (2 in.). 21319713.

Collection contains 10 television commercials used during Young's campaign for the 1973 Mayoral election in Detroit, Michigan. (Democratic Party).

YOUNG, Donald Edwin. 1933-. 1 sound tape reel (7 1/2 ips.). 5 videocassettes (3/4 in. & 1/2 in.). 22446479.

Collection contains 6 radio commercials and 4 television commercials used during Young's 1984 campaign and 11 television spots from his 1986 campaign for U.S. Congress in Alaska. (Republican Party).

YOUNG, Larry. 1 sound tape reel (7 1/2 ips.).

Collection contains 1 radio commercial used during Young's 1982 campaign for State House in District 39 of Maryland.

YOUNG, Milton Ruben. 1897-1983. 1 film reel (16 mm.). 21416232.

Collection contains 1 television commercial used during Young's campaign for the 1968 U.S. senatorial election in North Dakota. (Republican Party).

YOUNG, Mory D. 1 sound tape reel (7 1/2 ips.).

Collection contains 1 radio commercial used during Young's campaign for 1980 County Clerk in Kent County in Michigan.

YOUNG, Robert. 1 videocassette (3/4 in.).

Collection contains 2 television commercials used during Young's 1984 campaign for U.S. Congress in District 2 of Missouri. (Democratic Party).

YOUNG, William. 1 videotape (2 in.).

Collection contains 1 television commercial used during Young's campaign for the 1974 congressional election, District 22 in Illinois.

YOUNGER, Evelle. 1 videocassette (3/4 in.).

Collection contains the 1978 television debate in the California gubernatorial race, between Evelle Younger (Republican Party) and Jerry Brown. Debate was sponsored by the League of Women Voters.

YOUNGSTEIN, Francis. 1 film reel (16 mm.). 21630983.

Collection contains 1 television commercial used during Youngstein's campaign for the 1973 Mayoral election in New York. (Free Liberty Party).

ZDANOWICZ, John. 1 sound tape reel (7 1/2 ips.).

Collection contains 1 radio commercial used during Zdanowicz's campaign for a 1980 election in New York. (Libertarian Party).

ZEIGLER, Nick. 1 film reel (16 mm.).24350710.

Collection contains 4 television commercials used during Zeigler's campaign for the 1972 U.S. Senate election in South Carolina. (Democratic Party).

ZIEBARTH, Wayne. 1 film reel (16 mm.). 1 sound tape reel (7 1/2 ips.). 24350602.

Collection contains 3 television commercials and 2 radio spots used during Ziebarth's campaign for the 1972 U.S. Senate election in Nebraska. (Democratic Party).

ZIMMERMAN, Miles B. 1 sound tape reel (7 1/2 ips.).

Collection contains 1 radio commercial used during Zimmerman's 1972 campaign for State House in District 87 in Pennsylvania. (Republican Party).

ZIMMERMAN, Roy. 3 videotapes (2 in.). 2 videocassettes (3/4 in.).
24350610.

Collection contains 8 television commercials from Zimmerman's
1980 campaign and 8 television commercials used during his 1984
campaign for Attorney General in Pennsylvania. (Republican
Party).

ZINK, John. 1 videocassette (3/4 in.).

Collection contains 5 television spots from Zink's 1980 primary
campaign for U.S. Senate in Oklahoma. (Republican Party).

ZSCHAU, Ed.
12 videotapes (1 in.).
8 videocassettes
(3/4 in. & 1/2 in.).
24350620.

Collection contains 15
television commercials
used during Zschau's
1986 campaign for
U.S. Senate in
California. (Repub-
lican Party).

Ed Zschau's campaign against Senator Cranston in California used this spot.

ZUMWALT, Elmo R. 1920-. 1 film reel (16 mm.). 21416099.

Collection contains 6 television commercials used during
Zumwalt's 1976 campaign for U.S. Senate in Virginia. (Democratic
Party).